FAO-Unesco

Soil map of the world

1 : 5 000 000

Volume IX

Southeast Asia

FAO-Unesco

Soil map of the world

FOOD AND AGRICULTURE ORGANIZATION OF THE UNITED NATIONS

UNITED NATIONS EDUCATIONAL, SCIENTIFIC AND CULTURAL ORGANIZATION

FAO - Unesco

Soil map
of the world

1 : 5 000 000

Volume IX
Southeast Asia

Prepared by the Food and Agriculture Organization
of the United Nations

Unesco - Paris 1979

Printed by Tipolitografia F. Failli, Rome
for the Food and Agriculture Organization of the
United Nations
and the United Nations Educational, Scientific and
Cultural Organization

Published in 1979 by the United Nations
Educational, Scientific and Cultural Organization
Place de Fontenoy, 75700, Paris

© FAO/Unesco 1979
Printed in Italy

ISBN 92-3-101363-7

The project for a joint FAO/Unesco Soil Map of the World was undertaken following a recommendation of the International Society of Soil Science. It is the first attempt to prepare, on the basis of international cooperation, a soil map covering all the continents of the world in a uniform legend, thus enabling the correlation of soil units and comparisons on a global scale. The project, which started in 1961, fills a gap in present knowledge of soil potentialities throughout the world and provides a useful instrument in planning agricultural and economic development programmes.

The project has been carried out under the scientific authority of an international advisory panel, within the framework of FAO and Unesco programmes. The different stages of the work included comparative studies of soil maps, field and laboratory work, and the organization of international expert meetings and study tours. The secretariat of the joint project, located at FAO Headquarters, was vested with the responsibility of compiling the technical information, correlating the studies and drafting the maps and text. FAO and Unesco shared the expenses involved in the realization of the project, and Unesco undertook publication of its results. The services of an associate expert were made available by the Government of the Netherlands to assist in the preparation of the soil map of Southeast Asia.

The present volume, covering the soils of Southeast Asia, is the ninth of a set of ten which make up the complete publication of the Soil Map of the World. The first volume records introductory information and presents the definitions of the elements of the legend which is used uniformly throughout the publication. Each of the nine following volumes comprises an explanatory text and the corresponding map sheets covering the main regions of the world.

FAO and Unesco wish to express their gratitude to the government institutions, the International Society of Soil Science, and the many individual soil scientists who have contributed so much to this international project.

CONTENTS

This volume describes the Southeast Asian section of the 1 : 5 000 000 Soil Map of the World.

The map

The Soil Map of Southeast Asia is drawn on topographic base maps of the 1 : 5 000 000 series of the American Geographical Society. The map units are associations of soil units divided into texture and slope classes. They are marked on the map by symbols. The dominant soils are shown by colours and phase differences are shown by overprints.

A small inset map shows three grades of reliability of the soil information from which the map was compiled.

Detailed definitions of the soil units and full descriptions of all the terms used may be found in Volume I of the set.

The text

The first chapter describes the development of the project in Southeast Asia and gives some notes on uses of the map. The second acknowledges the cooperation of the agencies and the many persons who contributed to the map and text, and the third gives a summary of the material in Volume I on the map units, legend and sources of information.

The main chapters of this volume deal with environmental conditions, soil distribution and land use and soil suitability.

ENVIRONMENTAL CONDITIONS

Chapter 4 contains brief accounts of four environmental factors which influence the development and use of soils: climate, vegetation, geology and lithology, and physiography.

Climate is discussed on the basis of five broad climatic zones. Since the criteria used in delimiting units are those that are important to crop growth, the climatic map is supplementary to the soil map in the transfer of crop information from one part of the world to another. Here only the higher categories are discussed. The 15 climatic regions are outlined on a small-scale map (Figure 1).

Vegetation is discussed on the basis of 11 broad vegetation regions distinguished according to habitat (either climatic or edaphic) and the physiognomy and structure of the vegetation. The distribution of the vegetation regions is outlined on a small-scale map (Figure 2). The text gives some brief notes on the location and nature of each region.

Geology is considered under four morphostructural regions, 13 geological regions and 46 geological units. Oceanic basins and morphostructural regions are shown in Figure 3, and geological regions in Figure 4. *Lithology* is considered under 10 regions in Figure 5. The text outlines the geological origins and nature of the main surfaces at present exposed.

Physiography is considered under 10 physiographic regions and 30 physiographic units. A small-scale map (Figure 6) shows the physiographic regions. The text gives some brief notes on the landscape and location of each region and subregion.

SOILS AND LAND USE

Chapters 5 and 6, describing the soils of Southeast Asia, contain an extensive table of soil associations, an account of the distribution of the main soils, and a discussion of land use and soil suitabilities for agriculture.

The table of soil associations lists all the map units in alphabetical order of symbols. Other columns show:

Associated soils
Inclusions
Phases
Areas of units in 1 000 hectares
Climate symbols
Countries of occurrence

The *distribution of major soils* is discussed on the basis of 19 broad soil regions and 10 subregions which are outlined on a small-scale map (Figure 7). The main soils of each region are discussed in relation to factors of the environment.

Present land use and suitabilities for agriculture are discussed at first in general. Then the main soils are considered separately, their present use being described and their suitability outlined.

Conclusions

A general outline of the distribution of the main soil units and their suitability is given in Chapter 6.

The dominance of Acrisols, which cover 51 percent of the region, is noted, and stress is laid on the essential management inputs needed to allow for agricultural expansion and minimize risks of serious and widespread soil degradation.

The Appendix

Site and profile data, including profile descriptions and analyses, are given in the Appendix for some of the main soil units. For easier reference, the soil profiles are listed in alphabetical order of symbols.

Le présent volume décrit la partie relative à l'Asie du Sud-Est de la Carte mondiale des sols au 1 : 5 000 000.

La carte

La carte des sols de l'Asie du Sud-Est est établie d'après les fonds topographiques au 1 : 5 000 000 de l'American Geographical Society. Les unités cartographiques sont des associations d'unités pédologiques divisées en classes de texture et de pente. Elles sont indiquées sur la carte par des symboles. Les sols dominants sont représentés par des couleurs et les différences de phase sont indiquées en surcharge.

Une carte à petite échelle reproduite en carton sur la carte principale précise les trois degrés de fiabilité des données pédologiques utilisées pour l'établissement de la carte.

On trouvera dans le volume I de cette série les définitions détaillées des unités pédologiques et une description complète de tous les termes employés.

Le texte

Le chapitre 1 fait l'historique du projet en Asie du Sud-Est et donne quelques informations sur l'utilisation de la carte. Dans le chapitre 2, les auteurs rendent hommage aux institutions et aux nombreuses personnes qui ont collaboré à l'établissement de la carte et du texte. Le chapitre 3 donne un résumé du volume I relatif aux unités cartographiques, aux légendes et aux sources d'information.

Les principaux chapitres de ce volume traitent du milieu, de la répartition des sols, de l'utilisation des terres et de la vocation des sols.

LE MILIEU

Le chapitre 4 expose brièvement les quatre facteurs du milieu qui influencent la répartition et l'utilisation des sols: climat, végétation, géologie et lithologie, et physiographie.

Le *climat* est traité sur la base de cinq grandes subdivisions climatiques. Etant donné que pour délimiter ces unités on a retenu les critères importants pour la croissance des plantes, la carte climatique complète la carte des sols et doit être consultée pour le transfert des données sur les cultures d'une partie du monde à une autre. Il n'est tenu compte ici que des catégories supérieures. Les 15 régions climatiques sont délimitées sur la carte à petite échelle (figure 1).

La *végétation* est répartie en 11 grandes régions classées selon l'habitat (climatique ou édaphique), la physionomie et la structure de la végétation. Ces régions sont localisées sur une carte à petite échelle (figure 2). Le texte donne quelques brèves indications sur l'emplacement et la nature de chaque région.

La *géologie* est traitée sur la base de quatre régions morphostructurelles, 13 régions géologiques et 46 unités géologiques. La figure 3 indique les bassins océaniques et les régions morphostructurelles; la figure 4 donne les régions géologiques. La *lithologie* est étudiée sur la base de 10 régions (figure 5). Le texte indique l'origine géologique et la nature des principales surfaces qui sont actuellement exposées.

La *physiographie* est étudiée dans le cadre de 10 régions et de 30 unités physiographiques. Une carte à petite échelle (figure 6) montre les éléments du modelé de l'Asie du Sud-Est. Le texte donne quelques brèves indications sur le paysage et l'emplacement de chaque région et sous-région.

LES SOLS ET LEURS UTILISATIONS

Les chapitres 5 et 6, qui décrivent les sols de l'Asie du Sud-Est, comprennent un tableau détaillé des associations de sols, une étude de leur répartition par grandes régions pédologiques, et un examen de l'utilisation des terres et de leur vocation agricole.

Le tableau des associations de sols énumère toutes les unités cartographiques dans l'ordre alphabétique des symboles. Les autres colonnes sont consacrées aux rubriques suivantes:

  Sols associés

  Inclusions

  Phases

  Superficie en milliers d'hectares

  Climat

  Localisation par pays.

La *répartition des principaux sols* est étudiée sur la base de 19 grandes régions pédologiques et de 10 sous-régions qui figurent sur une carte à petite échelle (figure 7). Les principaux sols de chaque région sont étudiés en fonction des facteurs du milieu.

L'*utilisation actuelle des terres et leur vocation agricole* sont étudiées d'abord d'une manière générale. On passe ensuite à l'examen des principaux sols pris séparément; leur utilisation actuelle est indiquée et leur aptitude à l'agriculture est analysée.

Conclusions

Le chapitre 6 donne une description générale de la répartition des principales unités pédologiques et de leur vocation. Il signale la prédominance des acrisols, qui couvrent 51 pour cent de la région, et insiste sur les ressources qu'il est indispensable d'affecter à l'aménagement pour permettre l'expansion de l'agriculture et réduire au minimum les risques d'une grave dégradation générale des sols.

Annexe

On trouvera à l'annexe des renseignements concernant les sites et les profils, y compris des descriptions de profils et des analyses concernant certaines des principales unités pédologiques. Pour plus de commodité, les profils des sols sont donnés dans l'ordre alphabétique des symboles.

РЕЗЮМЕ

Резюме

В данном томе изложено описание раздела Юго-Восточной Азии почвенной карты мира масштаба 1: 5 000 000.

Карта

Почвенная карта Юго-Восточной Азии составлена на основе топографических базовых карт масштаба 1: 5 000 000 Американского географического общества. Картографические единицы - это Почвенные ассоциации, подразделенные на классы в зависимости от структуры и рельефа. Они показаны на карте индексами. Преобладающие почвы выделены цветами, а фазовые различия – штриховкой.

Малая карта-врезка показывает три степени достоверности данных о почве, на основе которых была составлена карта.

Подробные определения почвенных единиц и полные описания всех примененных терминов можно найти в I. томе комплекта.

Текст

В первой главе описывается разработка проектав Юго-Восточной Азии и содержатся некоторые заметки о пользовании картами. Во второй главе выражается признательность за сотрудничество учреждениям и многим лицам, которые приняли участие в составлении карты и подготовке текста, и в третьей главе дано резюме материалов, содержащихся в томе I, по картографическим единицам, легендам и источникам информации.

В основных главах этого тома освещаются условия окружающей среды, распределение почв и использование земли, а также пригодность почв.

УСЛОВИЯ ОКРУЖАЮЩЕЙ СРЕДЫ

В главе 4 приведены краткие сведения о четырех факторах окружающей среды, влияющих на формирование и использование почв: климате, растительности, геологии и литологии, физиографии.

Климат рассматривается на основе пяти обширных климатических зон. Поскольку для определения единиц использованы критерии, имеющие большое значение для роста зерновых, климатическая карта дополняет почвенную карту в плане передачи сведений о зерновых из одной части мира в другую. В данном случае рассматриваются лишь наиболее крупные категории. На мелкомасштабной карте /схема 1/ выделены 15 климатических зон.

Растительность рассматривается на основе 11 обширных зон растительности, выделяемых в зависимости от естественной среды /климатической или почвенной/, а также физиогномики и структуры растительности.

Распределение зон растительности указано на мелкомасштабной карте /схема 2/. В главе приводятся некоторые краткие замечания относительно расположения и характера каждой зоны.

Геология рассматривается по четырем морфоструктурным регионам, 13 геологическим регионам и 46 геологическим единицам. Бассейны океана и морфоструктурные регионы показаны на схеме 3, а геологические регионы - на схеме 4. Литология рассматривается по 10 зонам, показанным на

схеме 5. В тексте отмечается геоло-
гическая природа и характер основных
обнаженных в настоящее время повер-
хностей.

Физиография рассматривается по
10 физиографическим регионам и 30
физиографическим единицам. На мелкомасштабной карте /схема 6/ показаны
физиографические регионы. В тексте
приводятся некоторые краткие замечания относительно ландшафта и
расположения каждого региона и
субрегиона.

ПОЧВЫ И ИСПОЛЬЗОВАНИЕ ЗЕМЛИ

В главах 5 и 6, посвященных
почвам Юго-Восточной Азии, содер-
жится обширная таблица почвенных
ассоциаций, суммирующая сведения о
распределении основных почв, и
рассматривается вопрос о землеполь-
зовании и пригодности почвы для
сельского хозяйства.

В таблице почвенных ассоциаций
в алфавитном порядке индексов приво-
дится перечень всех картографических
единиц. В других колонках указаны:
   Сопутствующие почвы
   Спорадические
   Фазы
   Районы единиц в 1 000 гектаров
   Климатические индексы
   Страны их расположения
   Распределение основных почв
обсуждается на основе 19 обширных

почвенных зон и 10 подзон, которые
очерчены на мелкомасштабной карте
/схема 7/. Основные почвы каждой
зоны рассматриваются в связи с
факторами окружающей среды.

Современное использование земли
и ее пригодность для сельского хоз
яйства рассматриваются вначале в
целом. Затем основные почвы рассматриваются в отдельности одновременно
с указа нием на их применение в
настоящее время и их пригодность.

Выводы

В главе 6 дан общий обзор рас-
пределения основных почвенных единиц
и их пригодности. Отмечается пре-
обладание акрисолей, которые охваты-
вают 51 проц. зоны, и делается упор
на необходимость принятия важных мер
по управлению в целях обеспечения
развития сельского хозяйства и
снижения опасности серьезного и
широкого ухудшения почвы.

Приложение

В приложении приведены данные о
расположении и профилях, включая
описания и анализ профилей некоторых
основных почвенных единиц. Для
облегчения справок перечень профилей
почв приведен в алфавитном порядке
индексов.

En este volumen se describe la sección del Asia sudoriental del Mapa Mundial de Suelos a escala 1 : 5 000 000.

El mapa

El Mapa de Suelos, que comprende el Asia sudoriental, se ha trazado sobre los mapas topográficos base de la serie a escala 1 : 5 000 000, de la American Geographical Society. Las unidades del mapa son asociaciones de unidades de suelos divididas en clases texturales y de inclinación. Se indican en el mapa por medio de símbolos. Los suelos dominantes se muestran por colores, mientras que las diferentes fases se indican con sobreimpresiones.

Un pequeño mapa intercalado indica tres grados de fiabilidad de la información sobre suelos, que sirvió de base para la compilación del mapa.

En el Volumen I de la serie pueden encontrarse las definiciones detalladas de las unidades de suelos y descripciones completas de todos los términos utilizados.

El texto

En el primer capítulo se describe el desarrollo del proyecto en el Asia sudoriental y se dan algunas notas sobre los usos del mapa. En el segundo se da cuenta de la cooperación de organismos y del gran número de personas que han colaborado en los mapas y en el texto, y en el tercero se presenta un resumen del material contenido en el Volumen I sobre las unidades cartográficas, las leyendas y las fuentes de información.

Los capítulos más importantes de este volumen tratan de las condiciones del medio, de la distribución del suelo y de la utilización de las tierras y aptitud de los suelos.

CONDICIONES DEL MEDIO

El Capítulo 4 contiene breves reseñas de cuatro factores del medio que influyen sobre la formación y utilización de los suelos: el clima; la vegetación; la geología y litología, y la fisiografía.

El clima se estudia sobre la base de cinco amplias zonas climáticas. Como los criterios que se han seguido para la delimitación de las unidades son aquellos que tienen importancia para el desarrollo de los cultivos, el mapa climático es complementario del mapa de suelos para la transferencia de información sobre cultivos de una parte del mundo a otra. Aquí sólo se examinan las categorías superiores. Las 15 regiones climáticas se señalan en un mapa a pequeña escala (Figura 1).

La vegetación se estudia sobre la base de 11 amplias regiones de vegetación que se distinguen según el hábitat (ya sea climático o edáfico) y la fisionomía y estructura de la vegetación. La distribución de las regiones de vegetación se señalan en un mapa a pequeña escala (Figura 2). El texto contiene algunas breves notas sobre el emplazamiento y naturaleza de cada región.

La geología se examina con arreglo a cuatro regiones morfoestructurales, 13 regiones geológicas y 46 unidades geológicas. Las cuencas oceánicas y las regiones morfoestructurales se muestran en la Figura 3, y las regiones geológicas en la Figura 4. *La litología* se estudia con arreglo a 10 regiones en la Figura 5. El texto bosqueja los orígenes geológicos y la naturaleza de las principales superficies expuestas actualmente.

La fisiografía se examina con arreglo a 10 regiones fisiográficas y 30 unidades fisiográficas. Un mapa a pequeña escala (Figura 6) muestra las regiones fisiográficas. El texto contiene algunas notas breves sobre el paisaje y emplazamiento de cada región y subregión.

LOS SUELOS Y EL USO DE LA TIERRA

Los capítulos 5 y 6, en que se describen los suelos de Asia sudoriental, contienen un extenso cuadro de asociaciones de suelos, una reseña de la distribución de los suelos principales y un examen del uso de la tierra y de las aptitudes del suelo para la agricultura.

El cuadro de asociaciones de suelos enumera todas las unidades del mapa por orden alfabético de los símbolos. En las otras columnas se presentan:

Suelos asociados

Inclusiones

Fases

Superficie de las unidades en millares de hectáreas

Símbolos climáticos

Países en que se presentan

La distribución de los suelos principales se examina sobre la base de 19 amplias regiones edáficas y 10 subregiones, que se esbozan en el mapa a pequeña escala (Figura 7). Los suelos principales de cada región se estudian en relación con los factores del ambiente.

El uso actual de la tierra y su aptitud para la agricultura se examinan al principio en líneas generales. Se consideran después, por separado, los principales suelos, describiéndose su uso actual y esbozándose su aptitud.

Conclusiones

En el Capítulo 6 se da un bosquejo general de la distribución de las principales unidades edáficas y de su aptitud. Se pone de relieve la dominancia de los acrisoles, que cubren un 51 por ciento de la región, y se hacen resaltar los insumos de ordenación esenciales y necesarios para permitir una expansión agrícola y minimizar los riesgos de una degradación grave y generalizada de los suelos.

El Apéndice

En el Apéndice se dan datos sobre lugares y perfiles, incluidos las descripciones y los análisis de los perfiles para algunas de las principales unidades edáficas. Para facilitar la consulta, los perfiles de suelos se enumeran en orden alfabético de los símbolos.

1. INTRODUCTION

History of the project [1]

Recognizing the need for an integrated knowledge of the soils of the world, the Seventh Congress of the International Society of Soil Science held in 1960 in Madison, Wisconsin, United States, recommended that ways and means be found for the publication of soil maps of the great regions of the world. As a follow-up to this recommendation, FAO and Unesco agreed in 1961 to prepare jointly a Soil Map of the World based on the compilation of available soil survey material and on additional field correlation. The secretariat of the joint project was located at FAO Headquarters in Rome. It was responsible for collecting and compiling the technical information, undertook correlation studies and drafted the maps and text.

In June 1961 an Advisory Panel composed of prominent soil scientists representing various parts of the world was convened by FAO and Unesco to study the methodological, scientific, and various other problems related to the preparation of a Soil Map of the World. [2]

In June 1964 a meeting was convened in Tokyo on the classification and correlation of soils from volcanic ash.

A regional seminar on soil survey and soil fertility research in Asia and the Far East was held in New Delhi in February 1971.

In July 1972 the Government of Indonesia hosted the Second ASEAN (Association of South-East Asian Nations) Soil Conference in Jakarta. Field trips organized for the conference afforded opportunities for the correlation of many of the major soil units of the Southeast Asia region.

The final draft of the general Soil Map of Southeast Asia was compiled in the Soil Resources Development and Conservation Service of FAO in 1975. It incorporates updated information on soil distribution resulting from a number of FAO/UNDP field projects, and entirely revised soil maps for several countries such as Indonesia, Malaysia, the Philippines and Thailand.

The main sources of information used in the preparation of the Soil Map of Southeast Asia are described in Chapter 3.

Objectives

Transfer of knowledge and experience from one area of the earth to another can only be successful when allowance is made for similarities and differences in the geographical, soil and climatic conditions of the regions or countries involved. Furthermore, the economic feasibility of different management techniques under prevailing socio-economic conditions needs to be assessed before they can be recommended for adoption. In order to do so, reliable information on the nature and distribution of the major soils of the world is of fundamental importance. However, the preparation of regional and continental soil maps requires a uniform legend and nomenclature and the correlation of existing soil classification systems. One of the principal objectives of the FAO/Unesco Soil Map of the World project was to promote co-operation among soil scientists all over the world to agree on an international soil correlation system.

In Southeast Asia agricultural research is centred mainly on increased output from existing cropland and evaluation studies of the agricultural potential of vast areas which have scarcely been touched by man, together with the rehabilitation of land which has suffered degradation due to man's irresponsible activities. Many experts under international and bilateral programmes are assisting the governments in this task. This regional soils study attempts to present a synthesis of the knowledge available at the present stage of development of soil science in South-

---

[1] The history of the project as a whole is dealt with more completely in Volume I.

[2] The participants in this meeting were:
Consultants: G. Aubert (France), M. Camargo (Brazil), J. D'Hoore (Belgium), E.V. Lobova (U.S.S.R.), S.P. Raychaudhuri (India), G.D. Smith (United States), C.G. Stephens (Australia), R. Tavernier (Belgium), N.H. Taylor (New Zealand), I.V. Tiurin (U.S.S.R.) and F.A. van Baren (Netherlands).
Unesco Secretariat: V.A. Kovda and M. Batisse.
FAO Secretariat: D. Luis Bramao, R. Dudal and F. George.

east Asia. It is hoped that it will promote better understanding among soil scientists, planners and farmers, provide useful coordination of national and international soils work, and stimulate research and its application in the region.

Value and limitations of the map

The Soil Map of Southeast Asia is meant to be a source of factual data providing a basis and framework for further regional and national soil surveys at a more detailed scale. It may assist in selecting methods of reclamation, crop production, fertilizer application and general use of soils. Until now all attempts to make overall plans or forecasts for agriculture have been hampered by lack of uniformity in the terminology, nomenclature and classification of soils and by the lack of a comprehensive picture of the world's soil resources.

Through a systematic interpretation of the Soil Map of the World it will be possible to appraise the distribution and production potential of the major soils on a continental basis and to delineate broad priority areas which deserve further study. This inventory of soil resources will bring to light the limitations and potentialities of the different regions for increased food production.

In addition, a regional soil map such as the Soil Map of Southeast Asia can be a valuable teaching aid for the training of geographers, soil scientists, agronomists and all those who are interested in the study of the environment.

Although the publication of the map and text marks a significant step forward, it is necessary to point out its inherent limitations. The accuracy and detail of information which can be shown are obviously limited by the small scale of the map and by the fact that soil data for some areas are scarce because of inadequate field correlation or lack of direct observations. On the other hand, difficulties have arisen in the use of available information for the compilation of the regional map because of the difference in the methods of field and laboratory studies. These limitations may also apply to the interpretative data, since they can only be as accurate as the soils information on which they are based. Yet despite these shortcomings, the Soil Map of

Southeast Asia is the most recent and detailed inventory of soil resources based on international cooperation. Its limitations emphasize the necessity of intensifying soil correlation and obtaining better knowledge of the nature and distribution of soils in areas of the region where information is lacking or inadequate.

Use of the map and explanatory text

Against the background of the topographic base the soil map shows the broad pattern of dominant soils marked by different colours. Clusters of closely related colours have been used for soils which have similar characteristics, so that major soil regions can be recognized.

More detailed information about each map unit can be derived from the soil association symbols. The composition of 143 soil associations is given in Table 4 of Chapter 5, where they are listed alphabetically and numerically and are described in terms of climate, extension and main areas of occurrence. A table showing the composition of the soil associations is also given on the back of the map sheet.

The meaning of the textural and slope classes which accompany the symbols of the map units and the overprints which indicate phases are indicated on the soil map and further described in Chapter 3. The definitions of the soil units involved can be found in Volume I. The profile descriptions and analytical data in the Appendix illustrate and further clarify the soil definitions.

The geographical distribution of the broad soil regions is shown in Figure 7 and discussed in Chapter 5.

For information on the occurrence, land use, limitations, suitabilities and potentialities of the soil units, Chapter 6 should be consulted. Here the specific management problems of the soil units are discussed.

Those who are interested not only in the nature, distribution and suitabilities of the soils (the " agricultural angle "), but also in the natural environment, will find additional reading in Chapter 4. This chapter deals with climate, vegetation, geology and lithology, and physiography.

2. ACKNOWLEDGEMENTS

The preparation of the Soil Map of Southeast Asia could only have been accomplished with the cooperation of government institutions and many soil scientists.

Those who gave particular help to the project are listed below. Sincere appreciation is also expressed here to all those whom it has not been possible to single out.

Contributors

OFFICIAL AGENCIES

Burma	Land Use Bureau and Irrigation Department, Ministry of Lands and Forests, Rangoon
Democratic Kampuchea [1]	Ministère de l'agriculture, Phnom Penh
Indonesia	Soil Research Institute, Department of Agriculture, Bogor
Lao	Direction de l'agriculture, Ministère de l'économie et de la planification, Vientiane
Malaysia	Soil Science and Soil Survey Divisions, Department of Agriculture, Kuala Lumpur
Netherlands	Royal Tropical Institute, Amsterdam
Philippines	Bureau of Soils, Department of Agriculture and Natural Resources, Manila
Portugal	Missão de Estudos Agronómicos do Ultramar (Portuguese Overseas Organization for Agricultural Research), Lisbon
Singapore	Department of Geography, University of Singapore, Singapore
Thailand	Soil Survey Division, Land Development Department, Bangkok
United Kingdom	Land Resources Division, Ministry of Overseas Development, Surbiton, Surrey
United States	Agency for International Development (USAID), Washington, D.C.
Viet Nam [1]	Direction des études et recherches agronomiques, forestières et zootechniques, Ministère de l'agriculture, Ho-Chi-min city

Committee for Coordination of Investigations of the Lower Mekong Basin, Economic and Social Commission for Asia and the Pacific, Bangkok

INDIVIDUAL CONTRIBUTORS
(by country to which their work relates)

Burma	B.I. Gasanov [2], M.F. Purnell [2], B.G. Rozanov
Democratic Kampuchea [1]	G.D. Crocker
Indonesia	P. Driessen, F.J. Dent [2], J.F. Harrop [2], P.L.J. de Jongh [2], D. Muljadi, G.H. Robinson [2], M. Soepraptohardjo
Lao	J. Fromaget, W. van der Kevie [2], E. Saurin
Malaysia and Singapore	W.M. Law, P. Thomas, I.F.T. Wong
Philippines	J.A. Mariano, A.T. Valmidiano
Thailand	C. Changprai, F.J. Dent [2], W. van der Kevie [2], F.R. Moormann [2], S. Panichapong, G.H. Robinson [2], S. Rojanasoonthon, J.J. Scholten [2]
Viet Nam	V.M. Fridland, F.R. Moormann [2], A. Pécrot [2]

---

[1] Democratic Kampuchea was known as Cambodia and southern Viet Nam as the Republic of Viet Nam at the time the Soil Map of Southeast Asia was prepared.

---

[2] FAO staff.

Preparation of the map

In close collaboration with the above-listed government institutions, soil specialists and FAO staff, the overall map of Southeast Asia was assembled at FAO Headquarters in 1976 under the supervision of A. Pécrot. Intercontinental correlation was carried out by R. Dudal.

Grateful acknowledgement is made of the permission given by the American Geographical Society of New York to use its 1 : 5 000 000 World Map as a basis for the preparation of the Soil Map of the World.

Preparation of the explanatory text

The final draft of the text was completed and assembled by F.J. Dent at FAO Headquarters in August 1978. P. Arens contributed to the chapter on land use and soil suitability. Background information for the sections on climate, geology and lithology, and physiography was contributed by P.L.J. de Jongh.

Financial support

The costs of the preparation and the printing of the Soil Map of Southeast Asia were shared by FAO and Unesco. Acknowledgement is also made here to the Government of the Netherlands, which made the services of P.L.J. de Jongh available to the project from 1970 to 1972.

Topographic base

The soil map of Southeast Asia was prepared on the basis of the 1 : 5 000 000 topographic map series of the American Geographical Society of New York, assuming an average radius of the earth of 6 378 388 metres. For Southeast Asia this map is in one sheet, IX. The Miller oblated stereographic projection was used.

Areas of land surfaces measured directly on the map with a planimeter are subject to variations due to the projection of less than 8 percent. Distances between land points measured directly on the map are subject to errors of less than 4 percent. Accuracy can be greatly improved by use of the Key on the American Geographical Society map, which gives lines of equal scale departure and conversion tables based on mean scale departure ratio.

Map units

The map unit consists of a soil unit or of an association of soil units. The textural class is indicated for the dominant soil unit while a slope class reflects the topography in which the soil association occurs. Furthermore, the associations may be phased according to the presence of indurated layers or hard rock at shallow depth, stoniness and salinity. The soil units, classes and phases are defined in Volume I.

Each soil association is composed of dominant and subdominant soil units, the latter estimated to cover at least 20 percent of the delimited area. Important soil units which cover less than 20 percent of the area are added as inclusions.

The symbols of the map units show the soil unit, textural class and slope class as follows:

1. Soil units

The symbols used for representation of the soil units are those shown in Table 1.

2. Textural classes

The textural classes, coarse, medium and fine, are shown by the symbols 1, 2 and 3 respectively.

3. Slope classes

The slope classes, level to gently undulating, rolling to hilly, and strongly dissected to mountainous, are indicated by the letters a, b and c respectively.

Cartographic representation

SYMBOLS

The soil associations are noted on the map by the symbols representing the dominant soil unit, followed by a figure which refers to the descriptive legend on the back of the map in which the full composition of the association is outlined.

Examples: Bh24   Humic Cambisols and Humic Acrisols

Po27   Orthic Podzols, Albic Arenosols and Gleyic Podzols

Associations in which Lithosols are dominant are marked by the Lithosol symbol I combined with one or two associated soil units.

Examples: I-Lv   Lithosols and Vertic Luvisols
I-Lc-Bk   Lithosols, Chromic Luvisols and Calcic Cambisols

If information on the textural class of the surface layers (upper 30 cm) of the dominant soil is available, the textural class figure (1, 2 or 3) follows the association figure, separated from it by a dash.

Examples: Bh24-2   Humic Cambisols, medium-textured, Humic Acrisols and Lithosols

Po27-1   Orthic Podzols, coarse-textured, Albic Arenosols and Gleyic Podzols

TABLE 1. – SOIL UNITS FOR SOUTHEAST ASIA

J	FLUVISOLS	U	RANKERS	H	PHAEOZEMS	W	PLANOSOLS
Je	Eutric Fluvisols			Hh	Haplic Phaeozems	We	Eutric Planosols
Jc	Calcaric Fluvisols	T	ANDOSOLS	Hg	Gleyic Phaeozems	Wd	Dystric Planosols
Jd	Dystric Fluvisols					Ws	Solodic Planosols
Jt	Thionic Fluvisols	To	Ochric Andosols				
		Tm	Mollic Andosols	B	CAMBISOLS	A	ACRISOLS
		Th	Humic Andosols				
G	GLEYSOLS	Tv	Vitric Andosols	Be	Eutric Cambisols	Ao	Orthic Acrisols
				Bd	Dystric Cambisols	Af	Ferric Acrisols
Ge	Eutric Gleysols			Bh	Humic Cambisols	Ah	Humic Acrisols
Gd	Dystric Gleysols	V	VERTISOLS	Bg	Gleyic Cambisols	Ap	Plinthic Acrisols
Gm	Mollic Gleysols			Bk	Calcic Cambisols	Ag	Gleyic Acrisols
Gh	Humic Gleysols	Vp	Pellic Vertisols	Bc	Chromic Cambisols		
Gp	Plinthic Gleysols	Vc	Chromic Vertisols	Bv	Vertic Cambisols		
				Bf	Ferralic Cambisols	N	NITOSOLS
		Z	SOLONCHAKS				
R	REGOSOLS					Ne	Eutric Nitosols
		Zt	Takyric Solonchaks			Nd	Dystric Nitosols
Re	Eutric Regosols	Zg	Gleyic Solonchaks	L	LUVISOLS	Nh	Humic Nitosols
Rc	Calcaric Regosols						
Rd	Dystric Regosols			Lo	Orthic Luvisols		
		S	SOLONETZ	Lc	Chromic Luvisols	F	FERRALSOLS
				Lk	Calcic Luvisols		
I	LITHOSOLS	So	Orthic Solonetz	Lv	Vertic Luvisols	Fa	Acric Ferralsols
				Lf	Ferric Luvisols	Fo	Orthic Ferralsols
				Lg	Gleyic Luvisols	Fx	Xanthic Ferralsols
Q	ARENOSOLS	Y	YERMOSOLS			Fr	Rhodic Ferralsols
						Fh	Humic Ferralsols
Qc	Cambic Arenosols	Yh	Haplic Yermosols			Fp	Plinthic Ferralsols
Qf	Ferralic Arenosols	Yl	Luvic Yermosols	P	PODZOLS		
Qa	Albic Arenosols						
				Po	Orthic Podzols	O	HISTOSOLS
		X	XEROSOLS	Ph	Humic Podzols		
E	RENDZINAS			Pg	Gleyic Podzols	Oe	Eutric Histosols
		Xk	Calcic Xerosols			Od	Dystric Histosols

NOTE: This table follows the order of presentation of soil units in Volume I and lists all units occurring as associations or inclusions for the total land area of map sheet IX.

Where two groups of textures occur that cannot be delimited on the map, two figures may be used.

Example: Lo65-2/3 Orthic Luvisols, medium- and fine-textured, Humic Nitosols and Eutric Fluvisols

The slope class of the soil association is indicated by a small letter (a, b or c) immediately following the textural notation.

Example: Bh24-2c Humic Cambisols, medium-textured, Humic Acrisols and Lithosols, strongly dissected to mountainous.

In complex areas where two types of topography occur that cannot be delimited on the map, two letters may be used.

Example: Lf32-3bc Ferric Luvisols, fine-textured, and Lithosols, rolling to steep

If information on texture is not available, the small letter indicating the slope class will immediately follow the association symbol.

Example: Lc100-c Chromic Luvisols, Lithosols and Calcic Cambisols, strongly dissected to mountainous.

MAP COLOURS

The soil associations have been coloured according to the dominant soil unit. Each of the soil units used for the Soil Map of the World has been assigned a specific colour. The distinction between map units is shown by a symbol on the map.

The colour selection is made by clusters so that " soil regions " of genetically related soils will show up clearly.

In associations dominated by Lithosols, stripes of grey (the Lithosol colour) alternate with stripes of the colour of the associated soils.

PHASES

Phases are indicated on the Soil Map of Southeast Asia by overprints.

The petric and petroferric phases show the presence of concretionary and petroferric horizons, respectively, within 100 cm of the surface.

The stony or gravelly phase marks areas where the presence of gravel, stones, boulders or rock outcrops makes the use of mechanized agricultural equipment impracticable.

A lithic phase indicates shallow soils with an average depth of 10 to 50 cm.

The saline phase shows that certain soils of the association (not necessarily the dominant ones) are affected by salt to the extent that they have a conductivity greater than 4 mmhos/cm in some part of the soil within 125 cm of the surface for some part of the year. The phase is intended to mark present or potential salinization.

Sources of information

A map showing the sources of information of the Soil Map of Southeast Asia is shown as an inset on the soil map. A separation is made between the areas compiled from systematic soil surveys, soil reconnaissance, and general information supplemented by occasional local field observations.

About 19 percent of the Southeast Asia region is now covered by soil survey maps based on sufficient ground control to be placed in reliability class I. Inevitably, among these maps there is variation in accuracy depending on a number of factors such as scale, methodology and purpose of preparation. The use of diverse methods of classification also makes correlation more difficult and reduces the reliability of the map. Further uncertainty is introduced by the influence on soil boundaries of differing concepts used in defining the units.

Approximately 34 percent of the soil map in reliability class II has been prepared from soil reconnaissance designed to give, in combination with basic information on the natural environment, a fair idea of the composition of the soil pattern. Advantage was taken of marked changes in the vegetational, geomorphological, lithological and climatic patterns in the preparation of the soil maps of certain areas where coverage by soil surveys was insufficient.

Reliability class III, covering 47 percent of the region, refers to areas which are unexplored, or in which occasional soil studies have not supplied sufficient basic data for the compilation of more than a rough sketch of the soil pattern, even at 1 : 5 000 000 scale. To understand the soil pattern of these regions, therefore, further studies still need to be undertaken. Aerial photographs are seldom available. However, since these regions are mostly thinly populated and have poor accessibility, they usually have a low

priority position for development. It may take a long time before the necessary data for appreciably improving the map are at hand. New aerial photographs and other information that may become available through remote sensing from spacecraft and satellites may eventually be used.

In the preparation of the Soil Map of Southeast Asia a large number of documents was consulted. Although it is impossible to mention all of them, the main ones, covering the countries listed below or specifically prepared for the project, are recorded here by country of origin. Comment is also made on the reliability of the maps in the areas discussed.

DEMOCRATIC KAMPUCHEA

The main source of information was a general soil map of Cambodia at a scale of 1 : 1 000 000 compiled in 1963 by G.D. Crocker of USAID. The map is of a reconnaissance nature and was based on interpretations of available information on geology, geography, topography and soils supported by aerial photograph review and field observations and sampling.

INDONESIA

The main source of information was a general soil map of Indonesia at 1 : 2 500 000 scale compiled in 1973 by P.L.J. de Jongh, FAO Associate Expert, who completed a two-year assignment in Indonesia with the FAO/UNDP Land Capability Appraisal Project. The map is largely a desk study based on interpretations of soil maps prepared by the Soil Research Institute, and information available on geology, geomorphology, vegetation, climate and soils.

LAO

Very few soils data exist for Lao, consequently soil unit delineation and identification are based on interpretations of a geological map of Indochina at 1 : 2 000 000 scale compiled in 1952 by J. Fromaget and E. Saurin, and the 1 : 1 000 000 USAF K-10 Operational Navigation Chart published in 1965. Interpretations resulted in a general soil map of the lower Mekong basin at 1 : 5 000 000 scale compiled in 1972 by W. van der Kevie of FAO, who was seconded for three months to the Committee for Coordination of Investigations of the Lower Mekong Basin.

PENINSULAR MALAYSIA AND SINGAPORE

The main sources of information were the Soil Map of Malaya at 1 : 1 520 000 (approx.) compiled in 1962 by the Soil Science Division, Ministry of Agriculture; and the Generalized Soil Map of West Malaysia at a scale of 1 : 760 320 compiled in 1970 under the supervision of W.M. Law of the Department of Agriculture on the basis of systematic reconnaissance soil survey.

PHILIPPINES

The main source of information was the Soil Map of the Philippines at a scale of 1 : 1 600 000 compiled in 1972 by J.A. Mariano and A.T. Valmidiano of the Bureau of Soils, Department of Agriculture and Natural Resources. This map is based on interpretations of available information on soils, geology, land use, vegetation and climate.

SABAH

The main source of information was the Soil Map of Sabah at a scale of 1 : 5 000 000 compiled in 1974 by P. Thomas of the Regional Soil Survey and Land Capability Classification Project, Sabah, Malaysia. This map is based on a reduction of 1 : 250 000 to 1 : 100 000 scale soil maps of Malaysia.

SARAWAK

The main source of information was the Soil Map of Sarawak, Malaysia Timor, at a scale of 1 : 500 000 compiled in 1968 by the Soil Survey Division, Research Branch, Department of Agriculture, Sarawak, Malaysia, and printed in 1970. The map is based on interpretations of available information on soils, geology, geomorphology, vegetation and climate.

THAILAND

The main sources of information were the General Soil Map of the Kingdom of Thailand at a scale of 1 : 1 250 000 compiled in 1972 by F.R. Moormann of FAO and S. Rojanasoonthon of Kasetsart University, the Reconnaissance Soil Map of Peninsular Thailand at a scale of 1 : 750 000 compiled in 1972 by F.J. Dent of FAO, and a map of the main landforms of Thailand at a scale of 1 : 2 500 000 compiled in 1973 by J.J. Scholten of FAO and C. Siriphant of the Department of Land Development. Both soil maps were based on systematic reconnaissance soil surveys which cover all of peninsular Thailand and important parts of the remainder of the country.

VIET NAM

The main sources of information were the Soil Map of North Viet Nam at a scale of 1 : 3 000 000 compiled in 1961 by V.M. Fridland of the U.S.S.R. Academy of Sciences, and the General Soil Map of the Republic of Viet Nam at a scale of 1 : 1 000 000 compiled in 1961 by F.R. Moormann of FAO. Both maps were based on interpretations of available information on soils, geology, geomorphology, land use and climate supported by field observations and sampling.

References

CROCKER, G.D. *Reconnaissance survey of the soils of Cambodia.* 1963 Phnom Penh, Royal Cambodian Government Soils Commission/USAID.

DE JONGH, P.L.J. *Soils of Indonesia.* Bogor, FAO/Soil 1973 Research Institute. Working Paper No. 4.

DENT, F.J. *Reconnaissance soil survey of peninsular Thailand.* 1972 Bangkok, Department of Land Development. Report SSR No. 94.

FRIDLAND, V.M. *Nature of North Viet Nam,* explanatory text 1961 to *Soil map of North Viet Nam.* Moscow, U.S.S.R. Academy of Sciences.

FROMAGET, J. & SAURIN, E. *Carte géologique de l'Indochine.* 1952 2nd ed. (Lao and North Viet Nam)

LAW, W.M. *The generalized soil map of west Malaysia.* Kuala 1970 Lumpur, Department of Agriculture.

MALAYSIA. SOIL SCIENCE DIVISION. *Soil map of Malaya.* 1962 Kuala Lumpur, Ministry of Agriculture.

MALAYSIA. SOIL SURVEY DIVISION. *Soil map of Sarawak,* 1970 *Malaysia Timor.* Kuching.

MARIANO, J.A. & VALMIDIANO, A.T. *Classification of Philip-* 1972 *pines soils in the higher categories.* Manila, Bureau of Soils.

MOORMANN, F.R. *The soils of the Republic of Viet Nam.* 1961 Saigon, Ministry of Agriculture.

MOORMANN, F.R. & ROJANASOONTHON, S. *The soils of the* 1972 *Kingdom of Thailand.* Bangkok, Department of Land Development. Report SSR No. 72A.

SCHOLTEN, J.J. & SIRIPHANT, C. *Soils and landforms of* 1973 *Thailand.* Bangkok, Department of Land Development. Report SSR No. 97.

THOMAS, P. *Soil map of Sabah.* Regional Soil Survey and 1974 Land Capability Classification Project. Kota Kinabalu, Department of Agriculture.

U.S. AIR FORCE. *Operational navigation chart K-10 (Cam-* 1965 *bodia, Laos, Thailand, Viet Nam).* 3rd ed. St. Louis, Aeronautical Chart and Information Center.

VAN DER KEVIE, W. *General soil map of the lower Mekong* 1972 *basin.* Bangkok, Committee for Coordination of Investigations of the Lower Mekong Basin, Economic and Social Commission for Asia and the Pacific.

4. ENVIRONMENTAL CONDITIONS

In this chapter brief outlines are given of four aspects of the environment that are important in the development of soils. These are climate, vegetation, geology and lithology, and physiography.

These outlines indicate the location and nature of the major regions in which important variants of climate, vegetation, rock types and landscape occur. Small-scale maps illustrating these environmental factors appear at the back of this volume.

CLIMATE [1]

Climatic factors

The climate is generally determined by the monsoon regime, upon which agriculture is dependent. The rainfall pattern is modified by the orientation of important mountain ranges such as the Tenasserim mountains in eastern Burma, the Annam chain in Viet Nam, the Taman range in Peninsular Malaysia and the mountains in the eastern parts of Indonesia and the Philippines.

Average temperatures remain practically uniform (around 27°C) throughout the year in the coastal parts of Thailand and Democratic Kampuchea and most of the region lying south of 17°N. North of this latitude the mean range of temperature increases slightly with latitude over coastal regions but shows high variation over inland areas. These inland areas also have a large mean daily diurnal range owing to their continentality. In addition, altitude has a moderating influence on high summer temperatures and humidity.

Following is a brief description of the region's main climatic zones. A classification of its climatic and ecological regions is given in Tables 2 and 3.

---

[1] Information used in compiling this section was taken with the authorization of Unesco from P. Koteswaram's paper, Climate and meteorology of humid tropical Asia, in *Natural resources of humid tropical Asia*, Unesco, 1974.

1. THAILAND

The country is influenced by the northeast monsoon from October to February and by the southwest monsoon from May to September. The highest temperatures of the year are registered during the inter-monsoon season (March and April), when day temperatures rarely fall below 32°C.

Heavy rainfall does not normally occur, as the country is sheltered from the summer monsoon by the Tenasserim range and from the winter monsoon by the mountainous relief of Viet Nam. The mean annual rainfall ranges from 1 000 to 1 500 mm over much of the country, and in the south and southeast exceeds 2 000 mm. Following the thunder-showers of March and April, the bulk of the rainfall occurs from May to October. The southwest monsoon is established over the country by mid-May and retreats in October before the advancing northeast monsoon. The monthly rainfall pattern shows two maxima corresponding to these two periods. In June and July the Tenasserim coast receives heavy orographic rainfall due to the strong southwest monsoon current, while the interior receives very little precipitation. A branch of the moist southerly current also brings rainfall as high as 400 mm on the coast east of Bangkok. Rainy days are most numerous in September (10-15); there are about seven days each in July, August and October, and less than five days in other months.

The rainfall of the southwest monsoon is determined by the interaction of the monsoon trough with westward-moving perturbations at high altitudes. The southwest monsoon may also be intensified by remnants of typhoons moving eastward from the China seas. During the northeast monsoon the seasonal trough is far to the south of the country, often resulting in dry, cool, pleasant weather.

2. LAO, DEMOCRATIC KAMPUCHEA AND VIET NAM

The climate is tropical in the southern parts of these countries, but in the north winters are moderately cool. There are two main seasons, the northeast monsoon from October to March and the southwest monsoon from mid-May to late September, with short intervals between. The pattern of the relief features and their orientation in relation to the principal monsoon currents are the main factors affecting climatic contrasts, which are noticeable over even small areas. Most parts of these countries receive the major portion of their annual rainfall from May to October. The period from December to March is fairly dry, with the exception of the northeast coast of Viet Nam. Typhoons reach the coast north of latitude 15°N once or twice a year between early May and August, bringing gales and very heavy rain for two to three days.

Following the southward shift of the seasonal trough, the northwest monsoon commences in October and continues until March. Over the most northerly parts of Lao and Viet Nam, air currents from the Asian anticyclone are usually fresh and cool. Late in the season, occasional incursions of northeast trade winds across warmer seas into this area are associated with thick, very low clouds and drizzling rain which usually lasts for two to three days, and sometimes for as long as a week.

Along the northeast coast of Viet Nam, moisture-laden winds arrive after a long passage over the sea. The incidence of the northeast monsoon in October is characterized by the marked increase in the mean monthly rainfall of Quang Tri from 400 mm in September to 500 mm in October. Heavy rainfall occurs along the northeast coast during October and remains high (about 570 mm) in November, but usually diminishes during December and January, and by February is negligible. October and November are the wettest months of the year in this coastal area.

Toward the end of March and in April, as the land mass of Southeast Asia becomes increasingly warmer and the low-pressure zone develops over southwestern China, the northeasterlies of the winter monsoon are replaced by light variable winds. As the season advances, convective activity and thunderstorms become more frequent over the interior.

The southwest monsoon is established by the end of May and continues until late September. During this season the winds over the open sea vary from southeasterlies to westerlies. Inland they generally come from the southwest, but tend to follow the configurations of the terrain. For most parts of the area other than the central east coast, this is the principal rainy season of the year. Almost 80 percent of the annual rainfall occurs from May to September. Steady continuous precipitation is rare during the southwest monsoon, the rain usually falling in heavy showers and during thunderstorms, the frequency

of the latter usually being high in mountainous terrain. Typhoons which tend to weaken and sometimes deflect off the Annam range on the coast may bring several days of heavy continuous rain.

3. PENINSULAR MALAYSIA AND SINGAPORE

The climate is characterized by high humidity, abundant rainfall and little variation in temperature throughout the year. Owing to the maritime exposure of the peninsula, the annual mean daily range of temperature is no more than 9°C. The excessive day temperatures registered in continental areas are never experienced, the highest temperature ever recorded in the peninsula being 39.4°C. Nevertheless, because of the high humidity days are often oppressive in the plains from April to June. December and January have the lowest mean daily temperature.

The southwest monsoon and the northeast monsoon, associated with the periodic changes in prevailing winds, are the two main seasons in the year, with two shorter transitional seasons separating the monsoons. The times of commencement of the monsoons vary to some extent. The southwest monsoon is usually established by the latter half of May or early June, and ends in September. The northeast monsoon usually commences in late October or November and ends in March. In the two transition periods, April to May and October, winds are generally light and variable.

From April to November the region is overlain by a warm, moist, conditionally unstable equatorial maritime air mass. Heavy rain and thunderstorms develop in the Strait of Malacca and move with the prevailing southwesterly winds to west coast districts and Singapore.

Topography greatly affects the distribution of seasonal rainfall in Peninsular Malaysia. The major topographic features are oriented roughly north-northwest to south-southeast and comprise the western ranges, the central valley and the eastern ranges. During the northeast monsoon (November to January) the east coast districts receive the highest rainfall. June and July, during the southwest monsoon, are the driest months in most districts. The central and northwestern parts of the peninsula are sheltered from the northeast monsoon by the eastern ranges and from the southwest monsoon by the mountains of Sumatra; consequently the highest rainfall occurs between the monsoons, owing to convective activity. The monthly rainfall pattern therefore shows two maxima separated by two minima. The higher maximum generally occurs during the autumn transition. The southwest coastal area is also sheltered from the southwest monsoon by the highlands of Sumatra, but experiences frequent thunderstorms from May to August. In consequence, this area shows only one maximum (October to November) and one minimum (February) in the monthly rainfall pattern. Although it varies from place to place, the annual rainfall is high over the entire peninsula (2 000 to 3 000 mm) without the climate being extremely dry or wet.

Heavy precipitation is common but of short duration, except on the east coast during the northeast monsoon, particularly in November and December. Very heavy rain storms causing severe flooding are frequent, and more than 380 mm in 24 hours have been recorded along the east coast. On the west coast the heaviest daily precipitation rarely exceeds 300 mm, although 430 mm in eight hours have been recorded at Penang.

Dry spells lasting for three or four weeks occur occasionally.

4. INDONESIA, SABAH AND SARAWAK

Lying within 10° on either side of the equator and surrounded by warm tropical seas, this zone is generally characterized by a hot, humid climate in all seasons. However, this general tendency toward equatorial uniformity is significantly modified by the mountainous character of most of the islands and the variety of topographic and geographic features.

The main wind currents are different on either side of the equator during much of the year. South of the equator the year can be conveniently divided into two main wind regimes: the west monsoon from November to March, and the east monsoon from June to September.

During the west monsoon the area from southern Sumatra to Irian Jaya [1] lies on the northern side of the equatorial trough of the summer in the southern hemisphere. Here there is considerable weather change resulting from the warm, humid lower tropospheric westerlies and the westward-moving tropical perturbations. This is the principal rainy season for most localities in this area. The east monsoon brings a comparatively dry season owing to a relatively dry and divergent wind regime in lower tropospheric levels. Over Sumatra and most of Borneo [2] the annual rainfall is fairly uniformly distributed. However, in the southern part of the area there is a sharp distinction between dry and rainy seasons. In Java this distinction is well developed in the west and becomes much stronger in the

east and in places in the central part of the island, the greater part of which is practically rainless during several months. The dry season resulting from the east monsoon becomes more pronounced from west to east through eastern Java and the Lesser Sunda Islands, with Flores and Timor approaching a semiarid climate.

During the transition periods the weather over most of the zone is determined by the activity of the equatorial trough. In April and May the trough of the southern hemisphere shifts northward and approaches the equator. In consequence, the zone of convergence between the northeast and southeast trade winds of the two hemispheres becomes narrower than at other times of the year and leads to convective activity. The line of confluence fluctuates and shifts its position, often erratically, according to the strengthening and weakening of the conflicting trade wind circulations. When convergence is strong, the resulting large-scale vertical motion of the highly humid and unstable air mass along the entire narrow zone produces long lines of heavy cumulo-nimbus formations, bringing violent thunderstorms and heavy rainfall. When the trade wind regimes are weak, the weather is generally sultry with light winds or calms, and often oppressive.

Parts of the zone in the northern hemisphere experience a northeast monsoon (with the exception of northern Sumatra, which has a northwest monsoon) from November to March and a southwest monsoon from June to September with two short transition periods (April to May, October) between the two monsoons. Monthly rainfall distribution shows the lowest minimum during the southwest monsoon when the zone comes under a divergent wind regime in surface and lower tropospheric levels. During the spring transition (March and April) showery weather is frequent and in some places the frequency of thunderstorms is as high as fifteen per month. In autumn (October and November) the equatorial trough is relatively more active than in spring, with a well-marked zone of confluence running across the northern part of the zone. Consequently this is a period of maximum rainfall over most northern areas. The monthly rainfall pattern shows two maxima corresponding to the two transitions and two minima corresponding to the two monsoons. The higher maximum is reached during the autumn transition and the lower minimum during the southwest monsoon. Eddies normally occur in January and July over northern Sumatra, Borneo, and to the north of Irian Jaya.

Indonesia as a whole is free from tropical cyclones. However, the occurrence of a tropical cyclone in the neighbourhood of the Philippines influences the amount of precipitation received in Borneo and Java.

[1] Irian Jaya was previously called West Irian and later Irian Barat as shown on the topographic base of the Soil Map.
[2] The name Borneo is used to designate the entire island; Kalimantan designates the Indonesian part of the island of Borneo.

TABLE 2. – KEY TO CLIMATIC MAP OF SOUTHEAST ASIA (FIGURE 1)

Map symbol	Climate	Temperature regimes		Humidity regimes	Main locations
		Winter	Summer		
1.11	Ever-humid semihot equatorial	Ec	g	HU	Lowlands of Indonesia, Sabah, Sarawak and the Philippines
1.12	Humid semihot equatorial	Ec	g	Hu	Lowlands of Indonesia and Peninsular Malaysia
1.13	Moist monsoon semihot equatorial	Ec	g	MO[1]	Philippines; southern Viet Nam; Java
1.14	Moist/dry semihot equatorial	Ec	g	MO[2]	Timor; northern Philippines; southeastern Java
1.22	Humid semihot tropical	Tp	g	Hu	Northern Viet Nam
1.46	Moist/dry hot equatorial	Ec	G	MO[2]	Lowlands of Thailand, Democratic Kampuchea and Lao
1.47	Moist monsoon hot tropical	Tp	G	MO[1]	Southern Viet Nam; southeastern Democratic Kampuchea; Philippines
1.48	Moist/dry hot tropical	Tp	G	MO[2]	Central Thailand
1.71	Ever-humid tierra templada	Tp	c	HU	Central Kalimantan; southern Sabah
1.72	Humid tierra templada	Tp	c	Hu	Uplands of Indonesia, Malaysia and the Philippines
1.73	Moist monsoon tierra templada	Tp	c	MO	Uplands of Thailand, Lao and Viet Nam
1.75	Ever-humid/cool tierra templada	tp	T	HU	Highlands of Kalimantan
1.76	Humid/cool tierra templada	tp	T	Hu	Highlands of Indonesia, Lao, Viet Nam and the Philippines
2.25	Low tierra fria	Ct or colder	g	MO[3]	Highlands of northern Viet Nam and Lao
2.7	Andine taiga	Ti or milder	P	HU-Hu	Highlands of Irian Jaya

[1] 1-3 dry months. – [2] 4 or more dry months. – [3] 3-4 dry months.

KEY TO SYMBOLS IN TABLE 2

The following types of *winter* temperature regimes are recognized:

Ec   Sufficiently warm for equatorial crops (rubber, coconut)

Tp   Colder but frostless, too warm for cryophilous crops (wheat)

tp   *Idem*, sufficiently cool for cryophilous crops

CI   Non-frostless, but sufficiently mild for citrus and sufficiently cool for cryophilous crops

Ct   *Idem*, but marginal for cryophilous crops

Ti   Sufficiently mild for winter wheat but not for winter oats

The following types of *summer* temperature regimes are recognized:

G   Sufficiently warm for cotton, summer days very hot

g   *Idem*, but summer days less hot than G and warmer than c

c   Sufficiently warm for maize and cotton; summer days not so warm, nights cool but frostless; good for coffee growing

M   Cooler, but sufficiently warm for maize

T   Sufficiently long-warm for wheat but not for maize

P   Insufficiently long-warm for wheat, but sufficiently warm for forest

The following *humidity* regimes are recognized:

HU   Ever-humid

Hu   Humid

MO   Moist monsoon

NOTE: For more detailed characterization of temperatures and humidity regimes, see Papadakis (1966).

Lying on the equator an surrounded by large oceanic areas, Indonesia has a generally sultry climate, and the temperature is practically uniform throughout the year. However, on the high plateaus the climate is cool and bracing.

5. PHILIPPINES

The Philippines, extending north-south between latitudes 5°N and nearly 20°N, can be divided climatologically into three main areas.

During the northeast monsoon Luzon and adjoining areas receive very little rainfall and have a warm winter as a result of subsidence associated with the mid-tropospheric anticyclone which predominates over the area during this season.

The eastern parts of the Philippines receive the highest rainfall during the northeast monsoon as a result of the strong, humid monsoon current striking the highlands flanking the coasts. The drier period is from March to August, when the zone lies leeward of the prevailing winds.

Southern parts of the Philippines receive some precipitation during the northeast monsoon, but most rain falls during the southwest monsoon.

Therefore, with the exception of the eastern parts, the Philippines receive most of their annual rainfall from May to October, the percentage increasing toward the north.

Following the zenithal march of the sun southward across the equator in September, the seasonal trough shifts from Luzon southward across the zone during late September and October. During this transition period, frequent westward-moving tropical disturbances bring abundant rain. With the exception of places in the northern and eastern central parts of the Philippines, the patterns of monthly rainfall distribution show a double peak, with the higher maximum generally occurring in the transition period following the southwest monsoon.

Most of the typhoons and tropical depressions develop in the area between the Philippines and longitude 160°E, moving in an approximate west-northwesterly direction. They generally form from May to November, with the highest frequency in September. Typhoons developing east of the Philippines and having a west-northwesterly track bring gales, torrential rain and floods in Luzon during their passage, giving the Philippines a serious tropical cyclone problem.

Climatic regions

The climatic regions of Southeast Asia are shown in Figure 1. The climatic criteria selected (e.g.

TABLE 3. – CLIMATIC CHARACTERISTICS OF SOME PLACES REPRESENTING THE CLIMATIC REGIONS OF THE MAP

Climate [1]	Place	Winter type	Summer type	Humidity regime	Annual potential evapotranspiration [2]	Annual rainfall	Leaching rainfall [3]	Drought stress [4]	Humid season [5]	Dry season [5]
					.... mm					
1.11	Balikpapan, Indonesia	Ec	g	HU	800	2 227	1 420	—	11–10	0
1.12	Jakarta, Indonesia	Ec	g	Hu	980	1 798	690	117	10–6	0
1.13	Surabaja, Indonesia	Ec	g	MO	1 340	1 740	830	439	12–5	8–10
1.14	Kupang, Indonesia	Ec	g	MO	1 420	1 440	890	870	12–3	6–10
1.22	Hanoi, Viet Nam	Tp	g	Hu	890	1 681	900	113	4–10	0
1.46	Bangkok, Thailand	Tp	G	MO	1 330	1 397	610	548	5–10	1–4
1.47	Saigon, Viet Nam	Ec	G	MO	1 310	1 984	1 220	520	5–11	2–4
1.48	Chiang Mai, Thailand	Tp	G	MO	1 540	1 080	390	849	6–10	12–4
1.71	Tamansari, Indonesia	Tp	c	HU	760	1 610	1 870	—	10–9	0
1.72	Lembang, Indonesia	Tp	c	Hu	710	1 966	1 360	98	10–6	0
1.75	Tjibodas, Indonesia	Tp	M	HU	570	3 290	2 710	—	8–7	0
2.7	Pangrango, Indonesia	Ci	P	HU-Hu	410	3 454	2 820	—	8–7	0

[1] The meteorological definitions of the symbols and their agricultural potentialities are given in Papadakis (1966). – [2] Annual potential evapotranspiration is computed month by month on the basis of midday saturation deficit (Papadakis, 1961). – [3] Leaching rainfall is rainfall minus potential evapotranspiration during the humid season. – [4] Drought stress is the potential evapotranspiration minus rainfall during the non-humid season. – [5] A month is *humid* when rainfall exceeds potential evapotranspiration, it is *dry* when rainfall plus the water stored in the soil from previous rains covers less than half of potential evapotranspiration, and *intermediate* between these. The figures in the columns indicate the months when the season begins and ends. 11-10 means that the humid season begins with November (11), terminates with October (10); both November and October are included, so that it covers all the year. 0 means that there is no dry season. Months that are not mentioned in the humid or dry season are intermediate.

drought stress, duration of humid and dry seasons, and potential evapotranspiration) are closely related to crop requirements and distribution, so that the climatic regions delineated by Papadakis (1961, 1966) are of significance to agriculture.

Each region shown on the map has a number representing the climate. Main climatic characteristics and locations of ecological zones are outlined in Table 2 and the related keys. Climatic data from some representative places in the various regions are given in Table 3.

In the table of soil associations in Chapter 5 the type of climate as characterized in Table 2 and Figure 1 is given for each map unit.

VEGETATION [1]

The broad vegetation regions

Throughout Southeast Asia climax-type vegetation in equilibrium with the environment consists basically of forest. Dense evergreen forest covers regions that are sufficiently humid, and broadleaf deciduous forest develops in regions where the ecological, climatic or edaphic conditions are less favourable.

Human occupation of the region in general, and the practice of shifting cultivation by burning in particular, have resulted in a variety of more or less degraded types of secondary vegetation.

In the most favourable conditions, where limited stretches of land in dense humid evergreen forest are cleared for cultivation, heliophilic pioneer species grow rapidly again to form a forest with a complete upper canopy. The replacement by ombrophilous species which were part ot the original growth takes considerably longer, but the potential for reconstituting the climax is preserved.

In less favourable conditions, forest removal may result in greater destruction of the forest soil and the formation of savanna, which when regularly burned by man makes reconstitution of the climax impossible.

Southeast Asia is divided into 11 broad vegetation regions (Figure 2) based on the World Vegetation Map drafted by J. Schmithüsen. The regions are distinguished on the basis of habitat (either climatic or edaphic), and the physiognomy and structure of the vegetation.

---

[1] Information used in compiling this section was taken with Unesco's authorization from papers by P. Legris, R.O. Whyte and M. Jacobs in *Natural resources of humid tropical Asia*, Unesco, 1974.

1. TROPICAL LOWLAND EVERGREEN RAIN FOREST

Tropical lowland evergreen rain forest occurs in areas of low to medium altitude characterized by a relatively high rainfall (usually exceeding 2 000 mm) well distributed throughout the year, and lack of a prolonged dry season. The annual thermal amplitude is under 3°C. This forest type forms the climax vegetation over large areas of the Philippines, Irian Jaya, Borneo, Sulawesi, the Moluccas, western Java, Sumatra, the Malay Peninsula and southern Thailand. It also occurs at low altitude along the coast of Democratic Kampuchea and southern Viet Nam where high annual rainfall balances the effect of the short dry season and encourages the development of a dense humid forest of a quasi-equatorial type.

This forest is extremely complex and very rich in species. It is usually characterized by three tree storeys with an undergrowth of shrubs and seedlings and an abundance of lianas and epiphytes.

The dominant storey is usually 35 to 50 m high and is discontinuous with a few trees of up to 65 m in height and a girth of 3 m or more. This storey is characterized by a high occurrence (up to 50 percent) of evergreen Dipterocarpaceae, (e.g. *Dipterocarpus alatus*, *D. turbinatus*) with *Parashorea stellata*, *Anisoptera glabra*, *Hopea odorata* and *Shorea assamica*. Riverine evergreen forest is more homogeneous and is distinguished by the abundance of *Hopea odorata* and *Dipterocarpus alatus* in Viet Nam, while in Democratic Kampuchea *Eugenia cambodiana*, *E. fluviatilis*, *Diospyros helferi* and *Finetia rivularis* are common species.

The second storey forms an almost continuous canopy between 25 and 35 m in height, and consists of young trees of the upper storey species in association with a number of other species.

The lower storey contains young saplings of the dominant storeys together with shrub species. The grass layer consists mainly of young seedlings. Herbaceous vegetation is scarce because of light deficiency. There is no accumulation of litter owing to rapid decomposition of organic matter, and the organic matter content of the topsoil is low.

The secondary forest which develops after removal of the original vegetation is also a closed vegetation but does not show an orderly structure, and no strata can be distinguished in the first stages of development.

2. TROPICAL INUNDATED SWAMP AND BOG FORESTS

Swamp and bog forests occur in regions which are more or less permanently inundated by fresh water. Vast tracts of these forests are found on the east coast of Sumatra, the west coast of Borneo, the Meervlakte intermontane plain and the south coast of Irian Jaya, the west coast of the Malay Peninsula, and to a lesser extent the Chao Phaya, Mekong and Red river flood plains.

Trees belong mainly to primary rain forest genera. Most are taller than 20 m and are equipped with buttresses, pneumatophores, or stilt roots. Two main forest types are recognized: mixed swamp forest and " padang " forest.

Mixed swamp forest occurs on the fringes of the vast ombrogenous peat bogs of the region and on the less extensive topogenous bogs and swamps. Upper storey dominants common to mixed swamp forest in Borneo and Sumatra include *Alstonia pneumatophora* and *Lophopetalum multinervium* on shallow peat, *Campnosperma coriacea, Gonystylus bancanus, Palaquium burckii, Tetramerista glabra, Durio carinatus, Koompassia malaccensis, Parastemon urophyllum, Dyera lowii, Mezzettia leptopoda, Shorea platycarpa, S. teysmanniana*, and *S. uliginosa*. In the middle and lower storeys characteristic species include *Blumeodendron tokbrai, B. kurzii, Neoscortechinia kingii, Horsfieldia crassifolia, Gymnacanthera eugeniifolia, Eugenia elliptilimba, Engelhardtia serrata, Diospyros pseudomalabarica, D. siamang, Ilex sclerophylloides, I. hypoglauca, Mangifera havilandii, Santiria laevigata* and *S. rubiginosa*.

Padang forest occurs over central domed areas of ombrogenous peat bogs and is poorer in species than mixed swamp forest. In Borneo common padang forest species include *Palaquium cochleariifolium, Diospyros evena, Dactylocladus stenostachys, Lithocarpus dasystachyus, Parastemon spicatum, Garcinia cuneifolia, Sterculia rhoidifolia* and *Xylopia coriifolia*. These species are either absent, or have not yet been recorded in the padang forest of Sumatra, which is composed mainly of smaller trees of the same species that occur in mixed swamp forest.

Trees in mixed swamp forest have a larger diameter on average than those of padang forest, although basal areas per hectare are low in comparison with those of hill forest.

In the most extreme padang forest of Sarawak the trees are very small and stunted, giving the vegetation a savanna-like aspect.

3. MANGROVE FOREST

Mangrove forest occurs only within the tidal range of the estuaries and coastal mud flats of the region. It is composed almost entirely of evergreen sclerophyllous broadleaf trees and/or shrubs with either stilt roots or pneumatophores. Epiphytes are generally rare, with the exception of lichens on branches and adnate algae on the lower parts of trees.

The main areas of occurrence are the littoral fringes of the coastal plains of Thailand, Malaysia and Indonesia, and the Ca Mau region at the southern tip of Viet Nam. The most developed species belong to the genera *Rhizophora, Bruguiera, Ceriops, Avicennia, Carapa, Sonneratia, Heritiera* and *Lumnitzera*. Species of the first three genera listed produce valuable timber. Many mangrove forests are backed by almost pure stands of *Melaleuca leucadendron*, which is of local importance for the extraction of gomenol and the production of charcoal.

4. TROPICAL EVERGREEN SEASONAL RAIN FOREST

Seasonal rain forest occurs in humid bioclimates with an average dry season of up to four or five months and an annual rainfall of over 2 000 mm, or a shorter dry season of one or two months and an annual rainfall of 1 500 to 2 000 mm. It includes a number of physiognomical types varying considerably according to altitude and intensity of drought. Its floristic composition is largely determined by edaphic conditions.

Dipterocarpaceae are dominant in the upper storey of the dense forests of northern and central Thailand. Characteristic trees are *Dipterocarpus costatus, D. dyeri*, and *D. artocarpifolius, Anisoptera cochichinensis, Shorea vulgaris*, and *Sterculia lychnophora*. The dominant storey contains *Mesua ferrea, Vatica* and *Dalbergia*, while dominants in the undergrowth are often Euphorbiaceae, Anonaceae and Ebenaceae. An intermediate type of mixed semideciduous forest with *Lagerstroemia* and Leguminosae dominants also occurs. The degradation facies are brakes composed of Tiliaceae (*Grewia*), Hypericaceae (*Cratoxylon*) and Rubiaceae (*Psychotria, Ixora, Randia, Gardenia*). Further degradation results in the formation of *Imperata* scrub or its equivalent, the *Eupatorium* stands with a woody vegetation of fire-resistant species, *Albizzia, Careya* and *Phyllanthus*.

5. TROPICAL MOIST DECIDUOUS FOREST

Mixed moist deciduous forest occurs principally in northern and central Thailand and Java in areas with an annual rainfall of about 1 500 mm and a dry season of four to five months. The mean temperature of the coldest month lies between 15 and 20ºC. Two types are distinguished according to whether these forests are teak-bearing or not.

Teak-bearing forest (*Tectona grandis*) occurs mainly in areas with cooler humid bioclimates. This forest type frequently occupies valleys and foothills in northern Thailand and Java with well-drained soils, abundant occult precipitation and slight saturation deficits. Teakless mixed deciduous forest occurs mainly in central Thailand. Dominant species other than teak in both forest types include *Pterocarpus macrocarpus*, *Xylia kerii*, *Lagerstroemia calyculata*, *L. tomentosa*, *L. balansae*, *Schleichera trijuga*, *Afzelia xylocarpa*, *Adina cordifolia*, *Mitragyna javanica*, *Terminalia chebula*, *T. belerica*, *T. tomentosa*, *Anogeissus acuminata*, *Eriolaena candollei*, *Lannea coromandelica*, *Tetrameles nudiflora*, *Sponndias pinnata*, *Premna pyramidata*, *Grewia vestita*, *Milletia brandisiana*, *Dillenia* and *Sterculia*. Bamboos are prevalent in the undergrowth.

6. TROPICAL LOWLAND SEMIDECIDUOUS RAIN FOREST AND TROPICAL MOIST DECIDUOUS FOREST

An association of lowland semideciduous rain forest and moist deciduous forest occurs in Lao and northern Viet Nam. The former consists of dense hemi-ombrophilous forests containing a majority of evergreen species and a large proportion of deciduous species. The dominants in the arboreal storey are Dipterocarpaceae, Papilionaceae, Leguminosae, Meliaceae and Sapindaceae, while the middle storey is dominated by Anonaceae, Rubiaceae and Euphorbiaceae.

If the vegetation is cleared, its place is taken by a *Eupatorium* or *Saccharum arundinaceum* scrub which may ultimately develop into the original forest, but peniclimax open woodland may develop where exploitation is followed by repeated burning.

Two types of moist deciduous forest are distinguished: one on high ground, in which bamboos are prevalent, and the other in low-lying alluvial regions. The best represented families are the Leguminosae with fourteen species, the Verbenaceae with five species, and the Combretaceae with four species. The undergrowth consists of Gramineae and Bambuseae. Teak occurs in the moist deciduous forest of Lao, but is absent in similar forest in Viet Nam.

7. TROPICAL DRY DECIDUOUS FOREST

The typical Dipterocarpaceae open woodland is mainly confined to subhumid hot bioclimates with a five-to-six-month dry season and an annual rainfall of 1 000 to 1 500 mm. These climatic conditions are extremely conducive to outbreaks of fire and rapid degradation of the soil. This forest type occurs mainly in northeastern Thailand, Democratic

Kampuchea, Lao and Viet Nam, the Lesser Sunda Islands, and seasonal parts of Luzon.

Some forests of this type appear to be stabilized on permeable sandy soils (Koulens sandstone in Democratic Kampuchea), or on skeletal soils often of schistose origin (*Pentacme siamensis* and *Terminalia tomentosa* types) in Viet Nam. Open woodland on sandy soil frequently contains bamboos (*Oxytenanthera* sp.) and *Imperata cylindrica*. Another woodland in the wetter eastern Mekong regions (Stung Treng) seems to correspond to stages in the regeneration of the forest after removal of vegetation, which has not progressed further owing to regular outbreaks of fire.

In Thailand dry deciduous forest covers the Korat plateau, extending into the Savannakhet and Vientiane regions of Lao, and the northern half of Democratic Kampuchea. Typical dominants include *Dipterocarpus tuberculatus*, *D. obtusifolius*, *D. intricatus*, *Pentacme siamensis*, *Shorea obtusa*, *Terminalia tomentosa*, *T. mucronata*, *Buchanania lanzan*, and *Emblica officinalis*. In the graminaceous undergrowth there is a proliferation of *Cycas* and *Phoenix acaulis*.

8. TROPICAL MONTANE RAIN FOREST

The tropical montane rain forest of western Thailand, Malaysia, Indonesia and the Philippines is, in many respects, the poor relation of tropical lowland evergreen rain forest. There is no sharp distinction between the two, the main difference being a shift in the floristic composition of the dominants in the upper and main tree storeys. Many of the common lowland forest species occur in montane forest, although not frequently. The many montane forest species absent in the lowlands belong to families such as the Elaeocarpaceae, Ericaceae, Pagaceae, Lauraceae, Symplocaceae and Theaceae. Species common to the subtropics (conifers, tree ferns and herbs) also occur, and there is an increase of moss growth and epiphytes.

Except for big trees on ridge tops, the large trees of montane forest are usually shorter and slightly smaller than those of lowland forest. The density of wide-girth trees on ridge tops is greater than in lowland forest and there are correspondingly fewer trees in the under storey and the lower part of the main storey. The ground flora on ridge tops is usually extremely poor, owing in part to the common occurrence of the palm *Eugeissona triste*. The vegetation on the slopes is often poorly stocked in woody species and the under storey is rich in stemmed and stemless palms and rattans. In intermontane valley bottoms large woody species are comparatively poor, and the forest is characterized by the richness in the ground flora and shrub layer. *Alocasia* sp., *Colocasia* sp., *Donax grandis* and many ground ferns are common.

Montane ericaceous forest occurs in the cloud belt above 2 400 m or on exposed ridges and summits at lower altitudes. It is typically composed of a single tree storey with a dwarf structure seldom more than a few metres high. Trees are frequently gnarled and there is an increase in the development of liverworts, mosses and filmy ferns, both on the trunks of trees and on the ground. *Sphagnum* spp. are common. Oaks are limited to a few species and the forest is characterized by the presence of ericaceous species. Epiphytic orchids are common and rhododendrons frequent. This forest type is also characterized by an accumulation of acid humus and peat around the roots of the trees in which epiphytes, mosses, filmy ferns and herbs abound.

9. MONTANE LAUREL FOREST

The 20°C isotherm, which is located between 800 and 1 000 m at latitudes around 11 to 12°N, seems to correspond with the base of the Laurisylva belt in which most of the Lauraceae, Fagaceae, Magnoliaceae, Juglandaceae and conifers occur. It is also at this level that the low-altitude formations of Dipterocarpaceae, Leguminosae and Lythraceae largely disappear. Increasing altitude affects the bioclimates in the following ways: the dry season becomes progressively shorter and may even be absent; the mean monthly thermal amplitude diminishes, although daily amplitude increases; the rainfall becomes steadily higher up to intermediate altitudes of about 1 700 m on eastern slopes and from 800 to 1 000 m on western slopes.

In the Laurisylva belt there are patches of *Dacrydium* and *Podocarpus imbricatus* as well as open pine forest. *Pinus merkusii* and *P. khasya* occur in Lao and Viet Nam. *P. insularis*, which is closely related to *P. khasya*, has also been reported in Viet Nam. *P. dalatensis*, a five-leafed pine comparable with *P. excelsa* of the Himalayas, is found on the southern plateaus of Viet Nam.

The base of the true mountain belt, comprising Fagaceae, Ericaceae and conifers (*Pinus krempfii*, *P. armandii*, *Fokienia hodginsii*, *Keteeleria davidiana*), is situated, on average, at an altitude of 1 700 m in low latitudes. This belt is locally well preserved in Lao and Viet Nam.

The bioclimates in this belt are humid or very humid and are characterized by a fairly cool season in which the temperature is lower than 15°C and may occasionally fall below 0°C. As the latitude rises, the various vegetation belts are found at progressively lower elevations owing to the effect of diminishing temperatures and increasing thermal amplitude. Consequently, stands of Fagaceae grow at a lower altitude in the Hue region than in southern parts of Viet Nam.

Pine forests are also found in the mountains of northern Sumatra (*Pinus merkusii*), Luzon (*P. merkusii*, *P. insularis*), and Mindoro (*P. insularis*) at altitudes of 1 200 to 2 400 m. Here the undergrowth invariably consists of grass and bracken.

10. SAVANNA

Savanna, which represents destroyed monsoon forest, consists of grass vegetation with scattered trees which are often fire-resistant. Areas subjected to repeated and severe burning, such as the drier parts of northwestern Sumatra and the coastal plains of Viet Nam, have a vegetation consisting of little else but grass.

In Southeast Asia, Gramineae other than Bambuseae are of little importance in the climax formations. The occurrence of Gramineae characteristic of India and China appears to be related to human intervention. Gramineae play a much more important role in the secondary formations, particularly open forest and savanna. The first Gramineae to appear after forest removal are the Paniceae, *Cyrtococcum patens*, *C. trigonum*, *Panicum sarmentosum* and *Paspalum conjugatum*. On cultivated land *Digitaria marginata* and various species of *Paspalum* occur, while in the shade of plantations the swards are dominated by *Paspalum conjugatum*, *Axonopus compressus*, *Cyrtococcum trigonum* and *Centotheca lappacea*. After several years of shifting cultivation the sward gradually deteriorates to *Imperata cylindrica* savanna.

A particular type of ecological regression is seen in the extensive areas of non-forest land, called "veal" in Democratic Kampuchea, where the herbaceous cover is composed of *Cynodon dactylon*, *Pseudopogonatherum* sp., *Imperata cylindrica* (rare), various Rosaceae, Cyperaceae and small bamboos. The plain of Veal Trea is a treeless, jeep-high community of Cyperaceae, *Fimbristylis* sp., Commelinaceae, and above all the grasses, *Echinochloa crusgalli*, *Themeda* sp. and *Panicum luzonense*. These grasses are burned each year for hunting purposes, and become green again and flower with the first rains in May.

Delvert (1961) concludes that the "veal" is a secondary formation covering sites that were cultivated in ancient times, as aerial photographs of the area show former rice paddies, smaller in size than those of today, numerous ponds, old canals and roads. The "veal" must formerly have been covered by a mediocre flood forest, and its present vegetation is a form of anthropic savanna.

11. MONTANE VEGETATION ABOVE THE TREE LINE

An alpine climax vegetation, which is largely herbaceous and rich in remarkable species of temperate affinity, is found above the climatic timberline in the highlands of the Maoke mountains of Irian Jaya, and, owing to fires set by hunters, also extends far below that limit.

Where the subalpine forest is destroyed it is replaced by alpine grassland. A brief dry spell may be sufficient for the forest with its heavy moss cover to burn on by itself for some time once it has caught fire, for instance through the action of hunters. Grass also acts as a cover for the germination of forest tree species, but this is a slow process under the prevailing low temperatures, and there is always the possibility that fires will recur and disrupt the regeneration.

GEOLOGY AND LITHOLOGY

Geological regions

The description of the geology and lithology of Southeast Asia is based on four morphostructural regions:

A. The Sunda shelf area
B. The circum-Sunda orogenic system
C. The Sahul shelf area
D. The circum-Australian orogenic system.

The four morphostructural regions of Southeast Asia are bordered by the Indo-Australian, South China Sea, Philippine and Carolinan oceanic basins which range from 4 000 to 6 000 m in depth.

The oceanic basins and morphostructural regions are shown in Figure 3. The morphostructural regions are subdivided into 13 geological regions and 46 geological units which are outlined below and shown in Figure 4. The parent materials are shown in Figure 5.

A. Sunda shelf area

    A 1. Malay Peninsula and western Thailand geosynclinal system
        A 1.1 Malay Peninsula
        A 1.2 Western Thailand geosynclinal system
    A 2. Indochinese complex

A 3. Indochinese massif
    A 3.1 Korat and Vientiane massifs
    A 3.2 Eastern massifs
    A 3.3 Tonkin massif

A 4. Quaternary basins
    A 4.1 Mekong river basin
    A 4.2 Chao Phraya river basin

A 5. Borneo
    A 5.1 Continental Sunda shelf sector
    A 5.2 Embaluh zone
    A 5.3 Kuching and Meratus zones

B. Circum-Sunda orogenic system

    B 1. Philippines
        B 1.1 Luzon
        B 1.2 Mindoro
        B 1.3 Panay
        B 1.4 Negros, Cebu and Bohol
        B 1.5 Samar and Leyte
        B 1.6 Mindanao
        B 1.7 Palawan

    B 2. Moluccas
        B 2.1 Ceram
        B 2.2 Buru
        B 2.3 Misool
        B 2.4 Sula Islands
        B 2.5 Halmahera group

    B 3. Sulawesi
        B 3.1 Northern arm
        B 3.2 Central
        B 3.3 Southeastern arm
        B 3.4 Southern arm

    B 4. Lesser Sunda Islands
        B 4.1 Wetar
        B 4.2 Alor
        B 4.3 Flores
        B 4.4 Sumbawa
        B 4.5 Lombok
        B 4.6 Bali
        B 4.7 Sumba
        B 4.8 Timor
        B 4.9 Tanimbar

    B 5. Java and Madura
        B 5.1 Southern belt
        B 5.2 Central belt
        B 5.3 Northern belt

    B 6. Sumatra
        B 6.1 Northern mountains
        B 6.2 Barisan range
        B 6.3 Northeastern lowlands
        B 6.4 Islands west of Sumatra
        B 6.5 Islands east of Sumatra

C. Sahul shelf area

    C 1. Aru Islands

D. Circum-Australian orogenic system

    D 1. Irian Jaya

        D 1.1 Doberai Peninsula

        D 1.2 Central

        D 1.3 Southern alluvial plain

A. SUNDA SHELF AREA

The Sunda shelf comprises the Indochinese Peninsula, the greater part of Borneo, the east coast of Sumatra, Bangka and Belitung (Billiton) together with the shallow South China Sea. Toward the north it includes the Shan highlands.

The Sunda shelf has been stable for a considerable period of time, but at present is extensively inundated, with only its higher parts standing above the sea. Advanced peneplanation of the area is evident from the unconformity of the seas which now cover the continental shelf, and the presence of the Lingga and Riau archipelagoes and Bangka and Belitung islands, which may be considered monadnocks.

The basement complex of the Sunda shelf consists of rocks of Precambrian to Jurassic age. The oldest parts of the shelf, the Indochinese and eastern massifs, were affected by the Hercynian orogeny toward the end of the Carboniferous. The Kimmeridgian orogeny during the late Triassic and Jurassic affected the entire area, while the Himalayan orogeny probably only resulted in local rejuvenation.

A1. *Malay Peninsula and western Thailand geosynclinal system*

The Malay Peninsula consists of parallel ranges which run obliquely to its general direction and grade into the western Thailand geosynclinal system in the north. The latter unit, an extension of the Shan highlands of Burma, consists of an intensely folded old mountain system of shale, schist and limestone which is in an advanced stage of erosion. The cores of the mountain system, which consist of granite and other intrusives, are exposed in north-south-trending ranges.

A1.1. The Malay Peninsula consists of an alternation of locally metamorphosed limestone, shale and sandstone, and acid intrusives and extrusives. The limestone is massive and resistant. The sandstone and shale normally overlie the limestone and contain chert beds. In the eastern and southern parts of the peninsula the sandstone and shale have been metamorphosed to schist, quartzite, phyllite and slate. The acid intrusives consist of syenite and hornblende-granite. The Pahang volcanic series occurs locally in the central part of the peninsula. It is a mixed group of extrusives, mainly volcanic ash, pumice beds, lapilli and lava, varying from rhyolite to basaltic rocks.

A1.2. The western Thailand geosynclinal system comprises parts of the Shan highlands in the north and the Bilauktaung range in the centre, and grades into the mountains of the Malay Peninsula in the south.

The Carboniferous Kauchanabari system outcrops in the Shan highlands. This system consists mainly of shale, siltstone and other argillaceous sediments associated with greywacke, sandstone, limestone and marl, and local granitic intrusions. Permian and Carboniferous limestone, locally dolomitic, outcrops to the south. The rocks of the Bilauktaung range are thought to be Cambrian, and consist of the Phuket series composed of dark-coloured pebbly shale and sandstone which are metamorphosed around late Cretaceous or early Tertiary muscovite and biotite granite intrusions.

The Korat series west of Nakhon Si Thammarat which consists of sandstone, conglomerate and shale is locally metamorphosed to quartz-phyllite and slate. Permian limestone occurs near the mountains of the peninsula. The limestone is often dolomitic and is locally overlain by Devonian sandstone and shale.

A2. *Indochinese complex*

The Indochinese complex is the region between the western Thailand geosynclinal system and the Indochinese massif. The region consists of a number of depression zones appearing as long narrow troughs. These troughs were formed at the beginning of the Mesozoic, either from tectonic grabens, or from vast subsidence basins in which marine and continental sediments accumulated to form the Korat series. The Cardamom mountains, a peneplained, folded structure along the Gulf of Thailand, form the southeastern limit of the Indochinese complex.

The Korat series predominates throughout the region except for the area east of the Chao Phraya basin, where the Ratburi limestone complex outcrops. The Korat series contains sandstone, greywacke, arkose and conglomerate which are generally interbedded with various shales, limestones and coal seams. Pre-Permian gneiss and schist outcrop southeast of Bangkok and west of Vientiane. Basic and acid igneous rocks occur locally.

A3. *Indochinese massif*

The Indochinese massif is subdivided into the Vientiane massif, the eastern massif and the Tonkin massif to the north.

A3.1. The Korat and Vientiane massifs consist in the main of the Khok Kruat and Salt formations.

The Khok Kruat formation is largely composed of sandstone, shale and siltstone. The sandstone is very fine to fine grained, medium hard and feldspathic, and is locally cemented with iron. The interbedded shale and siltstone are soft.

The Salt formation, overlying the Khok Kruat formation, is less resistant and consists of sandstone, sandy shale and siltstone together with beds of gypsum, anhydrite and rock salt. The Phu Kadung and Kanchanaburi series occur in the western part of the Korat plateau. The Phu Kadung formation consists of sandstone, shale, siltstone and calcareous conglomerates, and the Kanchanaburi series of shale and sandstone which is metamorphosed in places to slate, phyllite and quartzite.

A3.2. The eastern massif consists, from north to south, of the Hue-Thakhek, Kontum and Annam massifs.

The greater part of the Hue-Thakhek massif is composed of limestone, dolomite and marble. Large masses of granite and granodiorite also occur, especially to the south.

The basement rock of the Kontum massif consists of gneiss, granite, gabbro, epidiorite and quartzite which in the southwest are covered by basalts.

The eastern part of the Annam massif is characterized by outcrops of acid effusive rocks such as dacite, rhyolite and andesite, and late Carboniferous basalts occur in the west. The greater part of the inter-massif zone consists of sandstones of the Korat series. The Plateau des Bolovens consists of basalts, and acid effusives occur to the south.

A3.3. The Tonkin massif consists of a basement of Precambrian and Paleozoic igneous and metamorphic rocks overlain by Mesozoic limestone and sandstone. The basement rocks consist of crystalline schists, gneiss, micaschist and amphibolite which are often intruded by granite. The western and northeastern parts of the Tonkin massif are locally covered by sandstones of the Korat series.

Permian limestones and sandstones outcrop along the Red river valley. The valley floor and delta of the river consist of Quaternary and recent deposits.

A4. *Quaternary basins*

Two extensive Quaternary basins occur in the Sunda shelf area: the Mekong and Chao Phraya river basins.

A4.1. The Mekong river basin consists of recent and older alluvial deposits of silt and clay which are sometimes interbedded with sandy layers. The higher river terraces are composed of sandy materials, while the Mekong delta alluvial deposits are generally clayey with occasional belts of fluvial sands in the coastal area. Isolated hills of granite, gabbro, sandstone and conglomerate are scattered throughout the river basin.

A4.2. The Chao Phraya river basin is made up of recent and older alluvium consisting of interbedded sand, silt and clay. In the north, laterite and weakly consolidated sediments occur together with gravel layers. Clayey alluvial deposits are found in the delta.

A5. *Borneo*

Although the eastern part of Borneo was slightly affected by the folding of the circum-Sunda orogenic system, the island as a whole forms part of the Sunda shelf and is divided into three main geological units.

A5.1. The continental Sunda shelf sector of Borneo consists of more or less stable parts of western Borneo which have not been subjected to Tertiary diastrophism. Three parts are distinguished:

In the northwest, the Chinese district consists of intensely metamorphosed Permo-Carboniferous deposits. Upper Triassic formations also occur as two facies: a metamorphosed flysch facies and a volcanic facies consisting of acid extrusives such as rhyolite.

In the south, the central axis, or Schwaner area, is almost entirely composed of a great quartz-diorite or tonalite plutonic massif.

The southern part of the Ketapang area consists of the Ketapang and Matan complexes. The Ketapang complex consists of a sandy shale with a typical flysch facies, but is almost entirely overlain by basaltic rocks of the Matan complex.

A5.2. The Embaluh zone consists of the Danau formation in the south grading northward to the Rajang formation. The Danau formation is composed of a complicated, intensely folded and overthrust succession of quartzite, shale, sandstone and limestone interbedded with ancient pyroclastic rocks. The Rajang formation consists of phyllitic and argillaceous sandstone. Mount Kinabalu in the north of the zone consists of granite, gneiss and schist.

A5.3. The Kuching zone extends east-west between the Upper Kapuas and the Schwaner mountains from Kuching toward the Makassar Strait and is characterized by gentle folds and fault structures of Paleogene age. The greater part of the Kuching zone consists of Paleogene and Neogene continental sandstone and Paleogene marine sandstone and marl.

South of the Kuching zone, the Meratus zone is made up of crystalline schists. The southern part of the Meratus range consists of basic intrusives including peridotite and pyroxenite.

B. Circum-Sunda orogenic system

The circum-Sunda orogenic system includes the Philippines in the northeast and merges southwestward into the great Sunda mountain system. Unlike the Sunda mountain system, no geosynclinal conditions appeared in the Philippines until after the Miocene period.

The great Sunda mountain system has a total length of about 7 000 km and extends from the Banda arc in the east along the Lesser Sunda Islands, Java, Sumatra and the Andaman and Nicobar Islands to the Arakan Yoma in Burma, where it meets the Himalayan system at a sharp angle of intersection. Throughout its length the Sunda mountain system consists of two parallel belts of mountain ranges, island arcs and submarine ridges. The inner belt is volcanic and the outer belt non-volcanic.

Two main phases of orogeny are recognized. An intensive phase which occurred toward the end of the Mesozoic and the beginning of the Tertiary was accompanied by intrusions of deep-lying igneous rocks, granites and peridotites. The second phase, which took place at the end of the Tertiary, was less violent than the first.

B1. *The Philippines*

The Philippines are characterized by high tectonic instability and volcanic activity. The basement consists chiefly of pre-Jurassic igneous rocks which outcrop in extensive areas of Mindanao, Palawan, Mindoro and Leyte. Two groups of igneous rocks are distinguished. The first comprises volcanic rocks and the second deep-lying plutonic rocks exposed by long, continuous erosion. Mesozoic sedimentary rocks outcrop, particularly in the north of Luzon, Mindoro and Panay. Granites and other plutonic rocks are more widely represented. Many are of Tertiary origin, contemporary with the great tectonic movements which began in the Miocene after a period of vigorous sedimentation during the Oligo-Miocene era resulting in the very thick deposit of the Vigo series. An unconformity, marking an erosion phase, separates these beds from the Pliocene Malumbang series.

Vertical movement continued until recent times, as can be seen by the uplifted Pliocene coral formations on Mount St. Thomas at an elevation of nearly 2 000 m. Post-glacial movements are best shown by raised beaches as high as 500 m above sea level, and filled-in valleys on the east coast.

The geology of the main islands of the Philippines is summarized as follows:

B1.1. The basic and ultrabasic intrusives which outcrop south of the Lingayen Gulf in Luzon are composed of gabbro, peridotite, pyroxenite and rhyolite. Effusives occupy a large part of the island. In the north they are composed of spilite and basalt, keratophyre and andesite of Cretaceous and Paleogene ages. The Pliocene and Quaternary volcanics which occur near Manila Bay and on the southeast arm of Luzon are composed chiefly of pyroxene-andesite and dacite, together with pyroclastics and basalt.

Much of Luzon is covered by the Vigo series, which is composed of marine Oligo-Miocene shelf deposits with greywacke, shale and limestone, and of the Mio-Pliocene molasse deposits of the Mulumbang series overlain by pyroclastics and tuffaceous sedimentary rocks. Reef limestone often occurs along the coast of Luzon. Extensive areas of recent and Pleistocene alluvial deposits are found in the plains of the Cagayan, Agno and Pampanga river valleys.

B1.2. The basement complex which outcrops on Mindoro consists of amphibolite, quartz and mica-schist, phyllite, quartzite and slate, together with some ultrabasic and basic plutonic rocks. In the eastern and western parts of the island the basement complex is overlain by the Tertiary Vigo series and Quaternary sediments.

B1.3. The greater part of Panay consists of the Vigo and Malumbang series, predominantly sandstone, shale and some limestone. Oligocene basic effusives including keratophyre and andesite occur in the northeast and northwest, often in association with pyroclastics.

B1.4. Volcanics occur in the north and south of the island of Negros. Their pyroxene-andesite core is surrounded by dacite and andesite flows and pyroclastics. The central part of the island consists of Mesozoic and Plio-Pleistocene clastic sediments, except for a small area in the southeast where Cretaceous metamorphics outcrop together with basic effusives.

Cebu and Bohol consist of the Malumbang series, Plio-Pleistocene limestone and sandstone, and some small outcrops of Cretaceous to Paleocene basic effusives.

B1.5. The northern part of Samar consists of the Malumbang series, which is locally overlain by pyroclastics. Cretaceous to Paleocene basic effusives occur to the south.

The greater part of Leyte is covered by the Malumbang series. The metamorphic basement complex outcrops over a small area in the northeastern part of the island.

B1.6. The western part of Mindanao consists of the metamorphic basement complex, which is overlain to the east by the Vigo series. The central part of the island consists of Tertiary and Quaternary volcanoes with pyroxene-andesite and dacite cores surrounded by pyroclastics and basalt. The eastern part is very complicated. In the northeast the basement complex outcrops together with basic intrusives. Tertiary sandstone, limestone, shale and conglomerate occur to the south. Near the Davao Gulf, Plio-Pleistocene volcanic products cover an extensive area. Recent alluvial deposits occur along the Agusan and Mindanao rivers.

B1.7. In the northern part of Palawan the metamorphic basement complex is covered by Jurassic clastic sediments including arkose, greywacke and mudstone. To the south there are Cretaceous ultrabasic and basic plutonic rocks, predominantly peridotite associated with gabbro and diabase dikes. The southern part of the island consists of metamorphosed lava flows of spilite, basalt, keratophyre and andesite which to the west are overlain by the Vigo series.

B2. *The Moluccas*

The Moluccas form a group of islands between Sulawesi (Celebes) and Irian Jaya. There is a strong contrast between volcanic islands and those formed mainly of sedimentary rocks. The volcanic islands are found in the Banda arc (Banda, Damar, etc.) and form a continuation of the active volcanic chain of Sumatra, Java and the Lesser Sunda Islands. The islands of this group are too small to be shown on the map.

The group comprising Ceram, Buru, Misool, Obi and their continuation in the Sula Islands are nonvolcanic. Here schists and granites are ringed with Mesozoic beds and overlain by Tertiary remnants. These are nearly horizontal in Misool and Obi, but are strongly folded in Ceram and Buru. The complexity of recent movements is shown by the very unequal uplifting of the Pliocene and Quaternary coral formations.

B2.1. The greater part of Ceram consists of Triassic sandstone of a flysch facies. It covers a belt of crystalline schists, predominantly phyllites, which outcrop in the southwestern part of the island. A belt of Quaternary deposits borders the northeast coast.

B2.2. The northern part of Buru consists of crystalline schist, gneiss, phyllite and amphibolite. Triassic flysch sandstone outcrops to the south.

B2.3. Misool consists almost entirely of limestone and marl of Jurassic to Pleistocene age. Triassic shale and quartzite outcrop only in a southern belt along the coast.

B2.4. The Sula Islands consist mainly of crystalline schists with granitic intrusions forming the basement complex. In the eastern part of Taliabu and the western part of Mangole, the schists are overlain by Jurassic and Cretaceous quartz-sandstone, calcareous sandstone and conglomerates.

B2.5. The core of the islands of the Halmahera group is formed by the crystalline basement complex which covers the southern part of the main island where basic intrusions also occur. To the north the basement complex is covered by Eocene tuff, sandstone and marl, and by andesitic and basaltic lava flows.

Cretaceous marl and limestone outcrop in several places, as do Tertiary and Quaternary limestone. Active volcanoes are found in the northern arm of the main island facing the Molucca Sea.

B3. *Sulawesi*

The irregular form of Sulawesi is due to many intersecting faults and important tectonic movements. During uplift in Tertiary and Quaternary times volcanism was very intense. The presence of raised Plio-Pleistocene coral reefs indicates that there have been repeated vertical movements during very recent or even contemporary times. The occurrence of several river captures supports this view.

B3.1. The northern arm of Sulawesi consists of the Minahasa zone in the east and the Gorontalo zone in the west. The Minahasa zone is characterized by active volcanoes and the surface consists of andesite and basalt flows, together with pyroclastics. Young Neogene sandstone outcrops along the west of the zone. The Gorontalo zone is east-west-trending. In the east, granite massifs are widely exposed. A polymetamorphic series of crystalline schist and phyllitic shale occurs toward the west.

B3.2. Central Sulawesi consists of three geologic zones. The Kolonodale zone in the eastern part is characterized by extensive outcrops of basic and ultrabasic igneous rocks, together with Mesozoic limestone and chert. The Poso zone in the central part consists largely of crystalline schist. The Palu zone in the west is characterized by extensive massifs of granodioritic rock, crystalline schist and sandstone.

B3.3. In the southeastern arm of Sulawesi south of the Kolonodale zone, metamorphic rocks consist of the Kolonabay beds of calcareous schist and shale, the Baitu beds of phyllite, quartzite and clay shale, and the Kendari beds of quartz-sandstone, quartzite and clay shale.

Muna and Butu islands consist of upper Triassic flysch deposits and Neogene marine sediments of limestone, marly shale and micaceous sandstone.

The core of Kabaena consists of ultrabasic peridotite and serpentinite, most of which are overlain by Neogene limestone.

B3.4. The southern arm of Sulawesi is divided into northern and southern parts, separated by an alluvial plain.

The Quarles and Latimodjong mountains of the northern part are composed of gneiss and crystalline schists, which also occur south of the alluvial plain. North of Mandar Bay and in the extreme south is the volcanic Maroro formation, which is composed of andesite, basalt and volcanic tuffs.

B4. *Lesser Sunda Islands*

The Lesser Sunda Islands are divided into the inner arc, comprising Wetar, Alor, Flores, Sumbawa, Lombok and Bali, and the outer arc, of which the main islands are Sumba, Timor and Tanimbar.

The significant difference between the two chains of islands is that the inner arc is volcanic, whereas the outer arc is covered by sedimentary formations.

B4.1. The western part of Wetar consists of andesite and dacite occurring as lava flows and volcanic breccia. In the east basalt becomes dominant with rhyolite occurring in places.

B4.2. Alor consists mainly of basalt and andesite with intercalated tuffs, limestone and marl showing characteristics of submarine volcanism. Quartz-andesite and dacite occur locally.

B4.3. Flores is almost entirely composed of dacite, andesite, basalt and some rhyolite effusives. Uplifted reef limestone of Plio-Pleistocene age occurs along the northwest coast. Miocene intrusive rocks, predominantly granodiorite, outcrop in small areas of central Flores.

B4.4. Sumbawa is composed of Neogene marine limestone and calc-alkaline rocks in the south, and in the north is crowned with volcanoes characterized by leucitic rocks.

B4.5. The southern part of Lombok consists of folded Tertiary volcanic breccias, tuffs and clay. The breccias contain andesite, dacite, trachite and liparite. In most places this complex is covered by limestone containing fragments of dacite tuff. Northern Lombok, separated from the south by an alluvial plain, consists of young basaltic and andesitic products.

B4.6. In the northern part of Bali young volcanism has produced basaltic rocks. The eastern part is mainly composed of the Batur complex consisting of andesite and basalt. The southern part of the island is composed of Miocene limestone.

B4.7. Sumba is covered by predominantly soft marl and limestone which are products of coral reefs uplifted during the Neogene. Igneous rocks such as rhyolite, andesite and basalt outcrop locally.

B4.8. The central part of Timor consists of the Sonnebait and Kekneno series, both composed of clastic sediments. The Sonnebait series is Permian and Mesozoic shallow-water sandstone and mudstone with some trachyt-basalt and olivine fragments. The Kekneno series is a Permian and Triassic flysch formation.

South of Dili the Palelo series, consisting of crystalline schists, is bounded on the east by the Ophiolite complex of ultrabasic and basic intrusives.

The greater part of the island is overlain by Neogene deposits, predominantly limestone, tuffaceous marls and shales.

B4.9. Much of Tanimbar consists of Mesozoic clastic sediments overlain by an upper Cretaceous limestone. Tertiary sediments, which cover the Mesozoic deposits in the southern part of the island, are predominantly limestone and marl.

B5. *Java and Madura*

Geologically, Java and Madura belong to the young Tertiary mountain system bordering the pre-Tertiary Sundaland.

Although older Cretaceous strata appear in small localities, Tertiary and Quaternary rocks are dominant and volcanic deposits are extensive.

The region is divided into three longitudinal belts.

B5.1. The southern belt is composed of Miocene limestone, marl, sandstone and conglomerate which are often mixed with volcanic materials. Clastic sediments occurring in the west consist of the Kebu beds composed of Miocene shale, tuffite and conglomerate, and the Butak beds composed of sandstone and shale.

The limestone plateaus consist of the Wonosari beds composed of platy marl and limestone, and the Kepek beds composed of Globigerine marl.

B5.2. The central belt is a volcanic zone composed of a succession of volcanoes whose products have covered the older landscape with lava, ash outpourings and lahars. Lapilli and volcanic ash cover the greater part of this area. Lavas are basic and consist mainly of pyroxene-andesite and basalt. In the extreme west is a granite massif covered by Eocene sandstone.

B5.3. The northern belt consists of the Rembang-Madura anticlinorium in the east and the alluvial plain near Jakarta.

The Rembang-Madura anticlinorium is composed of two belts of massive limestone separated by a low central belt of marly sedimentaries which are mostly overlain by Quaternary alluvial deposits.

On the northwestern side of this belt is Mount Murjo, a volcano consisting of leucite-tephrite, a basic effusive composed of calcic plagioclase and leucite.

B6. *Sumatra*

Geotectonically, Sumatra is divided into two parts: the wide coastal plains in the northeast, and the western mountain ranges.

The northeastern coastal plains form part of the Sunda shelf, and the western mountain ranges belong to the circum-Sunda orogenic system which continues on through the Arakan Yoma range in western Burma.

B6.1. In the northern mountains, metamorphic crystalline schists, orthogneiss, quartzitic sandstone and marble predominate around Atjeh, together with diabase, andesite and gabbro basic effusives. There are also some granitic outcrops. Tertiary formations of limestone, marl, conglomerate, sandstone and shale outcrop on the north coast.

South of Atjeh effusive liparitic tuffs occur in the vicinity of Lake Toba. These overlie Paleozoic quartzitic sandstone and slate, and have been partly eroded.

B6.2. The Barisan range forms the mountainous part of Sumatra south of Lake Toba. In the north are two parallel ranges: the western range composed of granite with micaschist and quartzite, and the eastern one composed of shale and limestone, with conglomerate, quartzite and some limestone to the south. The southern part of the Barisan range is mainly composed of basic and some acid effusives. The Tigapula range, however, consists of sandy clay shale and quartzitic sandstone. Tertiary sandstone and liparitic tuffs outcrop near the coast, but further inland these are overlain by young volcanic materials.

B6.3. In the northeastern lowlands the Tertiary deposits occurring adjacent to the Barisan range are clay marl overlain by a thick series of liparitic tuff and sandstone. Tertiary limestone, marl, conglomerate and some sandstone and shale are found near Atjeh. The remaining part of the lowlands is covered by alluvial deposits consisting mainly of fluvial sediments which for the greater part are interbedded with acid volcanic deposits.

B6.4. The islands west of Sumatra consist of limestone and sandstone locally covered by recent sediments. Simeulue Island in the north consists of Neogene sandstone, except on the east coast where coral limestone outcrops. Nias Island consists of Neogene sandstone, shale, tuffaceous siltstone and silty clay. Siberut Island is composed of limestone, calcareous and tuffaceous sandstone, and marl. The Mentawai Islands in the south consist mainly of quartz-sandstone and some marly limestone overlying pre-Tertiary quartzite and amphibolite.

B6.5. The biotite-granite core of Bangka and Belitung Islands east of Sumatra is mostly overlain by sedimentary formations of sandstone, quartzite and clay shale.

C. SAHUL SHELF AREA

As the main parts of the Sahul shelf fall within the Australasia region (Volume X), this area is only briefly discussed here.

The Sahul shelf is similar to the Sunda shelf in its morphology, and is the northern extension of the Australian continental mass that is partially inundated by the shallow Arafura Sea. The southern alluvial plain of Irian Jaya and the Aru Islands form part of the shelf, which was not affected by the Tertiary orogenies.

C1. *Aru Islands*

The Aru Islands lie on the northern edge of the Sahul shelf area. They are divided by three narrow channels which have been variously interpreted as remnant stream courses that once traversed the former land surface between Irian Jaya and the Aru Islands, or as fault lines.

The Aru Islands are mainly composed of horizontal beds of coraline limestone, although granite is exposed on the southern island of Trangan.

D. CIRCUM-AUSTRALIAN OROGENIC SYSTEM

As with the Sahul shelf, the greater part of the circum-Australian orogenic system falls within the Australasia region (Volume X) and is only briefly discussed here.

The circum-Australian orogenic system extends along the central axis of Irian Jaya through the archipelagoes east of Australia to New Zealand.

D1. *Irian Jaya*

The mountainous area of Irian Jaya consists mainly of sedimentary and low-grade metamorphic rocks. The majority of the lithological formations are of Tertiary to Pleistocene age, with considerable areas of Paleozoic rocks in the central part forming the backbone of the main island from northwest to southeast. Lithologically there appears to be a gradual decrease in acidity of the rocks from west to east. In the central parts of the main island the mountain ranges are of considerable width and contain several large intermontane valleys filled with Pleistocene and recent alluvial deposits.

D1.1 The northern part of the Doberai (Vogelkop) Peninsula consists of the Kemum formation composed of Paleozoic and Mesozoic sandstone and shale which for the greater part are metamorphosed to phyllitic slate and quartzitic greywacke. To the north and east this formation is overlain by the Betanta formation comprising basic effusive rocks of basalt, keratophyre, pyroclastics and tuffs.

The southern part of the peninsula consists of the Miocene Klasaman, Marchesa and Steenkool formations.

The Klasafat formation outcrops in a small area near Sorong and consists of Globigerina marl with lenses of limestone. The upper part is sandy. The Kais formation runs from Klamono in the west to Sarera (Geelvink) Bay in the east and consists of chalky limestone overlain by coral fragments in a matrix of marly clay.

The sandy clay Klasaman formation is marly in the lower part and intercalated with clayey and calcareous sand. It occurs in the western part of the Doberai Peninsula and Salawati Island together with the Marchesa formation, which consists of limestone debris from raised coral reefs.

The Steenkool formation in the southeastern part of the Doberai consists of clastic sediments of alternating sandstone and clay with intercalations of conglomerate.

The Bomberai Peninsula consists of the Plio-Pleistocene Buru formation, which is composed of thin-bedded sandy, silty and sometimes marly shale with abundant shells and carbonized plant remains.

The Onin Peninsula consists of the Eocene Onin formation composed of hard marl and limestone, with some minor sandstone and quartzitic layers.

The Kumawa mountains consist of the Oligocene Kumawa formation composed of argillaceous limestone overlain by sandy marl.

Waigeo Island northwest of the Doberai consists of basic intrusives and, to the south, the massive coral limestone deposits of the Waigeo formation.

D1.2. The central part of Irian Jaya consists of the Van Rees mountains which are separated from the Maoke mountains by the Meervlakte intermontane depression. The Van Rees mountains are mainly composed of the Plio-Pleistocene Mamberamo formation of sandstone and conglomerate with intercalations of limestone, marl and siltstone. Ultrabasic igneous rocks and local metamorphic greenschist occur near Djajapura (formerly Hollandia) and 50 km south of Sarmi.

The core of the Maoke mountains consists of Paleozoic and Mesozoic sediments largely metamorphosed to quartz-micaschist with some chlorite and graphite, and intruded with granite and granodiorite. On northern slopes toward the west is the Cretaceous Kembelangan formation consisting of shale and sandstone with intercalations of quartzitic sandstone. On southern slopes calcareous sediments predominate in the form of Mesozoic and Tertiary limestone and marl with a minor occurrence of shale and sandstone. The Buru formation outcrops along the southern foothills of the Maoke mountains. Chalky limestone with intercalations of calcareous clays of the Digul formation outcrop in the Digul river area.

D1.3. The southern alluvial plain consists of two dominant types of sediments: recent and subrecent alluvial and deltaic deposits, and Plio-Pleistocene alluvial deposits.

The recent and subrecent alluvial deposits in the lower parts of the alluvial plain comprise poorly drained level flood plains and swamps of recent alluvium, peat and locally some better drained levees and terraces. The Plio-Pleistocene alluvial deposits occur in a gently undulating to rolling landscape comprising the higher parts of the southern alluvial plain up to an elevation of 400 m.

PHYSIOGRAPHY

To facilitate description, Southeast Asia has been divided into 10 physiographic regions which are further subdivided into 30 physiographic units. The names given to these regions and units have meaning when applied to Southeast Asia as a whole and do not in all instances conform to national names. (For example, the Korat plateau as used here extends beyond the Korat plateau of Thailand.) The physiographic features of these regions and units are described in this section and shown in Figure 6.

1. Indochinese Peninsula
   1a. Malay Peninsula
   1b. Western highlands
   1c. Central highlands
   1d. Korat plateau
   1e. Eastern highlands
   1f. Northern highlands
   1g. Chao Phraya lowlands
   1h. Mekong lowlands

2. Borneo

3. Philippines
   3a. Luzon
   3b. Mindoro
   3c. Panay
   3d. Negros, Cebu and Bohol
   3e. Samar and Leyte
   3f. Mindanao
   3g. Palawan

4. Moluccas
   4a. Ceram
   4b. Buru
   4c. Misool
   4d. Obi
   4e. Sula Islands
   4f. Halmahera

5. Sulawesi

6. Lesser Sunda Islands
   6a. Wetar
   6b. Alor
   6c. Flores
   6d. Sumbawa
   6e. Lombok
   6f. Bali
   6g. Sumba
   6h. Timor
   6i. Tanimbar

7. Java and Madura

8. Sumatra

9. Aru Islands

10. Irian Jaya

1. INDOCHINESE PENINSULA

1a. *Malay Peninsula*

Physiographically, the Malay Peninsula is considered as the southern part of the Indochinese Peninsula, and extends to the alluvial plain of the Khirirat river in the north. The peninsula consists of a number of north-south-running parallel mountain ridges. In the central part eleven ridges are distinguished.

To the south six are recognized, diminishing in height southward until they disappear beneath the sea, emerging again as the hills of Lingga, Riau and Bangka islands. In general, relief is diversified, and there are extensive tracts of low undulating land. The Korbu range is the most continuous and rises to a height of 2 850 m near the frontier with Thailand.

West of the Korbu range the terrain is undulating and extensively developed. Large plains and extensive mangrove swamps occur along the west coast. Some of these lowlands are formed by alluvial deposits washed down by rivers, while others are the result of the denudation to base level of soft tracts of shale.

East of the Korbu range there are extensive forested mountains and the terrain is less developed than on the western side. Although generally hilly, the east coast comprises several broad open plains of varying extent which are usually under cultivation.

1b. *Western highlands*

These comprise the Bilauktaung range in the south and the southern part of the Shan highlands in the north. They consist of a narrow continuous area with parallel north-south-running ranges separated by narrow, steep-sided valleys. The mountains are largely sharp-crested with steep, highly dissected slopes and narrow V-shaped valleys. Several mountain and hill ranges, particularly in the south, have highly weathered limestone ridges with isolated pinnacles and numerous caverns and sinkholes.

1c. *Central highlands*

These are characterized by a series of discontinuous, north-south mountain and hill ranges separated by long, narrow valley plains and intermontane basins.

The northern part of the central highlands is an intensely folded old mountain system in an advanced stage of erosion. Mountains and hills with steep, dissected slopes predominate, becoming more rounded and flat-topped toward the south. The northernmost rivers join the Mekong, but for the greater part the area drains southward into the Chao Phraya. The valleys range from narrow forested gorges to broad, open cultivated tracts toward the south. Most plains and basins are rolling and dissected with small scattered hills. Wide banks of alluvium bordering the streams form the principal agricultural land. The highlands decrease in elevation toward the south. Along the Gulf of Thailand rugged uplands rise steeply above a narrow coastal plain. The Cardamom mountains and the Chaîne de l'Eléphant are nearly continuous ranges, but the western end of the uplands is quite broken, with hills and mountains separated by rolling and dissected plains. A number of alluvial valleys are found in the Cardamom mountains. The low hills of these peneplained folded rocks extend to the straight eastern side of the Bight of Bangkok where a fault structure extends the line of the Dong Paya scarp. Along the coast there are flat to gently undulating plains, and the coastline is fairly irregular with many rugged headlands and steep cliffs.

1d. *Korat plateau*

The Korat plateau is a large saucer-shaped basin tilted toward the southeast and surrounded by hills and mountains. The basin floor, a flat to gently rolling plain 150 m in elevation, is drained by the Mekong, which skirts its northern and eastern edges. The landscape is characterized by broad, flat, incised valleys and flat-topped mesa-like interfluves where the water table remains well below the surface for most of the year. Salt-affected soils occur, especially in regions under cultivation. Wide marshy tracts extend along the Nam Mun and Nam Chi rivers. The Mekong enters a gorge-like valley below the confluence with the Nam Mun. During heavy rains this gorge causes the Nam Mun valley to inundate far upstream. Numerous scattered hills occur in rolling and dissected plains of the Korat plateau. The nearly continuous Pnom Dang Rek hill range forms the edge of the plateau in the south and southeast, and the western limit is formed by the Dong Paya scarp.

1e. *Eastern highlands*

The eastern highlands mainly consist of the Annam range, a massive range of mountains and hills 50 to 330 km wide which extends some 1 000 km from north to south to form the watershed of the Mekong river basin. In the west the Annam range extends into Lao through a series of plateaus, including the Plateau des Bolovens in the north and the Mong plateau in the south.

Mountains dominate the north and central parts of the eastern highlands, but to the south dissected hills and rolling to hilly plateaus are more common. In the north the Khammouane plateau is largely surrounded by an extensive hilly limestone area containing a maze of steep ridges and pinnacles with numerous sinkholes, caves and disappearing streams. Upland plains and plateaus are most extensive in the Kontum and Dar Lac areas. Along the western periphery smaller upland plains are common, comprising generally rolling or dissected terrain with numerous scattered small hills. Along the coast, narrow discontinuous plains are separated by rugged mountains and hilly outliers of the main range. In most places the mountains and hills of the Annam range are rugged, steeply sloping and highly dissected. The valleys are narrow and steep-sided, especially on the eastern side. In the south the hills are generally less rugged and the crests are more rounded.

Along the coast a narrow strip of alluvium has accumulated between the scarp of the Annam range and the belt of sand dunes piled up by tide and wind which form a long island off the mouth of the Hue river.

1f. *Northern highlands*

The greater part of the northern highlands consists of an extensive rugged mountain area in which the main ranges trend northeast-southwest. The mountains are rough and sharp-crested with steep, highly dissected slopes and narrow V-shaped valleys. There are some scattered hill areas and numerous intermontane basins, and on the Xieng Khouang plateau is the large Plain of Jars upland. Although the mountains are not particularly high, in the north they form a great square block of tangled and densely forested highlands.

The Red river has incised its course in the northern highlands, and toward the Gulf of Tonkin the valley plains of this river and its tributaries, especially the Song Bo (Black river), cover a great area. The Red river is extremely difficult to control. Its estimated annual silt load is 2 000 million m^3, most of which is carried into the sea. Owing to the deposition of sediments in the river bed, the river level near Hanoi is sometimes 6 m above that of the bordering alluvial land. The delta of the Red river, most of which lies at less than 3 m above sea level, is a network of distributaries carrying off water from the Red river and other streams rising in the deforested northern highlands.

1g. *Chao Phraya lowlands*

The Chao Phraya lowlands form a large lowland plain extending northwest from the Gulf of Thailand for about 650 km. The lowlands are drained primarily by the southward-flowing tributaries of the Chao Phraya river. In the north, narrow plains extend into the highlands along major streams. Flat to gently rolling plains predominate. In the south the extremely flat, poorly drained plains of the Chao Phraya delta are crisscrossed by numerous canals, drainage ditches and streams. The plains lie barely above sea level and are subject to regular annual flooding. They are drained by slow-running rivers, of which the Chao Phraya is the largest. Its bed has been raised several metres above the level of the plain by alluvial accumulation.

Several groups of hills and mountains interrupt the monotony of the plains, and isolated limestone pinnacles and ridges are scattered throughout. The coastline is low and irregular.

1h. *Mekong lowlands*

The Mekong lowlands comprise an extensive lowland plain drained primarily by the north-south-trending Mekong and the northwest-southeast-trending Lake Tonle. The lowlands extend for about 800 km north to south and 600 km east to west. The surface consists of flat to gently rolling plains which become more rolling and dissected toward the north and east. South of Phnom Penh the poorly drained flat plains of the low-lying Mekong delta are crossed by numerous canals, ditches, small streams, and the wide Mekong tributaries. Natural levees occur along the larger streams which contain numerous large, flat islands. Many small groups of hills, isolated hills and a few mountain groups are scattered throughout the area, except in the extreme south. The coastline is fairly regular, with few embankments and hilly promontories. Mudflats border most of the coast and tidal streams. Large areas of the delta are still occupied by marshes, and other areas such as the Plaine des Joncs are flooded during part of the year.

2. BORNEO

Borneo, with an area of 740 000 km², is the second largest island of the Indonesian archipelago. It is flanked on the west and south by shallow seas scarcely 50 m deep, but to the north and east there is only a narrow continental platform and the sea floor slopes steeply to depths of 3 000 to 4 000 m.

A broad mountain system traverses the island from the Kinabalu range in the north with mount Kinabalu (4 101 m), via the Muller mountains, to the Schwaner range in the southwest. This complex mountain system forms the divide of the island from which other chains branch off to the east and west. The western branches of the central mountain system are the Upper Kapuas mountains, the Hose mountains and the Dulit range. The eastern branches are the Brassey range, ending in the peninsula north of Darvel Bay, and a second mountain range ending in the Mangkalihat Peninsula. In the southwestern part of the island only a few isolated peaks reach 1 000 m, but in the east the highland forms a compact mass with peaks reaching an altitude of 2 000 m. In the southeastern part of the island the north-south-trending Meratus range has a more isolated position.

Large parts of the central Borneo highlands have reached an advanced stage of geomorphological maturity, varying from the rounded slopes of igneous rocks to the flat-topped interfluves of sandstone country, such as the Madi plateau in which ravine-like valleys have been cut.

Much of the island is covered by dense forest, and lowlands are so poorly drained that little cultivation is practised. In the north and northeast the hills and mountains almost reach the sea, while in the south and southwest the coastal plains extend far inland. Here the coast consists of a succession of deltaic swamps and peat formations, some of them 100 km wide, fringed with mangrove swamps and Nipa palms. On the east coast the Mahakam and Mentarang rivers have built up extensive deltas.

3. THE PHILIPPINES

The Philippines consist of 10 large islands and about 7 000 smaller ones, most of which are little more than isolated rocks or corals standing above the sea. Except for the shallow sea to the south, the Philippines are separated from the Asiatic mainland by deep seas, including the Mindanao Trench, which is over 10 km deep.

3a. *Luzon*

Two north-south-trending mountain ranges extend into northern Luzon: the central mountains in the west, including Luzon's highest peak, Mount Pulog (2 929 m); and the Sierra Madre in the east. They are separated by the Cagayan valley, which is one of the most important cropland areas in the Philippines. Toward the south the central lowlands run from Manila Bay to the Lingayen Gulf, forming a generally flat plain which for the most part rises only a few metres above sea level. The rugged, densely forested Zambales area along the west coast is separated from the sea by a narrow coastal plain consisting of raised coral reefs and recent alluvium.

The southern peninsula of Luzon consists of an alternation of northwest-southeast-trending mountains, volcanoes including the active 2 462-metre-high Mount Mayon, and interior plains.

3b. *Mindoro*

The northwestern part of the island is an area of recent volcanic activity. The mountain chain traversing the island from northwest to southeast includes Mount Halcon (2 600 m) and Mount Baco (2 500 m). Toward the east and west this chain is bordered by coastal plains.

3c. *Panay*

A mountain range bordering the west coast, it has peaks of over 2 000 m. To the north and east is an extensive plain which in places is occupied by marshes, especially where deltas have built up.

3d. *Negros, Cebu and Bohol*

Negros consists of a north-south-trending mountain range and, to the northwest, of a 30-km-wide coastal plain covered with volcanic deposits. Volcanoes occur at the northern and southern extremities of the mountain range; Mount Canlaon, an active volcano in the north, is nearly 2 500 m high.

Cebu consists of a single mountain chain surrounded by erosional surfaces with coral deposits uplifted to varying levels.

Bohol shows an advanced stage of karstic evolution with numerous limestone hills rising from a plateau.

3e. *Samar and Leyte*

The island of Samar is a deeply incised plateau of Tertiary and volcanic rocks. Leyte is characterized by longitudinal ridges which are mostly rugged remnants of volcanoes rising to 1 300 m above sea level. Extensive lowlands, some of them marshy, occur in the northern part of Samar and on both islands near the narrow San Juanico Strait.

3f. *Mindanao*

Mindanao is characterized by two great tectonic depressions that were filled in in recent times. These are the plain of the Agusan river in the northeast and that of the Cotabato river in the southwest. Both plains are formed by the silting up of an arm of the sea. They are littered with lakes, swamps and creeks, and are fringed with mangrove swamps along the coast. The Agusan plain is separated from the east coast by the Dinata range, which rises to a height of 2 200 m at Mount Kampalili in the south. A north-south-trending range rising to the west of the plain includes Mount Apo (2 965 m), the highest peak in the Philippines. A huge volcanic complex west of this range includes Lake Lanao, which was formed by a lava-dam at an altitude of 700 m. The western part of Mindanao is formed by the 10-km-wide isthmus of the Zamboanga Peninsula. Ridges with flat tops at about 1 800 m are surmounted by eroded volcanoes such as Mount Malindang (2 425 m). The ridges are tilted toward the west and disappear beneath the sea, forming the Sulu Islands which connect Mindanao with northern Borneo.

3g. *Palawan*

The island of Palawan consists of an elongated, northeast-southwest-trending mountain range which is immediately bordered by the sea, almost without coastal plains. The highest peak of the island is Mount Mantalingajan (nearly 2 100 m) in the south.

4. THE MOLUCCAS

The Moluccas comprise most of the islands between Sulawesi (Celebes) and Irian Jaya and between the Philippines and Timor. Structurally, the islands are grouped into three arcs. The first arc passes through Damar and Banda as a continuation of the active volcanic chains of Sumatra, Java and the Lesser Sunda Islands. These islands are all of volcanic origin, but are too small to warrant separate description. The second arc consists of the nonvolcanic islands of Ceram and Buru. The third arc runs from Obi through Misool to the Sula Islands with a northern outlier formed by Halmahera Island.

4a. *Ceram*

Ceram is predominantly mountainous, rising to 3 000 m in the centre. Toward the eastern part of the island the ranges become hilly and there are several low and swampy plains. The mountain ranges are generally undulating, without clearly defined peaks. Most of the island is densely forested. The Ambon islands southeast of Ceram are of volcanic origin.

4b. *Buru*

Buru is an oval-shaped non-volcanic island. In the high mountains in the western part, Mount Tomaku reaches an altitude of 2 400 m. Toward the east the mountains are comparatively low, and a wide circular level plain surrounds Kajeli Bay. Most of the island is forested; only the northern part is bare of trees. Extensive marshy lowlands occur along the coast.

4c. *Misool*

Misool is flat to gently rolling in the north, and becomes hilly toward the south, with peaks rising to almost 1 000 m. The island is surrounded by many coral islets.

4d. *Obi*

The island of Obi is very mountainous, rising to over 2 000 m in the centre. A 10-km-wide coastal plain borders the sea on the east and west, but on the north and south the densely wooded mountains descend steeply to an irregular coastline.

4e. *Sula Islands*

The Sula Islands consist of three large islands and many smaller ones. They are non-volcanic, have hilly interiors, and are fringed with swampy coastal plains. The greater part of the islands is densely forested.

4f. *Halmahera*

Halmahera is shaped roughly like Sulawesi. The four long peninsulas are high, densely forested mountain chains which join in the centre of the island. The northern peninsula is volcanic with three active peaks. Broad flat valleys border the mountains and coral formations occur in the island interior.

5. SULAWESI

Sulawesi has an irregular shape and consists of a series of mountain ranges and plateaus intersected in places by tectonic depressions and river valleys, often forming narrow gorges. Lakes are numerous, particularly in the central part of the island. Some lakes were formed tectonically and are very deep, such as Lake Poso (500 m) and Lake Matana (600 m). Other lakes have been filled in and form marshy inland flats. The generally rocky coast often rises in steep cliffs fringed by coral reefs.

The Minahasa peninsula of the northern arm of Sulawesi is characterized by volcanoes such as Mount Kiabat (2 022 m). To the northeast the mountains diminish in height and disappear below the sea, forming scattered small islands. To the west, the Gorantalo sector comprises a mountain chain which merges southward into the Palu zone, where the highest point is Mount Nokilalaki (3 300 m).

To the south Mount Gandadiwata (3 074 m) forms the highest peak of the central highlands. To the west of these highlands is a broad marshy plain where the Lariang river has built up its delta. To the east the highlands grade into a peneplain-type plateau which is dissected by a tectonic depression in which lies Lake Poso.

The northeastern peninsula is formed by the Bulutumpu range. Along the coast extensive alluvial plains are bordered by mangrove swamps.

The southeastern arm is separated from central Sulawesi by an extensive alluvial plain. To the west is a mountain massif, and in the eastern part of the southeast arm there are extensive marshy lowlands. The Muna and Butung islands, separated from the southeastern peninsula by the shallow Tioro and Butung straits, are mainly lowlands fringed with mangrove swamps.

The southern arm of Sulawesi consists predominantly of lowlands with elevations of less than 200 m. Only Mount Rantekombola (3 455 m) in the north, which is an extension of the central highlands, and the more isolated Mount Lompobatang (2 371 m) in the south are surrounded by uplands. Extensive lowlands, often fringed with mangrove swamps, occur along the coast, while the Sidereng-Tempe lake belt traverses the southern peninsula from west to east.

6. LESSER SUNDA ISLANDS

The Lesser Sunda Islands are divided into the volcanic inner arc, consisting of Wetar, Alor, Flores, Sumbawa, Lombok and Bali, and the non-volcanic outer arc of Sumba, Timor and Tanimbar.

6a. *Wetar*

The island of Wetar is formed by volcanoes, the highest of which exceeds 1 000 m. The terrain is hilly and almost bare of trees. The coast is irregular and steep and is fringed with coral reefs.

6b. *Alor*

Alor is very mountainous, the highest peaks being the old volcanoes of Mount Kolana (1 900 m) in the east and Mount Mina (1 400 m) in the southwest. Five volcanoes on the island are active. The surface, dissected by steep ravines, comprises a plateau and a number of small coastal plains. The coast is mainly rocky with few indentations, but on the west coast Kalabahi Bay separates a northwestern promontory from the rest of the island, with which it is connected by a very low narrow alluvial isthmus. The island is covered mainly by low trees and alang-alang grass (*Imperata cylindrica*).

6c. *Flores*

Flores is the most mountainous island of the Lesser Sunda group. Elevations reach 2 400 m and there are practically no lowlands. Mountain areas and plateau areas in the east are deeply dissected by extensively branched streams. Valleys are narrow, steep-sided, deeply incised, and extend to within a short distance of the coastline, leaving a very narrow coastal plain. There are numerous active volcanoes on the island.

6d. *Sumbawa*

Sumbawa is a partially volcanic mountainous island. The highest point is the active volcano of Mount Tambora (2 850 m). A mountain chain traverses the island from east to west, decreasing in height in the central part, where it forms a narrow land bridge.

There are only a few stretches of alluvium along the coast and the island is surrounded by coral reefs. Most of the island is under forest.

6e. *Lombok*

The greater part of the island consists of rolling plains extending from the coast to an interior elevation of 500 m above sea level. The central part is traversed by an alluvial depression running from east to west which separates the southern mountains from the northern Rindjani range. The entire landscape shows the effects of volcanism.

6f. *Bali*

Bali is dominated by volcanism. A chain of active volcanoes occurs in the northern part of the island. Mount Agung (3 150 m) is the highest, and Mount Batur the most active. The northern slopes of the volcanoes are scored by short streams. On southern slopes large streams fan southward to build an inclined alluvial plain.

6g. *Sumba*

The dominant physiographic features of Sumba are extensive marine terraces and the mountains along the south coast. The marine terraces extend from the coastline some 20 to 30 km inland to elevations of 600 m. The upper terraces grade into hilly and deeply dissected plateaus. The central plains and plateaus are surrounded by slightly higher and more rugged terrain, but elevations are generally less than 800 m. The south coast mountains are eroded and bare, and reach elevations of up to 1 200 m.

6h. *Timor*

Timor is a mountainous non-volcanic island. The Mutis mountains in the southwest, rising to 2 450 m at Mount Miumafo, are separated by a central alluvial depression from the northeastern range, which attains an elevation of 2 900 m. The mountains rise steeply from the north and east coasts. To the south they grade into low hills and plains, but the width of the coastal plain, in which the rivers end as marshes, barely exceeds 5 km. In eastern Timor a series of karstic Triassic limestone plateaus surrounded by mesas rise to 1 200 m.

6i. *Tanimbar*

The Tanimbar Islands consist of a group of 66 islands, of which Jamdena is the largest. All the islands are non-volcanic and low-lying, with elevations rarely exceeding 200 m. Much of the terrain consists of impenetrable swamps. The higher parts of Jamdena island are under forest.

7. JAVA AND MADURA

Physiographically, Java and Madura are divided into four units: the north coast limestone platforms, the southern mountains, the volcanic zone and the northern alluvial belt.

The north coast limestone platforms of Rembang (Java) and Madura consist of a nearly continuous karstic plateau with an average height of 250 m. In Rembang the plateau consists of gently sloping hills interrupted by wide valleys. In Madura a low longitudinal belt with undulating relief runs through the middle of the island. A very narrow alluvial plain fringes the Rembang coast and the cliff-like limestone hills. In the extension into Madura, the alluvial fringe is discontinuous and only small alluvium embayments separate the steep limestone cliffs.

The southern mountains consist of a number of limestone plateaus which rise steeply from the coast and form a landscape of tropical karst. The limestone is porous and the surface generally barren with no surface rivers. The coast is rocky and strongly indented by deep inlets.

In Java volcanoes are mainly distributed along the medial ridge and valley belt comprising an older, mature dissected landscape. They rise steeply to great heights above all other relief forms; 14 cones exceed 3 000 m. The landscape pattern depends on whether the volcanic ejecta were deposited as molten lava, ash, or lahars. The latter is a mud flow resulting from a torrential flow of water acting upon volcanic debris.

The northern alluvial belt is divided into two parts. The discontinuous, inner portion near the uplands is lined by low terraces running roughly parallel to the coast. It rises in places to altitudes of 100 m and has an irregular topography due to the incision of watercourses below terrace level. The outer portion of the alluvial belt is flat and less than 15 m above sea level. Rapid delta formation is taking place, at a rate which increases temporarily whenever there is an outburst of volcanic activity in the interior.

8. SUMATRA

The physiography of Sumatra is fairly simple. Its backbone is formed by the Barisan range extending into the northern mountains and including the Semanko rift zone. The slopes toward the Indian Ocean are generally steep and consequently the southwest coastal belt is mountainous. The northeastern part of the island is occupied by broad, hilly tracts of Tertiary formations, and a very extensive lowland plain occurs along the northeast coast.

The Barisan range with its northern extension is 1 650 km long and about 100 km wide. It runs along the entire southwest coast and consists of small ranges, jagged ridges and plateaus of tuff often broken by canyons and volcanoes. The moutain area is grooved by the longitudinal trough of the Semanko rift zone, which can be followed from the northwest to the extreme southeast. The altitude of the Semanko rift zone is variable, and it is often interrupted by volcanoes such as the Batak hills containing Lake Toba. Nearly all recent volcanoes, of which there are about one hundred, are found in this trench or on its edge. Twelve are still active.

The northeastern lowlands occupy roughly half of Sumatra. On the equator and in the latitude of Palembang these lowlands are about 200 km wide. In central Sumatra the alluvial plain is for the greater part covered by volcanic deposits originating from the Toba hill mass.

A band about 100 km wide along the coast contains extensive oligotrophic ombrogenous peat swamp formations which are fringed with mangrove swamps.

The islands off the east coast are related to the Malay Peninsula. Here ridges and hills suddenly rise from gently undulating surfaces, reaching heights of nearly 1 200 m in Pulau and Lingga. Mangrove swamps fringe the coast in many places, particularly on the Riau and Lingga islands.

9. Aru Islands

The Aru group consists of around a hundred islands, of which only five are large. The entire group is closely packed, with individual islands being separated by narrow water channels. The terrain is flat and low; it consists of extensive marshes along the coasts and river banks and is broken by low hills which are densely forested. On the southern islands grassy plains are fringed with mangrove swamps along the coasts and rivers.

10. Irian Jaya

Irian Jaya is an area of great physiographic contrasts. Rugged mountain ranges, some 2 000 to 4 000 m high, rise abruptly from the sea, forming young alluvial flood plains, or are flanked by lower foothills which are generally dissected. Very extensive plains are found on the south and north coasts. Intermontane plains such as the Meervlakte also occur widely.

Physiographically, Irian Jaya is divided into the Raja Ampat area, the Doberai (Vogelkop) Peninsula, the Maoke mountains, the Meervlakte intermontane depression, the Van Rees mountains, and the southern alluvial plain.

The Raja Ampat area and the western part of the Doberai are formed by a large number of islands separated by deep channels. The islands generally have steep cliff coastlines. The largest island, Waigeo, is hilly to mountainous with pinnacle topography in its calcareous part.

The Doberai Peninsula consists of a massive mountain complex in its northern part rising to the 3 100-metre peak of Mount Gwamongga. Northern slopes fall steeply to the Pacific Ocean, almost without a coastal plain. Southern slopes diminish in height to form an extensive rolling plain grading to marshy lowlands which are separated from the sea by belts of tidal mangrove swamps or a series of low beach ridges. The Bomberai Peninsula consists almost entirely of an extensive marshy alluvial plain which is bounded on the south and west by the Kumawa and Onin mountains.

The Maoke mountains form a complex rugged mountain system with a maximum altitude of over 5 000 m — the highest in Southeast Asia. The ranges are dissected by river valley systems. Large dome-shaped masses of intrusive rocks commonly stand out in the landscape.

The Meervlakte, which is only 50 m above sea level, is an intermontane depression situated between the Maoke mountains and the Van Rees mountains. The plain is entirely covered with recent and subrecent alluvium of the Taritatu (Idenburg) and Tariku (Rouffaer) rivers which join in the north to form the Mamberamo river.

The southern part of Irian Jaya consists mainly of a swampy plain traversed by numerous tidal rivers that carry large amounts of silt. A sandy beach ridge often occurs along the coast. In the southern plain remnants of old river terraces occur locally, forming flat-topped narrow hills composed of sandy material with small well-rounded pebbles.

References

CLIMATE

KOTESWARAM, P. Climate and meteorology of humid tropical
1974 Asia. In *Natural resources of humid tropical Asia*,
        p. 27-85. Paris, Unesco.

PAPADAKIS, J. *Climatic tables for the world.* Buenos Aires.
1961

PAPADAKIS, J. *Climates of the world and their agricultural*
1966 *potentialities.* Buenos Aires.

VEGETATION

ANDERSON, J.A.R. Observations on the ecology of five peat
1976 swamp forests in Sumatra and Kalimantan. In *Peat
        and podzolic soils and their potential for agriculture in
        Indonesia*, p. 45-55. Bogor, Soil Research Institute.
        Bulletin No. 3.

DELVERT, J. *Le paysan cambodgien*. Paris and The Hague,
1961 Mouton. 740 p.

JACOBS, M. Botanical panorama of the Malesian archipelago
1974 (vascular plants). In *Natural resources of humid tropical Asia*, p. 263-294. Paris, Unesco.

LEGRIS, P. Vegetation and floristic composition of humid
1974 tropical continental Asia. In *Natural resources of humid tropical Asia*, p. 217-238. Paris, Unesco.

SCHMITHÜSEN, J. *Atlas zur Biogeographie*. Mannheim/Wien/
1976 Zürich, Geographisch-Kartographisches Institut Meyer.

VAN STEENIS, C.G.G.J. *Vegetation map of Malaysia*. 1:
1958 5 000 000. Paris, Unesco.

WHYTE, R.O. Grasses and grasslands. In *Natural resources
1974 of humid tropical Asia*, p. 239-262. Paris, Unesco.

WYATT-SMITH, J. A preliminary vegetation map of Malaya
1964 with descriptions of the vegetation types. *J. trop. Geogr.*, 18: 200-213.

GEOLOGY AND PHYSIOGRAPHY

ANON. *Nusa Tenggara survey report*, p. 10-57.
1961

BIROT, P. *Les régions naturelles du globe*, p. 282-298. Paris,
1970 Masson.

BRÜNING, K. *Harms Erdkunde*. Band 3. *Asien*, p. 12-14.
1958 München, Paul List Verlag.

CRESSEY, G.B. *Asia's lands and peoples*. New York, McGraw
1963 Hill. 663 p.

DAMES, T.W.G. *The soils of east central Java*, p. 11-18.
1955 Bogor, General Agricultural Research Station. Contribution No. 14.

DOBBY, E.H.G. *Southeast Asia*. London, University of
1967 London Press. 415 p.

DOBBY, E.H.G. *et al*. Paddy landscapes of Malaya. *The
1955 Malayan Journal of Tropical Geography*, Vol. 4. 94 p.

ENGINEER AGENCY FOR RESOURCES INVENTORIES. *Land reform
1968 Viet-Nam. Pilot drainage and irrigation project, Thanh Quoi, An Giang province. Feasibility study*, p. 19-21. Washington, D.C., Department of the Army.

ENGINEER AGENCY FOR RESOURCES INVENTORIES. *Vietnam
1970 subject index maps*, p. 49, 53-55. Washington, D.C., Department of the Army.

FAO/UNDP. *Soil fertility survey and research. The Philip-
1969 pines. Field experiments, plant nutrition and soil classification*. Rome. 220 p. LA:SF/PHI 10. Technical Report No. 1.

HAANTJES, H.A. *et al*. *Major soil groups of New Guinea and
1967 their distribution*. Amsterdam, Royal Tropical Institute. 87 p.

HAWORTH, H.F. *et al*. *Ground water resources development of
1966 northeastern Thailand*, p. 18-50. Bangkok, Ground Water Division, Department of Mineral Resources, Ministry of National Development. Ground Water Bulletin No. 2.

KENNEDY, R. *Islands and peoples of the Indies*. Washington,
1943 D.C., Smithsonian Institution.

KING, L.C. *The morphology of the earth*. London, Oliver
1962 and Boyd. 699 p.

LEE, W. *Reconnaissance geological report on northeastern
1923 Thailand*. Reprinted October 1954. U.S. Operations Mission to Thailand.

LYDE, L.W. *The continent of Asia*. London, Macmillan,
1933 777 p.

MOHR, E.C.J. *De boden der tropen in het algemeen en die
1937 van Nederlandsch-Indie in het bijzonder*. 5 vols. Amsterdam, De Bussy. 816 p.

MOORMANN, F.R. & ROJANASOONTHON, S. *Soils of Thailand*,
1968 p. 1-7. Bangkok, Department of Land Development. Report SSR No. 72.

REYNDERS, J.S. A pedo-ecological study on soil genesis. In
1964 *The tropics from sea-level to eternal snow. Star mountains, central New Guinea*, p. 9-11, 21-39. Utrecht, University of Utrecht. (Thesis)

REYNDERS, J.S. *The landscape in the Maro and Koembe river
1961 district*, p. 104-119. Boor en Spade 11.

ROBEQUAIN, C. *Malaya, Indonesia, Borneo and the Philippines*,
1966 p. 8-27, 113-258. London, Longmans.

SCHROO, H. An inventory of soils and soil suitabilities in
1963 West Irian. Reprint, *Neth. agric. Sci.*, 11 (4-5), 12 (1). 29 p.

SION, J. *Géographie universelle*. Tome 9. *Asie des moussons*.
1929 Paris, Armand Colin. 548 p.

STAMP, L.D. *Asia*. 12th ed. London, Methuen. 731 p.
1967

UNESCO/ECAFE. *Geological map of Asia and the Far East*.
1972 *Explanatory note*. 2nd ed. Paris, Unesco. 100 p.

UNITED NATIONS. *Atlas of physical, economic and social
1968 resources of the lower Mekong basin*, p. 1-71. New York.

VAN BEMMELEN, R.W. *Geology of Indonesia*. Vol. 1. The
Hague. 732 p.

VISSER, W.A. & HERMES, J.J. Geological results of the explo-
1962 ration for oil in Netherlands New Guinea. In *Verhandelingen van het Koninklijk Geologisch Mijnbouwkundig Genootschap*. Part 20.

WONG, I.F.T. *Reconnaissance soil survey of Selangor*, p. 3-6.
1966 Kuala Lumpur, Ministry of Agriculture, Co-operatives and Lands. Malayan Soil Survey Report No. 6/1966.

GEOLOGICAL MAPS USED FOR THE COMPILATION OF FIGURE 4.

Undated *Carte géologique de l'Indochine, 1 : 500 000*.

Undated *Map of the Republic of the Philippines, 1 : 600 000*. M.M. Alicante, Bureau of Soil Conservation.

1896 *Soil map of Java, 1 : 1 000 000*. Verbeek and Fennema.

1938 *Atlas van Tropisch Nederland*.

1948 *Geological map of Malaya, 1 : 300 000*.

1949 Geological maps. *In* R.W. van Bemmelen, *Geology of Indonesia*, Vol. 3.

1949 *Physiographic sketch map of Java, 1 : 1 000 000*. Pannekoek.

1957 *Geological map of Burma, 1 : 2 000 000*. Burma Geological Department.

1961 *Geological map of Asia and the Far East*. UN/ECAFE.

1962 Geological map of West Irian. *In* W.A. Visse and J.J. Hermes, *Geological results of the exploration for oil in Netherlands New Guinea*.

1963 *Geological map of the Philippines, 1 : 1 000 000*. Department of Agricultural and Natural Resources. Bureau of Mines.

1964 Geological map of northeastern Thailand, *1 : 750 000*. In: *Ground water resources development in NE Thailand*.

1965 Soil map of New Guinea. *In* H.A. Haantjes *et al.*, *Major soil groups of New Guinea and their distribution*.

1968 *Atlas of physical and social resources of the lower Mekong delta*, Plates p. 3 and 22. United Nations.

5. THE SOILS OF SOUTHEAST ASIA

The legend of the Soil Map of Southeast Asia consists of 347 map units in 143 different soil associations, each of which is composed of one or more soils occupying characteristic positions in the landscape. The sequence of their occurrence is related mainly to topography, physiography and lithology.

Each soil association is characterized by the dominant soil — the soil occupying the largest area in the map unit — and by associated soils and inclusions which occur in lesser proportion. Fifty different dominant soils have been indicated on the map.

For convenience and brevity the soil associations have been listed in Table 4.[1] The following information is given:

Map symbol. The map symbol of the dominant soil, followed by the number specifying the composition of the soil association, a second number indicating the textural class of the dominant soil, and a small letter indicating the slope class of the soil association. Textural class numbers are: (1) coarse, (2) medium and (3) fine. Slope class letters are: (a) level to undulating, (b) rolling to hilly and (c) steeply dissected to mountainous.

Associated soils. Subdominant soils which cover more than 20 percent of the map unit.

Inclusions. Inclusions of important soils occupying less than 20 percent of the map unit.

Phase. Phases related to the presence of indurated layers, hard rock, salinity or alkalinity in the soil.

Extension. An estimate of the area of the unit in thousands of hectares.

Climate. The climate symbols.[2]

Occurrence. The countries or regions of occurrence.

---

[1] The soil associations listed in Table 4 refer only to Viet Nam, Democratic Kampuchea, Lao, Thailand, Malaysia, Indonesia and the Philippines. Other soil associations shown on map sheet IX are listed in Volume VII (South Asia), Volume VIII (North and Central Asia) and Volume X (Australasia).

[2] According to the Papadakis system. See J. Papadakis, *Climates of the world and their agricultural potentialities*, Buenos Aires, 1966.

Distribution of major soils

The environmental conditions in Southeast Asia vary considerably. This applies to climate, vegetation, physiography, geology and lithology, and consequently to soils.

To aid in understanding the soil geography, Southeast Asia has been divided into 19 soil regions and 10 soil subregions (Figure 7). Each is described in terms of climate, natural vegetation, main rocks, and distribution of the main soils.

1. FLUVISOL-GLEYSOL ASSOCIATION OF THE CHAO PHRAYA, MEKONG AND RED RIVER DELTAS

This region comprises the deltas and alluvial plains of the Chao Phraya, Mekong and Red rivers, which form the most extensive area of Fluvisols in Southeast Asia. The relief is generally level, but becomes undulating along the inland borders of the region. Raised natural levees along the main rivers, their tributaries and their distributaries form a distinctive microrelief. Mudflats line much of the coast and tidal streams, and are inundated daily by sea water. Elevation is at or near sea level, and much of the region is either permanently saturated or subject to regular annual floods which coincide with peak discharge periods of the main rivers during the humid months (May to October). Annual rainfall ranges from 1 300 to 2 000 mm.

The soils are developed from recent alluvial deposits and unconsolidated materials, most of which show hydromorphic properties. Fluvisols predominate in the present flood plains and deltas of the rivers. The majority of Fluvisols of the region are fine textured; coarser textures are generally restricted to natural levees.

Eutric Fluvisols, generally developed from non-calcareous sediments, predominate in the flood plains of all three rivers. However, in the deltas and on coastal alluvial plains Thionic Fluvisols have developed from brackish-water clays that have a high content of sulphides which have been fixed and accumulated by reduction of sulphates from sea water. Physically and chemically unripe soils formed on sulphide-rich,

TABLE 4. — SOIL ASSOCIATIONS AND RELATED INFORMATION

Map symbol	Associated soils	Inclusions	Phase	Extension (1 000 ha)	Climate	Occurrence
Af11-2/3a		Fx Jd			1.11	Sumatra
Af-11-2/3a		Fx Jd		1 908	1.11, 1.12, 1.72	Java
Af11-2/3a		Fx Jd			1.11, 1.12	Kalimantan
Af55-3b	Bf Ap	Bd			1.11	Irian Jaya
Af55-3b	Bf Ap	Bd	Petric	3 452	1.11	Sulawesi
Af55-3b	Bf Ap	Bd	Petric		1.11	Sumatra
Af56-2a	Qf	Ap Ag	Petric	980	1.12, 1.11	Sumatra
Af57-2a	Ag Od	Qf Ap	Petric		1.12	Kalimantan
Af57-2a	Ag Od	Qf Ap	Petric	3 380	1.12, 1.11	Sumatra
Af59-1/2ab		Ag Ao	Stony	684	1.46	Lao
Af59-1/2ab		Ag Ao	Stony	1 017	1.48, 1.46	Thailand
Af60-1/2ab	Ao Bf	Ag Q1		41	1.46	Lao
Af60-1/2ab	Ao Bf	Ag Q1		2 251	1.76, 1.46, 1.47, 1.22	Viet Nam
Af60-1/2ab	Ao Bf	Ag Q1		6 615	1.47, 1.48, 1.46, 1.12, 1.73	Thailand
Af60-1/2ab	Ao Bf	Ag Q1		2 505	1.47, 1.46	Democratic Kampuchea
Af60-1/2ab	Ao Bf	Ag Q1		121	1.12	Peninsular Malaysia
Af61-1/2ab	Ap	Ag Gd		388	1.73, 1.46	Lao
Af61-1/2ab	Ap	Ag Gd		1 690	1.22, 1.47, 1.13, 1.46	Viet Nam
Af61-1/2ab	Ap	Ag Gd		2 544	1.11, 1.12	Peninsular Malaysia
Af61-1/2ab	Ap	Ag Jd		58	1.11	Singapore
Af61-1/2ab	Ap	Ag Jd		1 601	1.46	Democratic Kampuchea
Ag15-2/3a		Jd Rd		140	1.12	Java
Ag16-2a	Ao Lg	Ap Sg Gd		1 276	1.73, 1.46	Lao
Ag16-2a	Ao Lg	Ap Sg Gd		324	1.47	Viet Nam
Ag16-2a	Ao Lg	Ap Sg Gd		3 668	1.73, 1.48, 1.46, 1.47, 1.12	Thailand
Ag16-2a	Ao Lg	Ap Sg Gd		3 466	1.47, 1.46	Democratic Kampuchea
Ag17-1/2ab	Af Bf Lg	Wd Gd		415	1.22	Viet Nam
Ag17-1/2ab	Af Bf Lg	Wd Gd		7 028	1.47, 1.73, 1.48, 1.46, 1.13	Thailand
Ah25-2c		Ao Fh I		365	1.11, 1.75	Sarawak
Ah25-2c		Ao Fh I		83	1.75	Sabah
Ah25-2c		Ao Fh I			1.71, 1.75, 1.12	Kalimantan
Ah25-2c		Ao Fh I		6 228	1.76	Sulawesi
Ah25-2c		Ao Fh I			1.11	Irian Jaya
Ah25-2c		Ao Fh I			1.11, 1.76	Sumatra
Ah26-3c		Tv Th I		797	1.11, 1.76	Sumatra
Ah27-2/3c	I	Nd	Lithic	6 648	1.11, 1.12	Kalimantan
Ah27-2/3c	I	Nd	Lithic		1.76, 1.11, 1.72	Sumatra
Ao70-2/3b	Bd	Jd Ag Af		241	1.73, 1.14	Lesser Sunda Islands
Ao70-2/3b	Bd	Jd Ag Af			1.11, 1.12	Kalimantan
Ao70-2/3b	Bd	Jd Ag Af			1.12	Java
Ao70-2/3b	Bd	Jd Ag Af		7 041	1.11, 1.12	Sulawesi
Ao70-2/3b	Bd	Jd Ag Af			1.11	Moluccas
Ao70-2/3b	Bd	Jd Ag Af			1.11	Irian Jaya
Ao70-2/3b	Bd	Jd Ag Af			1.11, 1.72	Sumatra

TABLE 4. — SOIL ASSOCIATIONS AND RELATED INFORMATION *(continued)*

Map symbol	Associated soils	Inclusions	Phase	Extension (1 000 ha)	Climate	Occurrence
Ao71-2/3c		I Ah			1.11	Irian Jaya
Ao71-2/3c		I Ah		561	1.11	Moluccas
Ao71-2/3c		I Ah			1.12, 1.72	Java
Ao82-2/3b		Jd Fo Qf			1.72	Java
Ao82-2/3b		Jd Fo Qf		8 564	1.76	Sulawesi
Ao82-2/3b		Jd Fo Qf			1.11, 1.71	Moluccas
Ao82-2/3b		Jd Fo Qf			1.11, 1.12	Sumatra
Ao83-2/3c		I Fo Bd			1.72, 1.12	Java
Ao83-2/3c		I Fo Bd		1 038	1.12	Lesser Sunda Islands
Ao83-2/3c		I Fo Bd			1.11	Sumatra
Ao90-2/3c		Ah Bd I	Lithic	16 244	2.25, 1.48, 1.46, 1.76, 1.73	Lao
Ao90-2/3c		Ah Bd I	Lithic	11 890	2.25, 1.76, 1.47, 1.13, 1.46, 1.22, 1.73	Viet Nam
Ao90-2/3c		Ah Bd I	Lithic	4 041	1.76, 1.47, 1,46	Democratic Kampuchea
Ao90-2/3c		Ah Bd I	Lithic	15 240	1.76, 1.46, 1.73, 1.48, 1.13, 1.12, 1.47	Thailand
Ao90-2/3c		Ah Bd I	Lithic	3 840	1.72, 1.12	Peninsular Malaysia
Ao103-3ab	Ah	Fx Jd		1 178	1.11	Moluccas
Ao103-3ab	Ah	Fx Jd			1.11	Kalimantan
Ao104-2/3c	Ah Bd	Bc Ag		7 105	1.71, 1.11, 1.75	Sarawak
Ao104-2/3c	Ah Bd	Bc Ag		3 537	1.71, 1.11, 1.13	Sabah
Ao104-2/3c	Ah Bd	Bc Ag		136	1.71, 1.75, 1.11	Brunei
Ao104-2/3c	Ah Bd	Bc Ag			1.71, 1.12, 1.11	Kalimantan
Ao104-2/3c	Ah Bd	Bc Ag			1.11, 1.12, 1.76	Sulawesi
Ao104-2/3c	Ah Bd	Bc Ag		23 508	1.11	Moluccas
Ao104-2/3c	Ah Bd	Bc Ag			1.11	Irian Jaya
Ao104-2/3c	Ah Bd	Bc Ag			1.11, 1.76, 1.12	Sumatra
Ao105-2/3c	I	Ah	Lithic	1 128	1.11	Kalimantan
Ao105-2/3c	I	Ah	Lithic		1.76	Sumatra
Ao106-2/3b	Af L	Gd		2 608	1.71, 1.11	Sarawak
Ao106-2/3b	Af L	Gd		1 865	1.11, 1.71, 1.13	Sabah
Ao106-2/3b	Af L	Gd		258	1.11	Brunei
Ao106-2/3b	Af L	Gd		651	1.11	Sulawesi
Ao106-2/3b	Af L	Gd			1.11	Kalimantan
Ao107-2bc	Af Nd	Bf I		3 294	1.48, 1.46, 1.73	Lao
Ao107-2bc	Af Nd	Bf I		5 035	1.22	Viet Nam
Ao107-2bc	Af Nd	Bf I		3 379	1.47, 1.48, 1.46, 1.13, 1.12, 1.73	Thailand
Ao107-2bc	Af Nd	Bf I		75	1.46	Democratic Kampuchea
Ao108-2ab	Af Nd	Ag Vc		3 539	1.72	Peninsular Malaysia
Ao108-2ab	Af Nd	Ag Vc		2 805	1.48, 1.46, 1.13, 1.12, 1.73	Thailand
Ao109-2/3c	Bd I	Ah Nd		7 143	1.14, 1.47, 1.11, 1.13, 1.12, 1.72, 1.76	Philippines
Ap25-2/3a	Af	Qf Ag		665	1.11	Sumatra
Ap27-2a	Ag	Bf J Fo Hg		1 046	1.11, 1.12	Irian Jaya

TABLE 4. — SOIL ASSOCIATIONS AND RELATED INFORMATION *(continued)*

Map symbol	Associated soils	Inclusions	Phase	Extension (1 000 ha)	Climate	Occurrence
Bd58-2c	R Ao	Bf I U Lo			1.11, 1.71	Moluccas
Bd58-2c	R Ao	Bf I U Lo			1.11	Ewab
Bd58-2c	R Ao	Bf I U Lo		4 460	2.7, 1.11, 1.72	Irian Jaya
Bd58-2c	R Ao	Bf I U Lo			1.12	Lesser Sunda Islands
Bd58-2c	R Ao	Bf I U Lo			1.11, 1.72	Sumatra
Bd59-3c	Ge Lg	Be E I A		732	1.11	Irian Jaya
Bd62-2/3a	Gd	Jd Rd		295	1.12	Aru
Bd62-2/3a	Gd	Jd Rd			1.11	Sumatra
Bd63-2/3b	Ao	Af Fo	Stony	457	1.11	Moluccas
Bd63-2/3b	Ao	Af Fo	Stony		1.12	Sumatra
Be116-2c		Tv Re I			1.12, 1.76	Sulawesi
Be116-2c		Tv Re I		757	1.12, 1.72	Lesser Sunda Islands
Be116-2c		Tv Re I			1.72	Java
Be116-2c		Tv Re I			1.11, 1.76	Sumatra
Bf13-2/3b		Ah Fo		24	1.11	Sarawak
Bf13-2/3b		Ah Fo		522	1.11, 1.12	Kalimantan
Bg7-2/3a	Gh	Je		56	1.12	Java
Bg8-2/3a	Bd Be Lg	G Vp		3 360	1.14, 1.47, 1.11, 1.13, 1.12, 1.72	Philippines
Bh17-2bc		Jd Ah		2 727	1.11, 1.76, 1.77	Sumatra
Bh21-2c	U Bd	I R		2 497	2.7	Irian Jaya
Bh21-2c	U Bd	I R			1.72	Sumatra
Bh24-2c	Ah	I		2 721	1.11, 1.72	Irian Jaya
Bv17-3a		Vp Je Ge		140	1.12, 1.13	Java
E13-2c	Od I	Lc Ah Lg		1 122	2.7	Irian Jaya
E18-3c	Lc I	Re		160	1.11	Irian Jaya
E18-3c	Lc I	Re	Lithic		1.11	Irian Jaya
E18-3c	Lc I	Re	Lithic		1.12	Lesser Sunda Islands
E18-3c	Lc I	Re	Lithic	830	1.11, 1.72	Sumatra
E18-3c	Lc I	Re	Lithic		1.11	Ewab
E18-3c	Lc I	Re	Lithic		1.12	Sulawesi
E21-3ab	Re	I			1.12	Sulawesi
E21-3ab	Re	I			1.11	Moluccas
E21-3ab	Re	I		1 332	1.12	Aru
E21-3ab	Re	I			1.12	Lesser Sunda Islands
Fa14-3ab		Af F I		221	1.76	Viet Nam
Fh12-2/3c		Ah I	Petroferric	460	1.11, 1.72	Sumatra
Fh12-2/3c		Ah I	Petroferric		1.11	Kalimantan
Fh13-2b	Qf	Jd	Petric	1 577	1.11	Kalimantan
Fh14-2/3c	Ah	I	Petroferric		1.11	Kalimantan
Fh14-2/3c	Ah	I	Petroferric	3 815	1.11, 1.76	Sulawesi
Fh14-2/3c	Ah	I	Petroferric		1.11, 1.72	Irian Jaya

TABLE 4. — SOIL ASSOCIATIONS AND RELATED INFORMATION *(continued)*

Map symbol	Associated soils	Inclusions	Phase	Extension (1 000 ha)	Climate	Occurrence
Fo101-2b		Qf	Petroferric		1.11	Kalimantan
Fo101-2b		Qf	Petroferric	4 048	1.12, 1.76	Sulawesi
Fo101-2b		Qf	Petroferric		1.11, 1.72	Moluccas
Fo101-2b		Qf	Petroferric		1.12, 1.11, 1.76, 1.72	Sumatra
Fo102-3ab	Fh	Af G		121	1.76	Viet Nam
Fo102-3ab	Fh	Af G		247	1.48	Thailand
Fr31-2/3b		Jd Ag	Petric	153	1.73	Lesser Sunda Islands
Fr31-2/3b		Jd Ag	Petric	421	1.11	Kalimantan
Fr32-2/3c		Ao	Petroferric		1.11, 1.76	Sulawesi
Fr32-2/3c		Ao	Petroferric	497	1.72	Irian Jaya
Fr32-2/3c		Ao	Petroferric		1.11	Kalimantan
Fr33-3ab	Fo	Nd I V		1 681	1.76, 1.47, 1.46	Viet Nam
Fr33-3ab	Fo	Nd I V		72	1.12, 1.72	Peninsular Malaysia
Fr33-3ab	Fo	Nd I V		368	1.46	Democratic Kampuchea
Fx32-2ab	Of	Jd Ag	Petric	931	1.11	Sumatra
Fx32-2ab	Of	Jd Ag	Petric		1.11	Kalimantan
Fx38-2c	Fh	Ah I	Petric	236	1.11	Kalimantan
Gd28-3a	Gh Bg	Jd Od		180	1.11	Kalimantan
Gd28-3a	Gh Bg	Jd Od		275	1.11	Sarawak
Gd28-3a	Gh Bg	Jd Od		317	1.11	Sabah
Gd29-3a		Gm Gh Je		1 850	1.48, 1.46	Thailand
Gd29-3a		Gm Gh Je		64	1.46	Lao
Gd29-3a		Gm Gh Je		920	1.22, 1.47	Viet Nam
Gd29-3a		Gm Gh Je		165	1.12	Peninsular Malaysia
Ge54-3a	Gh	Je Re		95	1.13	Java
Ge54-3a	Gh	Je Re			1.12	Kalimantan
Ge55-3a		Bg Jt	Saline	440	1.22, 1.47	Viet Nam
Ge55-3a		Bg Jt	Saline	1 456	1.47, 1.46, 1.13, 1.12	Thailand
Ge55-3a		Bg Jt	Saline	689	1.11, 1.12	Peninsular Malaysia
Ge55-3a		Bg Jt	Saline	174	1.47	Democratic Kampuchea
Ge56-3a	Gm	Gh Je		2 547	1.22, 1.47, 1.13	Viet Nam
Ge56-3a	Gm	Gh Je		22	1.46	Lao
Ge56-3a	Gm	Gh Je		92	1.46	Thailand
Ge56-3a	Gm	Gh Je		1 646	1.46	Democratic Kampuchea
Ge57-3a		Gm Je		1 099	1.46	Democratic Kampuchea
Ge58-1/2a	Je Bg			302	1.47, 1.13	Philippines
Ge59-2/3a	Bg Be			353	1.47, 1.11, 1.13	Philippines
Gh20-3a	Jd	Od Jt			1.76	Sulawesi
Gh20-3a	Jd	Od Jt		3 969	1.11, 2.7	Irian Jaya
Gh20-3a	Jd	Od Jt			1.11, 1.12	Kalimantan
Gh20-3a	Jd	Od Jt			1.11	Sumatra
Gh21-3a	Wd	Jd Bd		617	1.11	Irian Jaya
Gh21-3a	Wd	Jd Bd			1.11	Sumatra
I-Af-3c				—	1.22, 2.25	Viet Nam
I-Ao-2/3c				713	1.72, 1.12, 1.11	Java

TABLE 4. — SOIL ASSOCIATIONS AND RELATED INFORMATION *(continued)*

Map symbol	Associated soils	Inclusions	Phase	Extension (1 000 ha)	Climate	Occurrence
I-E-3bc					1.11, 1.12, 1.14	Java
I-E-3bc				1 010	1.12	Sulawesi
I-E-3bc					1.11	Moluccas
I-E-3bc					1.12	Lesser Sunda Islands
I-Lc-3b				1 812	1.13, 1.14	Java
I-Lc-3b					1.71, 1.12	Lesser Sunda Islands
I-Lc-Bk-c				1 356	1.48, 1.46, 1.73	Thailand
I-Lc-Bk-c				465	1.46, 1.73	Lao
I-Lc-Bk-c				907	2.25, 1.22	Viet Nam
I-Lc-Bk-c				400	1.12, 1.72	Peninsular Malaysia
I-Lc-Bk-c				42	1.46	Democratic Kampuchea
I-Lk-3bc				1 572	1.73, 1.14	Lesser Sunda Islands
I-Lv-3b				457	1.13	Java
I-Od-U-1c				785	2.7, 1.72	Irian Jaya
Jd9-2/3a	Gd	Bd Rd Od			1.11	Irian Jaya
Jd9-2/3a	Gd	Bd Rd Od			1.11, 1.12	Sumatra
Jd9-2/3a	Gd	Bd Rd Od		9 897	1.11	Moluccas
Jd9-2/3a	Gd	Bd Rd Od			1.11, 1.12	Sulawesi
Jd9-2/3a	Gd	Bd Rd Od			1.12	Java
Jd9-2/3a	Gd	Bd Rd Od			1.11, 1.12	Kalimantan
Jd10-2/3a	Bd	Gh Rd			1.12	Java
Jd10-2/3a	Bd	Gh Rd		2 272	1.11, 1.76	Sulawesi
Jd10-2/3a	Bd	Gh Rd			1.11, 1.72	Irian Jaya
Jd10-2/3a	Bd	Gh Rd			1.12	Sumatra
Jd11-1a	Rd	Od Gh		252	1.11, 1.12	Kalimantan
Jd12-2/3a	Od	Jt Gd		2 642	1.11, 1.12	Sulawesi
Jd12-2/3a	Od	Jt Gd			1.11	Sumatra
Je13-1a	Ge			72	1.14, 1.47	Philippines
Je62-2/3a	Be	Ge Vp			1.12, 1.14, 1.12, 1.73	Lesser Sunda Islands
Je62-2/3a	Be	Ge Vp			1.76	Sumatra
Je62-2/3a	Be	Ge Vp			1.11	Irian Jaya
Je62-2/3a	Be	Ge Vp		2 467	1.11	Moluccas
Je62-2/3a	Be	Ge Vp			1.11, 1.12	Sulawesi
Je62-2/3a	Be	Ge Vp			1.13, 1.12, 1.76, 1.72	Java
Je62-2/3a	Be	Ge Vp			1.12	Kalimantan
Je63-2/3a	Ge	Re Vp			1.12	Kalimantan
Je63-2/3a	Ge	Re Vp			1.13, 1.76	Java
Je63-2/3a	Ge	Re Vp		589	1.12, 1.11	Sulawesi
Je63-2/3a	Ge	Re Vp			1.12	Lesser Sunda Islands
Je63-2/3a	Ge	Re Vp			1.72	Sumatra
Je70-3a	Gh	Oe Re		230	1.11	Kalimantan
Je72-2a	Ge	Gm		1 265	1.48, 1.46, 1.73	Thailand
Je72-2a	Ge	Gm		595	1.22, 1.47	Viet Nam
Je72-2a	Ge	Gm		557	1.46, 1.47	Democratic Kampuchea
Je73-3a	Jt Zg	Re	Saline	543	1.13, 1.47	Viet Nam
Je73-3a	Jt Zg	Re	Saline	413	1.11, 1.12	Peninsular Malaysia

TABLE 4. — SOIL ASSOCIATIONS AND RELATED INFORMATION (continued)

Map symbol	Associated soils	Inclusions	Phase	Extension (1 000 ha)	Climate	Occurrence
Je73-3a	Jt Zg	Re	Saline	216	1.47	Democratic Kampuchea
Je84-3a	Oe	Jd Hh		600	1.11	Irian Jaya
Je85-3a	Oe	Gh Jd		2 250	1.11, 1.12	Irian Jaya
Jt12-3a	Od	Gd R P	Saline	281	1.12, 1.11	Kalimantan
Jt12-3a	Od	Gd R P	Saline	53	1.11	Sarawak
Jt12-3a	Od	Gd R P	Saline	400	1.11	Sabah
Jt13-3a		Gh		1 119	1.22, 1.47	Viet Nam
Jt13-3a		Gh		222	1.47, 1.46	Democratic Kampuchea
Jt14-3a	Gh	Gd		1 424	1.46, 1.13, 1.47, 1.12	Thailand
Jt14-3a	Gh	Gd		531	1.47	Viet Nam
Jt14-3a	Gh	Gd		427	1.11, 1.12	Peninsular Malaysia
Lc78-3c	Bh	E Lk I	Stony		1.14, 1.71, 1.12	Lesser Sunda Islands
Lc78-3c	Bh	E Lk I	Stony	} 4 662	1.11, 1.72	Irian Jaya
Lc78-3c	Bh	E Lk I	Stony		1.12, 1.76	Sulawesi
Lc78-3c	Bh	E Lk I	Stony		1.13, 1.12, 1.11, 1.72	Java
Lc97-3b		Je Gh		} 1 504	1.12	Lesser Sunda Islands
Lc97-3b		Je Gh			1.11, 1.72, 1.12	Sumatra
Lc98-3c	Ne	Th I			1.11	Kalimantan
Lc98-3c	Ne	Th I		} 971	1.13, 1.12	Java
Lc98-3c	Ne	Th I			1.12	Sulawesi
Lc98-3c	Ne	Th I			1.12, 1.71, 1.14	Lesser Sunda Islands
Lc99-2b	Nd	G I		236	1.13, 1.47	Viet Nam
Lc100-c	I	Bk	Lithic	408	1.73, 1.22	Viet Nam
Lc100-c	I	Bk	Lithic	638	1.73, 1.46	Thailand
Lf32-3bc		I	Petric	64	2.25	Lao
Lg39-3ab	Lo Ge	Ag Je		24	1.73	Lao
Lg39-3ab	Lo Ge	Ag Je		678	1.73, 1.48	Thailand
Lg39-3ab	Lo Ge	Ag Je		641	1.46	Democratic Kampuchea
Lk19-2/3a	Lc	R		84	1.11	Sabah
Lo65-2/3b	Nh	Je			1.12	Lesser Sunda Islands
Lo65-2/3b	Nh	Je			1.12, 1.11	Sulawesi
Lo65-2/3b	Nh	Je		} 794	1.11	Moluccas
Lo65-2/3b	Nh	Je			1.11	Sumatra
Lo65-2/3b	Nh	Je			1.72, 1.12	Java
Lo66-2/3c		Lc Je I			1.11, 1.12	Kalimantan
Lo66-2/3c		Lc Je I		} 2 011	1.11, 1.12	Java
Lo66-2/3c		Lc Je I			1.11, 1.12, 1.76	Sulawesi
Lo67-2/3c	Fo Lc	Bc I Nd		1 160	1.71, 1.11	Sabah
Lo67-2/3c	Fo Lc	Bc I Nd		359	1.11	Kalimantan
Lo68-2/3b	Be Lg	Ao F		3 433	1.14, 1.47, 1.11, 1.13, 1.12, 1.72	Philippines
Lv5-3b		Th Tv		} 1 198	1.72	Lesser Sunda Islands
Lv5-3b		Th Tv			1.13, 1.72, 1.14, 1.76	Java
Lv6-3b	Ne	Lc		90	1.12	Java

TABLE 4. — SOIL ASSOCIATIONS AND RELATED INFORMATION *(continued)*

Map symbol	Associated soils	Inclusions	Phase	Extension (1 000 ha)	Climate	Occurrence
Nd54-3b		Ah I			1.11	Kalimantan
Nd54-3b		Ah I		457	1.12	Java
Nd54-3b		Ah I			1.11, 1.72, 1.12	Sulawesi
Nd54-3b		Ah I			1.11	Sumatra
Nd64-3a		Fh Jd		393	1.12	Java
Nd65-3ab	Bd	Vc E I		28	1.12	Peninsular Malaysia
Nd65-3ab	Bd	Vc E I		955	1.76, 1.46, 1.73	Lao
Nd65-3ab	Bd	Vc E I		1 930	1.48, 1.46, 1.12, 1.73	Thailand
Nd65-3ab	Bd	Vc E I		257	1.46	Democratic Kampuchea
Nd66-2/3b	Ne Ao	Be Lo		10 170	1.14, 1.47, 1.12, 1.11, 1.13, 1.76, 1.77	Philippines
Ne60-3b		Je Lc		575	1.13, 1,12	Java
Ne60-3b		Je Lc			1.76	Sulawesi
Ne65-3bc	Nd To	I		2 343	1.72, 1.47, 1.11, 1.13	Philippines
Nh9-3a		Jd Nd Vp		250	1.11	Sumatra
Nh9-3a		Jd Nd Vp			1.11	Kalimantan
Nh10-3b		Th Be		112	1.11, 1.12	Kalimantan
Od19-a		Jd Gh		1 485	1.11	Sarawak
Od19-a		Jd Gh			1.11, 1.12	Kalimantan
Od19-a		Jg Gh		10 968	1.11	Sumatra
Od19-a		Jd Gh			1.11	Irian Jaya
Od20-a	Gh	R Jd Jt		292	1.11	Sarawak
Od20-a	Gh	R Jd Jt		165	1.11	Sabah
Od20-a	Gh	R Jd Jt		183	1.11	Brunei
Od20-a	Gh	R Jd Jt		3 024	1.11	Kalimantan
Od20-a	Gh	R Jd Jt			1.11, 1.12	Sumatra
Od21-a		Gh Jt		183	1.47	Viet Nam
Od21-a		Gh Jt		68	1.12	Thailand
Od21-a		Gh Jt		763	1.11, 1.12	Peninsular Malaysia
Oe9-a	Ge		Saline	84	1.12	Irian Jaya
Oe10-a		Je Gh		14	1.13	Java
Oe11-a	Od	Je Gh		4 988	1.11 1.12	Irian Jaya
Oe12-a	Zg	Je Gh	Saline	1 964	1.11, 1.12	Irian Jaya
Oe12-a	Zg	Je Gh	Saline		1.11	Aru
Pg4-1a		Gh Od		23	1.11	Sarawak
Pg4-1a		Gh Od		1 377	1.11, 1.12	Kalimantan
Ph12-1b	Qa	Pp		2 104	1.11	Kalimantan
Ph12-1b	Qa	Pp			1.72	Irian Jaya
Po27-1a	Qa	Pg		2 478	1.76, 1.11	Sumatra
Qa17-1a	Po	Jd		171	1.11	Sarawak
Qa17-1a	Po	Jd		2 923	1.11	Kalimantan
Qc59-1ab	Bd	Ah Jd		4 746	1.11, 1.12	Kalimantan
Qc59-1ab	Bd	Ah Jd			1.11, 1.12	Sumatra

TABLE 4. — SOIL ASSOCIATIONS AND RELATED INFORMATION *(continued)*

Map symbol	Associated soils	Inclusions	Phase	Extension (1 000 ha)	Climate	Occurrence
Qc60-1a	Bd J	Ge		323	1.47, 1.13	Philippines
Qf48-1b	Af	Ag Fo		440	1.11	Moluccas
Rc46-1a		Bc		112	1.12	Sulawesi
Rd10-1a	Gd Od	Gh Jt S		} 28	1.11	Kalimantan
Rd10-1a	Gd Od	Gh Jt S			1.72	Irian Jaya
Re62-1ab		Je Gh		65	1.12, 1.72	Lesser Sunda Islands
Re82-1bc	Tv	Ah Gh	Stony	} 314	1.12	Lesser Sunda Islands
Re82-1bc	Tv	Ah Gh	Stony		1.13, 1.76, 1.14	Java
Re83-1ab	Qf Qa	G Je P		603	1.47, 1.13, 1.22	Viet Nam
Re83-1ab	Qf Qa	G Je P		314	1.13, 1.12	Thailand
Re83-1ab	Qf Qa	G Je P		130	1.12	Peninsular Malaysia
Th17-2c	Tv	Be Re I		} 2 384	1.12, 1.76, 1.72	Java
Th17-2c	Tv	Be Re I			1.72, 1.76	Sulawesi
Th17-2c	Tv	Be Re I			1.76, 1.11, 1.72	Sumatra
Th18-2ab	Gh	Be Re		682	1.12	Sumatra
Tm23-2c	Tv	I Re		} 898	1.76, 1.13, 1.14	Java
Tm23-2c	Tv	I Re			1.11	Moluccas
Tm23-2c	Tv	I Re			1.72, 1.71, 1.12	Lesser Sunda Islands
To24-2c	Tv	I Re		} 1 627	1.76, 1.72, 1.12	Java
To24-2c	Tv	I Re			1.11	Moluccas
To24-2c	Tv	I Re			1.12, 1.71	Lesser Sunda Islands
To25-2b	Lv	Je		} 567	1.76, 1.14	Java
To25-2b	Lv	Je			1.12	Lesser Sunda Islands
To26-2bc	Be Ne			734	1.47, 1.11, 1.13, 1.72	Philippines
To27-2/3bc	I	Ne		514	1.47, 1.11, 1.13, 1.72	Philippines
Tv38-1bc	Re	Th To	Stony	} 1 470	1.12, 1.13, 1.72, 1.76	Java
Tv38-1bc	Re	Th To	Stony		1.76	Sulawesi
Tv38-1bc	Re	Th To	Stony		1.11	Moluccas
Tv38-1bc	Re	Th To	Stony		1.76, 1.11, 1.72	Sumatra
Tv38-1bc	Re	Th To	Stony		1.12, 1.72	Lesser Sunda Islands
Vc57-3ab	Lc	Je		213	1.72, 1.12	Java
Vc59-3a		Bg Ge		87	1.47	Philippines
Vp61-3a	Bv	Je		} 805	1.13	Java
Vp61-3a	Bv	Je			1.12	Sulawesi
Vp61-3a	Bv	Je			1.14, 1.12	Lesser Sunda Islands
Vp62-3b	Lc	I		} 525	1.13, 1.12	Java
Vp62-3b	Lc	I			1.12	Lesser Sunda Islands
Vp63-3ab	Lv	Je		} 561	1.13, 1.14	Java
Vp63-3ab	Lv	Je			1.12, 1.11	Sulawesi
Vp63-3ab	Lv	Je			1.12	Lesser Sunda Islands
Vp64-3a	I Vc	F G	Lithic	330	1.48, 1.46	Thailand
Vp64-3a	I Vc	F G	Lithic	159	1.73	Lao

TABLE 4. — SOIL ASSOCIATIONS AND RELATED INFORMATION (concluded)

Map symbol	Associated soils	Inclusions	Phase	Extension (1 000 ha)	Climate	Occurrence
Vp64-3a	I Vc	F G	Lithic	596	1.76, 1.47, 1.46	Viet Nam
Vp64-3a	I Vc	F G	Lithic	901	1.46	Democratic Kampuchea
Vp65-3a	Ge	Bg Lo		991	1.14, 1.47, 1.11, 1.13, 1.76	Philippines

permanently saturated clays in brackish water with a Rhizophora-Bruguiera mangrove forest cover are potentially acid sulphate soils. Where natural or artificial drainage has occurred, the material has slowly ripened to form acid sulphate soils whose high acidity is due to the formation of sulphuric acid through oxidation. Both are grouped as Thionic Fluvisols, which are most extensive in the Chao Phraya and Mekong deltas. In the Red river delta they cover a relatively limited area. Eutric Fluvisols also occur along the littoral fringes of the deltas, and on banks of rivers and tidal channels. Saline-phase Eutric Fluvisols occur on the littoral fringes of the Chao Phraya and Mekong deltas, while the Eutric Fluvisols of the Red river delta are succeeded by Eutric Regosols along the coast.

Eutric Gleysols have developed in the plains and deltas where better natural or artificial drainage conditions have resulted in the ripening of materials in which little sulphide has accumulated, or which contain neutralizing components that prevent strong acidification after oxidation of the sulphides upon drainage. Saline Eutric Gleysols occur along the littoral fringes of the Chao Phraya and Mekong deltas. Gleysols are the principal rice-growing soils of the region.

The main inclusions of other soils within the region are fine-to-medium-textured Gleyic Acrisols which have developed from subrecent alluvium on old terraces bordering the present flood plains. An inclusion of Pellic Vertisols developed from lacustrine deposits borders the Chao Phraya flood plain in the east.

2. FLUVISOL-GLEYSOL ASSOCIATION OF IRIAN JAYA, THE CIRCUM-SUNDA ARCHIPELAGOES AND THE MALAY PENINSULA

Narrow coastal plains occur along the east coast of the Malay Peninsula, the northeast coast of Sumatra, the north coast of Java, and the west coasts of Sulawesi and Irian Jaya. The formations are characteristic of emergent shorelines, and while the majority of the individual plains are too small to

appear on the soil regions map, five of the largest occurrences have been combined to form the second Fluvisol-dominant soil region of Southeast Asia. The relief is predominantly level, with an undulating microrelief occurring on natural levees and beach ridges of the littoral fringe. Elevation is at or near sea level, and much of the region is either permanently saturated or subject to annual flooding during the rainy season. Annual rainfall ranges from 1 500 to over 2 000 mm.

The soils are developed from recent alluvial deposits and unconsolidated materials. The Fluvisols of the region are mainly unripe and permanently saturated, but Gleysols have ripened to some degree owing to better natural or artificial drainage. The majority of Gleysols and the Fluvisols of northern Java are used for rice growing, while other Fluvisols are under mangrove forest and marsh vegetation.

Fine-textured Thionic Fluvisols and Eutric Gleysols have developed from non-calcareous materials bordering Lake Thale in southern Thailand. Eutric Regosols are formed from beach and dune sediments along the littoral fringe, and inclusions of fine-to-medium-textured Gleyic Acrisols occur inland.

Medium-to-fine-textured Dystric Fluvisols developed from non-calcareous materials occupy the coastal plains of northeastern Sumatra, northern Java and western Sulawesi. Inland inclusions are mainly Orthic Acrisols, although in Java Chromic Vertisols and Dystric Nitosols also occur.

Fine-textured Humic Gleysols and medium-to-fine-textured Dystric Fluvisols occupy the extensive, marshy alluvial plain of the Bomberai Peninsula of Irian Jaya. The principal inclusions are Eutric Histosols in the marshy interior, and fine-textured Rendzinas and Chromic Luvisols in the bordering uplands.

3. GLEYSOL-VERTISOL ASSOCIATION OF LAKE TONLE

This region consists of the Lake Tonle and Mekong basins north of Phnom Penh, which form the principal lowlands of Democratic Kampuchea. The relief is predominantly level. An undulating microrelief characterizes the natural levees of the Mekong river, and a " gilgai " microrelief the Vertisols found in the east of the region. The average elevation is less than 50 m above sea level, and much of the region is inundated during the rainy season (May to October), when the flood waters of the Mekong river flow back into the immense Lake Tonle. The average annual rainfall is 1 400 mm.

These predominantly fine-textured soils are developed from recent and subrecent lacustrine deposits of mixed origin: clay and silt-laden flood waters of the Mekong river, and local mixed basic and acid source materials to the north, west and south of the lake. There are significant inclusions of montmorillonitic clays.

Eutric Gleysols are the dominant soils of the region. They encircle Lake Tonle and are submerged annually to depths of two to four metres during the rainy season, drying out in the dry season when the lake empties the flood waters back into the Mekong river. Fresh water mangrove forest occurs adjacent to Lake Tonle. Large areas are planted to " floating rice " when the water is high during the rainy season. Upland crops are planted locally during the dry season when the flood waters recede.

The fine-textured Pellic Vertisols predominating east and north of the Mekong river above Phnom Penh are developed from subrecent unconsolidated calcareous materials. These soils, which occupy slightly higher positions than the Gleysols, are rarely inundated and are used extensively for the cultivation of cotton, bananas, rice and pineapples.

Medium-textured Eutric Fluvisols, developed from recent alluvial deposits on the levees of the Mekong river, are traditionally settlement sites. Medium-textured Gleyic Acrisols are the principal inclusions along the northern, eastern and southern borders of the region, while fine-textured Gleyic Luvisols occur to the west in the vicinity of Battambang.

4. LITHOSOLS

Lithosols are by definition soils limited in depth by continuous coherent hard rock within 10 cm of the surface. In Southeast Asia they are found in small spots in areas of excessive relief. They may have a forest or savanna cover, or may be bare of vegetation, and may occur in any climatic region. The majority of occurrences are too small to appear on the Soil Map of Southeast Asia and hence on the soil regions map. However, in a number of areas these soils are extensive and have been combined to form the Lithosols soil region.

The main areas of occurrence have one feature in common. In every case the parent material consists of carbonate sediments, usually consolidated

limestone or dolomite. The landscape is typically tropical karstic with highly weathered limestone ridges, isolated pinnacles and numerous caverns and sinkholes.

The Lithosols of the Tonkin massif of Viet Nam, the eastern massifs of Lao and Viet Nam, the western highlands of Thailand and the Malay Peninsula occur on Carboniferous-Permian and Ordovician limestone which is massive and locally dolomitic. The principal associated soils are fine-textured Chromic Luvisols and Calcic Cambisols. Lithosols occur in association with fine-textured Ferric Acrisols along the border between Viet Nam and China. In each instance the slope class is steeply dissected to mountainous.

The Lithosols of the southern belt of Java, Sumbawa, Sumba and Timor occur on barren, rolling-to-hilly karstic plateaus of Triassic limestone rising steeply from the coast. The main associated soils are fine-textured Chromic Luvisols in Java, Sumbawa and Sumba. The Lithosols of Timor occur in association with fine-textured Calcic Luvisols.

5. ARENOSOL-ACRISOL ASSOCIATION OF BORNEO

This region, located on the continental Sunda shelf part of western Borneo, consists of a central core of metamorphic and acid effusive and intrusive rocks surrounded by a belt of Mio-Pliocene coastal deposits. Forest and forest-savanna cover most of the region. The relief is level to undulating in peripheral parts of the area, but becomes rolling, hilly and steeply dissected in places in the interior. Elevation ranges from 50 to over 1 000 m, but is less than 200 m throughout most of the region. The soils are well to excessively drained. Annual rainfall exceeds 2 000 mm and is evenly distributed throughout the year.

Arenosols have developed from coarse-textured clastic deposits in the Mio-Pliocene coastal belt. Acrisols have developed from metamorphic rocks and remnants of old acid effusive and intrusive complexes.

The coarse-textured Mio-Pliocene deposits of the coastal belt consist of a thick layer of white quartz sand. Cambic Arenosols have developed on leached sands, while Albic Arenosols have developed on slightly finer materials. Texture, however, remains coarse and most of these soils are excessively drained. The Arenosols grade inland to medium-to-fine-textured, well-drained Orthic Acrisols which have developed on metamorphic rocks and acid effusives. Orthic Acrisols developed from metamorphic rocks have a rolling to hilly relief, while those developed from acid effusives are steeply dissected.

The main inclusions are fine-to-medium-textured Orthic Ferralsols and Rhodic Ferralsols developed from acid intrusive and acid effusive rocks, respectively. Dystric Fluvisols occupy the narrow valleys of the main rivers.

6. RENDZINAS

Rendzinas are not extensive in Southeast Asia, but occur locally in parts of the Indonesian archipelago where they are intimately associated with shallower Lithosols and deeper Luvisols and Cambisols. They rarely exist as a continuous unit covering extensive areas. Principal occurrences are in parts of Irian Jaya, the Aru, Kai (Ewab) and Lesser Sunda Islands, the Moluccas, Sulawesi and Sumatra. These have been combined to form the Rendzinas soil region.

Rendzinas occur under climates ranging from ever-humid semihot equatorial in Sumatra to humid semihot equatorial as in Sulawesi and the Moluccas, and approach Andine taiga in Irian Jaya. Under ever-humid conditions a special type of rain forest relatively poor in species occurs. Areas of these soils with a more pronounced dry season support only a poor natural vegetation which in places is xerophytic. Where moisture supply is sufficient, Rendzinas are locally used for the production of fruit crops.

Rendzinas, developed on carbonate sediments of limestone and marl, are of two distinct types. The first type consists of well-drained Rendzinas developed on massive limestone rocks of Tertiary or older age which occur in northern Sumatra, southeastern Sulawesi and western Irian Jaya. Slopes are often steeply dissected and elevations range from sea level to over 2 000 m on the southern slopes of the Maoke mountains of Irian Jaya. These Rendzinas are fine textured and occur in association with Chromic Luvisols in Sulawesi, Lithosols, Dystric Cambisols and Humic Cambisols in Irian Jaya, and lithic Humic and Orthic Acrisols in Sumatra.

The second type of Rendzinas is developed on raised Neogene and Paleogene coral reefs. Main occurrences are in the Moluccas and the Aru, Kai and Lesser Sunda Islands on undulating to rolling terraces in littoral zones at elevations mainly below 100 m. These Rendzinas are well drained and fine textured and occur in association with Chromic Luvisols, Dystric Cambisols and Orthic Acrisols.

7. ANDOSOLS OF THE MOLUCCAS AND LESSER SUNDA ISLANDS

This region consists of the volcanic inner arc of the Lesser Sunda Islands and its northeast extension through the Banda arc of the Moluccas. The volcanic islands of Bali, Lombok, Flores, Alor, Wetar and the northern peninsula of Halmahera form the easterly continuation of the active volcanic chain of the great Sunda mountain system. Individually these islands are of small extent, but are combined as a soil region because of their unique soil landscape features.

Most of the islands comprising this region are entirely volcanic in origin. Gently rolling lowlands are virtually non-existent. The majority of slopes are steeply dissected to mountainous, and volcanoes rise virtually out of the sea to elevations of 1 000 to 3 750 m.

The prevailing climate is modified by altitude. Lower slopes experience a humid semihot equatorial climate with a distinct dry season (everhumid on Halmahera), while the higher peaks have a humid tierra templada climate.

Although the intensively cultivated areas of Bali support a high population density, most of the region remains under monsoon forest stratified according to elevation. The slopes of the more active volcanoes are under pioneer vegetation where the original cover has been destroyed by volcanic eruptions and ash falls.

The Andosols of the region are developed on recent andesitic to basaltic pyroclastic material. The exchange complex of most of these soils is dominated by amorphous material (allophane and related minerals). Bulk densities are commonly low and many of these soils have a smeary consistency when moist.

Mollic Andosols developed from andesitic volcanic ash or andesitic to basaltic pyroclastic materials occur on long slopes of recent volcanoes in Bali, Lombok, Flores and Halmahera. They are generally medium textured and well to somewhat excessively drained.

Ochric Andosols are developed from andesitic pyroclastic materials on the slopes of young andesitic volcanoes in Bali, Flores, Alor, Wetar and Halmahera. They are generally medium-to-fine-textured and well drained.

Vitric Andosols, the coarse-textured, gravelly and stony members of the Andosols, are developed from andesitic volcanic ejecta comprising pumice and volcanic glass. These soils are somewhat excessively drained and are located on the slopes of young volcanoes and mudflows in Bali, Lombok, Alor and Halmahera.

The principal soil inclusions of the region are Eutric Cambisols and Regosols in Bali, Vertic Luvisols and Pellic Vertisols in Lombok, Chromic Luvisols and Lithosols in Flores and Alor, and Orthic Luvisols in Wetar and Halmahera.

8. ANDOSOL-LUVISOL ASSOCIATION OF JAVA

The central volcanic belt of Java is composed of a succession of volcanoes whose products have covered the older maturely dissected landscape forms with lava, ash and lahars. Much of the area has rolling to hilly slopes punctuated by steep-sloped volcanoes. About 14 of these cones have elevations exceeding 3 000 m. The prevailing climate of the region is marked by the influence of altitude and the increase in dry months toward the east. Higher slopes have a humid tierra templada climate, while the climate of lower slopes grades from humid semihot equatorial in the west to moist monsoon semihot equatorial in the east. This region is one of the most intensively cultivated and populous areas in Southeast Asia. Little original monsoon or rain forest vegetation remains. Most of the rolling to hilly land has been terraced and planted to permanent food crops for generations, and as population pressure has increased, many of the higher slopes have been cleared and planted intermittently or permanently to food crops despite the danger of soil degradation.

The Andosols and Luvisols of the central volcanic zone of Java are intimately linked with the volcanic origins of the region. Andosols are developed from recent andesitic and basaltic pyroclastic materials, and exchange complexes are dominated by amorphous material (allophane and related minerals). Luvisols are largely developed on older volcanic complexes with kaolinite being the dominant clay mineral in combination with some illitic clays. The characteristic volcanic downslope catena of the region is Andosols on young materials grading to Luvisols on older deposits, with Vertisols rich in montmorillonitic clays occupying intervening volcanic plains.

In the humid western part of the region medium-textured, well-drained Humic Andosols are developed from recent andesitic pyroclastic materials on the higher volcanic cones. These are succeeded by medium-textured, well-drained Ochric Andosols on steeply dissected upper slopes. Rolling to hilly lower slopes are characterized by well-drained, medium-to-fine-textured Orthic Luvisols and fine-textured Vertic Luvisols. The main inclusions in this part of the region are Lithosols, Orthic Acrisols and Eutric Cambisols on steeply dissected upper slopes, and Dystric Nitosols and Chromic Vertisols on lower slopes and volcanic plains, respectively.

Unlike the west, the eastern part of the region has a pronounced dry season, and most soils have a higher percentage of base saturation. Medium-textured, well to somewhat excessively drained Mollic Andosols and Ochric Andosols are developed from recent andesitic to basaltic pyroclastic materials on the steeply dissected upper slopes. Coarse-textured, somewhat excessively drained Vitric Andosols have also developed on recent andesitic volcanic ejecta. Rolling to hilly lower slopes are dominated by well-drained fine Vertic Luvisols developed on older volcanic deposits. The main inclusions in the eastern part of the region are Eutric Regosols and Lithosols on upper slopes and Pellic Vertisols on volcanic lahars.

9. VERTISOL-FLUVISOL ASSOCIATION OF JAVA AND MADURA

The northern belt of eastern Java and Madura consists of the Rembang-Madura anticlinorium which is made up of two longitudinal belts of massive limestone separated by marly sedimentaries and overlain by Quaternary alluvial deposits. In Java the nearly continuous karstic plateau is characterized by gently sloping hills interrupted by wide valleys with a narrow fringe of alluvial plain along the coast. Madura consists of a low longitudinal belt with undulating relief fringed by a discontinuous alluvial plain along the coast. The elevation of the karstic plateau rarely exceeds 250 m. The prevailing climate is moist monsoon semihot equatorial. Annual rainfall usually exceeds 1 500 mm, but there is a distinct dry season from August to October. Most of this region is intensively cultivated and has a very high population density. Where sufficient irrigation water is available, rice, sugar cane and a variety of annual or perennial crops are grown. Limestone scarp slopes are planted to teak forest.

The Vertisols of this region are developed from weathering products of limestone and marl. They consist of fine-textured material and develop deep cracks when dry. The soils are self-mulching and often show " gilgai " microrelief. The dominant clay mineral is montmorillonite. Fluvisols are developed on recent alluvial deposits consisting of medium-to-fine-textured materials. Except for the better-drained soils on the natural levees of the main rivers, most Fluvisols in the area show hydromorphic characteristics and are inundated annually during the rainy season.

Pellic Vertisols are the dominant soils of the area. Their macrorelief is nearly flat to slightly undulating in the central belt of marly sediments, and rolling to hilly over much of the karstic plateau. The natural drainage of these soils is imperfect to poor in the rainy season. During the dry season they dry quickly and crack deeply.

Eutric Fluvisols are the principal soil components of the alluvial plains along the coastal fringe. They are medium-to-fine-textured and are generally poorly drained.

The main inclusions on the karstic plateau are Lithosols and Vertic Luvisols, with Chromic Luvisols occurring on steeply dissected slopes.

10. CAMBISOLS OF IRIAN JAYA

The Cambisols of Southeast Asia generally occur in small patches in hilly or mountainous country. One of the largest continuous areas of occurrence lies in the rugged mountains of Irian Jaya: the Van Rees ranges and the Maoke mountains, which are separated by the Meervlakte intermontane plain. The macrorelief of this region is predominantly steeply dissected to mountainous, and the maximum altitude exceeds 5 000 m. The prevailing climate is influenced by altitude and ranges from ever-humid semihot equatorial through humid tierra templada to Andine taiga. Annual rainfall usually exceeds 2 000 mm and is uniformly distributed throughout the year, with no distinct dry season. Most of the region is under rain forest which is stratified according to elevation and contains valuable hardwood trees. Shifting cultivation is practised in low-lying and more accessible parts of the region.

Cambisols are young soils developed on parent materials that are subject to continuous erosion or have recently accumulated. These conditions are found on steep slopes and talus slopes of colluvium over much of the Van Rees mountains and the northern slopes of the Maoke mountains in Irian Jaya. In the Van Rees mountains Cambisols are developed on weathering products and colluvium derived from Plio-Pleistocene deposits consisting mainly of sandstone and conglomerate. The Cambisols of the Maoke mountains are developed on Paleozoic and Mesozoic formations consisting of quartz micaschist with intrusions of granite and granodiorite.

Humic Cambisols generally occupy higher parts of both mountain systems and are medium textured and well to somewhat excessively drained. Dystric Cambisols occur on lower slopes south and east of the Meervlakte, and are medium textured and well drained.

The principal soil inclusions of the Van Rees mountains are Humic Ferralsols and Ferric Acrisols. Eutric Fluvisols occur along narrow river valleys and Lithosol-Dystric Histosol associations are found on the northern slopes of the Maoke mountains.

11. CAMBISOL-ANDOSOL ASSOCIATION OF SUMATRA

The active volcanic inner arc of the great Sunda mountain system is represented in Sumatra by the Barisan range, which forms a mountainous southwestern coastal belt rising steeply from the Indian Ocean to elevations of up to 3 800 m. Eastern slopes

rising from the adjacent dissected peneplains have a less severe macrorelief which is predominantly hilly, and in some places steeply dissected. The climate of the area is influenced by altitude and ranges from ever-humid semihot equatorial through humid tierra templada. Annual rainfall usually exceeds 2 000 mm and is uniformly distributed throughout the year with no distinct dry season. Large areas remain under rain forest which is stratified according to elevation. Highland coffee and pepper are grown locally, and shifting cultivation is practised on lower, more accessible slopes.

Andosols developed on intermediate to acid pyroclastic deposits occur extensively on the higher slopes of recent and subrecent volcanoes. Volcanic parent material is generally more acid in Sumatra than in Java and the Lesser Sunda Islands. Cambisols are developed from older pyroclastic materials on midslopes in the southern part of the region. In the northern part they are developed on steep slopes subject to continuous erosion and talus slopes of colluvium derived from granite, micaschist and quartzite.

Medium-textured, well-drained Humic Andosols with a steeply dissected macrorelief are developed on upper-slope pyroclastic deposits of recent and subrecent volcanoes. Coarse-textured, gravelly and stony Vitric Andosols are developed from volcanic ejecta consisting of pumice and volcanic glass. These soils are somewhat excessively drained, have a steeply dissected macrorelief, and are located on the slopes of recent volcanoes and mudflows.

Medium-textured, well-drained Humic and Dystric Cambisols are developed on weathering products and colluvium derived from older volcanic material, granite, micaschist and quartzite. Humic Cambisols usually occur on upper and eastern slopes, while Dystric Cambisols are more common on westward-facing mid-slopes. A small patch of Eutric Cambisols also occurs on more basic volcanic material in the extreme southern part of the region.

The main soil inclusions along the eastern flanks of the Barisan range are lithic Humic Acrisols, Orthic Acrisols and Orthic Ferralsols. A narrow belt of Orthic Acrisols and discontinuous inclusions of Dystric Fluvisols and Dystric Histosols fringe the southwest coast, and Chromic Luvisols occur in the southeastern tip of the region.

12. CAMBISOL-LUVISOL-NITOSOL ASSOCIATION OF THE PHILIPPINES

The central part of Luzon southwest of a line drawn between the Lingayan Gulf in the northwest and the Ragay Gulf in the southeast consists of the central lowlands, the western Zambales mountains, the southern extremity of the Sierra Madre mountains in the east, and the Bondoc Peninsula in the south. Except for the narrow eastern and western mountainous zones, the macrorelief is gently undulating to rolling. The maximum elevation in the mountains is 1 200 m, but most of the region is below 100 m. A moist monsoon hot tropical climate prevails. Annual rainfall ranges from 1 500 to 2 000 mm. There is a distinct dry season, and the rainy season occurs between May and October. The greater part of the region has been cleared and cultivated, principal crops being rice and coconut. However, natural monsoon forest vegetation remains on the rugged Zambales mountains.

Cambisols are developed on weakly stratified recent alluvial deposits of slightly dissected low continental river terraces. Luvisols are developed from Pliocene-Miocene marine clastic sediments, principally greywacke, shale and reef limestone. Nitosols are developed on Pliocene-Quaternary volcanics composed of pyroxene, andesite and dacite, together with pyroclastics and basalt. Medium-to-coarse-textured Gleyic Cambisols occur mainly in the central lowlands between the Lingayan Gulf and Manila Bay. They are poorly drained soils and ground water stands close to the surface during part of the year; some have been artificially drained. Their macrorelief is nearly flat to undulating. Medium-to-fine-textured Orthic Luvisols are dominant in the Bondoc Peninsula. They are well-drained soils with a rolling to hilly macrorelief.

Fine-to-medium-textured Dystric Nitosols occur on hilly to mountainous terrain along the eastern and western borders of the region and are developed on pyroxene, andesite and dacite. Fine-textured Eutric Nitosols are developed from pyroclastics and basalt. The macrorelief of both soils is predominantly rolling to hilly, but in some places is steeply dissected. The soils are well drained.

The main soil inclusions in the central lowlands and narrow coastal plains are Eutric Fluvisols, Eutric Gleysols and Cambic Arenosols developed on recent coarse-textured alluvium, and Pellic Vertisols developed from fine-textured weathering products of limestone and basalt. Steeply dissected, medium-to-fine-textured Orthic Acrisols are developed from the Cretaceous-Paleogene peridotite and gabbro which form the core of the Zambales mountains. Ochric Andosols occur on upper slopes of volcanoes.

13. LUVISOLS

Luvisols are generally found in regions with a long distinct dry season, an annual rainfall of less than 1 500 mm, and a mean annual temperature of over 20°C. This combination of climatic conditions is uncommon in humid Southeast Asia, and consequently occurrences of those soils tend to be localized and are rarely continuous or extensive. Elsewhere in this chapter, Luvisols are described for soil regions where they occur as inclusions or as secondary components of associations. However, in a number of places they are dominant. The two main types of occurrence are combined to form the Luvisols soil region.

The first type consists of Gleyic Luvisols developed on Quaternary alluvium and colluvium from mixed basic and acid sources. These soils are fine textured and poorly to somewhat poorly drained. Their macrorelief is nearly flat to gently rolling. The prevailing climate is moist monsoon to hot tropical. Annual rainfall ranges between 1 000 and 1 500 mm. There is a pronounced dry season, and the rainy season occurs from May to October. During the peak of the rainy season ground water approaches the soil surface for short periods. These soils are primarily used for rice cultivation. They occur mainly in the Ping and Yom basins of northern Thailand and the Battambang outwash plains of Democratic Kampuchea. The principal inclusions are Eutric Fluvisols and Gleysols developed on recent alluvium. Orthic Acrisols, Ferric Acrisols and Dystric Nitosols occur along upland borders.

The second type consists of medium-to-fine-textured Orthic and Chromic Luvisols developed on olivine basalt and limestone plateaus. These soils are well drained and their macrorelief ranges from rolling to steeply dissected. They occur mainly in the southeastern tip of Sumatra and Siberut Island, northeastern Kalimantan, central Irian Jaya, and southern and southeastern Sulawesi. The prevailing climate is humid semihot equatorial. Annual rainfall exceeds 1 500 mm. There is no distinct dry season. Natural monsoon forest vegetation remains on the steeper slopes in Irian Jaya and southeastern Sulawesi, but much of the area has been subjected to shifting cultivation, resulting in the spread of anthropic savanna. The main inclusions are Eutric Fluvisols and Dystric Cambisols in narrow valleys and small coastal plains. Eutric Cambisols, Humic Andosols, Vitric Andosols, and Rendzinas occur locally in mountainous areas.

14. PODZOLS OF SUMATRA AND BORNEO

Lowland Podzols occur on nearly level to gently rolling old coastal terraces in southern Borneo and on the islands of Bangka and Belitung (Billiton) off the east coast of Sumatra. Elevations are usually less than 50 m. The prevailing climate is ever-humid semihot equatorial. Annual rainfall exceeds 2 000 mm and is uniformly distributed over the year. These lowland Podzols have a characteristic natural vegetation known as "kerangas" forest which includes species such as *Dacrydium elatim, Casuarina sumatrana, Agathis dammara, A. alba* and *Whiteodendron moultanian*. When degraded, the kerangas forest is replaced by "padang" vegetation consisting of scattered stunted trees over patches of ground mosses. White pepper is grown on these soils in Bangka and Belitung, while in Borneo farmers use them for pig rearing.

The Podzols of the region are coarse textured and are developed on Neogene siliceous sand deposits probably derived from Mio-Pliocene coastal sediments.

In southern Borneo Podzols occupy a wide belt between the coastal peat swamps and the uplands of the interior. Gleyic Podzols occupy low positions and exhibit hydromorphic characteristics within 50 cm of the soil surface. At slightly higher elevations Humic Podzols are more extensive. They are well drained, but probably evolved in conditions of impeded drainage. The main inclusions along the coastal strip are Dystric Histosols, Humic Gleysols and Dystric Fluvisols. Inland, Humic Podzols grade to Orthic Acrisols and Albic Arenosols. The latter are probably developed on reworked material from old Podzols.

Orthic Podzols are extensive in the islands of Bangka and Belitung. They are coarse textured and well drained, but like the Humic Podzols of Borneo, probably evolved under conditions of impeded drainage. Inclusions of Dystric Histosols and Humic Gleysols occur along the coast, and Xanthic Ferralsols developed on acid volcanic tuff and Neogene sand deposits occupy slightly higher positions.

15. ACRISOLS

Acrisols are the most widespread soils of Southeast Asia. They are estimated to cover some 197 million ha, representing 51 percent of the region. Their macrorelief ranges from nearly level to steeply dissected or mountainous. They occur over a wide range of elevation and climate, although most are found in regions where annual rainfall exceeds 1 500 mm and there is no marked dry season. These soils form on acid to moderately basic parent materials, mostly on residuals of sedimentary, igneous or metamorphic rocks, and on terraces and dissected peneplains of old alluvial deposits. Acrisols are very poor in nutrients and highly susceptible to erosion. Hence successful continuous cultivation of these soils requires improved agricultural practices including fertilizer application, soil conservation and water storage. Consequently their use, or misuse, varies considerably throughout the region.

To aid in understanding the soil geography of Acrisols, the region has been subdivided into ten soil subregions.

15a. *Acrisols of continental Southeast Asia*

Fine-to-medium-textured and well to somewhat excessively drained, lithic Orthic Acrisols occur over vast tracts of steeply dissected terrain of the main mountain systems of Viet Nam, Lao, Democratic Kampuchea and Thailand. They are developed on residuals of consolidated clastic sediments and metamorphic and acid intrusive rocks. Most remain under natural broadleaf and pine forest, but are locally used for shifting cultivation by itinerant hill tribes, and for tea in Viet Nam.

Deeper, well-drained medium-textured Orthic Acrisols developed on residual materials and old alluvial deposits occur on steeply dissected foothills and rolling terraces, respectively. Steeper slopes remain under forest, while much of the rolling terrain is used for shifting cultivation, maize, and locally for rubber in southeastern Thailand, Democratic Kampuchea and Viet Nam.

Coarse-to-medium-textured, well to moderately well-drained Ferric Acrisols and poor to somewhat poorly drained Gleyic Acrisols are developed on old alluvium and occur on nearly level to rolling lower terraces. The original forest vegetation has been cleared in most places. Shifting cultivation is practised on these soils, with extensive areas being abandoned to anthropic savanna. Flat, low-lying Gleyic Acrisols are used for rice growing.

The main inclusions are Lithosols and Dystric Nitosols, with Eutric Gleysols and Eutric Fluvisols and Dystric Fluvisols occurring in river valleys.

15b. *Acrisols of the Malay Peninsula*

Fine- and medium-textured, well to somewhat excessively drained lithic Orthic Acrisols on steeply dissected terrain are dominant on the mountain ranges which form the backbone of the peninsula. They are developed on residuals of granite intrusives and metamorphic and consolidated clastic rocks. Most remain under dense rain forest vegetation, although tea is grown locally in Malaysia.

Deeper, well-drained, medium-textured Orthic Acrisols on foothills and rolling old terraces are widely used for rubber in southern Thailand and Malaysia. Oil palm is grown in Malaysia and coconuts are planted on Orthic Acrisols occupying littoral zones of the west and east coasts.

Coarse- and medium-textured, well to moderately well-drained Ferric Acrisols and poorly to somewhat poorly drained Gleyic Acrisols developed on old alluvium on lower terraces support poor stands of rubber and are often abandoned to anthropic savanna. Rice is grown on flat, low-lying Gleyic Acrisols.

The main inclusions are Rhodic Ferralsols, Dystric Nitosols and Lithosols. Eutric Gleysols, Eutric Fluvisols and Dystric Fluvisols occur in river valleys and narrow coastal plains, and Eutric Regosols are found on beach ridges and dunes fringing the east coast of the peninsula.

15c. *Acrisols of Sumatra*

Fine- and medium-textured, well-drained lithic Humic Acrisols are dominant on the steeply dissected forested slopes of the northern mountains of Sumatra. They are developed on residuals from metamorphic and acid igneous rocks. Orthic Acrisols occupy similar physiographic positions where the natural forest vegetation has been cleared. Coffee and tea are grown locally.

The dominant soils on the Neogene landscape of the northeastern lowlands are medium- and fine-textured, well-drained Orthic Acrisols on rolling to hilly dissected peneplains, and petric Ferric Acrisols on nearly level to undulating lower old terraces. They are developed on a thick series of Neogene liparitic tuff and sandstone. Most of these soils have been cleared of the original forest vegetation and have long been subjected to shifting cultivation. Rubber is an important component within the shifting cycle throughout the subregion, but over wide areas a fire disclimax of anthropic savanna, or " alang-alang " (*Imperata cylindrica*) vegetation occurs.

The main inclusions are a petroferric phase of Orthic Ferralsols developed on andesitic material, Humic Andosols and Vitric Andosols developed on recent volcanic materials, Cambic Arenosols developed on coarse Neogene deposits, and Orthic Podzols developed on coarse-textured liparitic tuff. Dystric Histosols, Humic Gleysols and Dystric Fluvisols occur along the eastern transition between the lowlands and the extensive coastal peat swamps.

15d. *Acrisols of Borneo*

The dominant soils of the mountain system comprising much of Borneo are medium- and fine-textured, well-drained Orthic Acrisols, and to a lesser extent Humic Acrisols, including a lithic phase. These soils are developed on residuals of non-calcareous consolidated clastic sediments, metamorphic and gneous rocks. Most of the steeply sloping mountainous terrain remains under a primary forest vegetation which forms the basis of a flourishing timber industry.

Orthic Acrisols are also the principal soils of the foothills and limited areas of rolling old terraces. A petric phase of Ferric Acrisols developed from Neogene liparitic tuff and sandstone occurs on lower nearly level to undulating terraces. Rubber, oil palm, coconut, and in Sabah, cocoa, are the main crops grown on Orthic Acrisols having gentler relief. However, although agricultural exploitation is increasing, most of the area is still under natural rain forest.

The main inclusions are petric and petroferric Orthic Ferralsols and Humic Ferralsols developed on igneous rocks, Cambic Arenosols and Albic Arenosols developed on Mio-Pliocene coastal deposits, and Orthic Luvisols developed on limestone, olivine basalt and pyroclastic rocks. Dystric Histosols, Humic Gleysols, Eutric Fluvisols and Dystric Fluvisols occur in the transition between the coastal belt and the uplands of the interior.

15e. *Acrisols of Sulawesi*

Medium- and fine-textured, well-drained Humic Acrisols and Orthic Acrisols with a steeply dissected to mountainous macrorelief are widespread throughout northern, central and southeastern Sulawesi. They are developed on granite, quartzite, crystalline schist and phyllitic shale. In central Sulawesi small areas of fine- and medium-textured, well-drained Orthic Acrisols and petric Ferric Acrisols with a rolling to hilly macrorelief are developed on Neogene sandstone and liparitic tuff.

Most of the Acrisols of Sulawesi remain under natural forest. Gently sloping and accessible areas are used locally for shifting cultivation.

The main inclusions are petroferric phases of Humic Ferralsols and Orthic Ferralsols developed from igneous and strongly metamorphosed rocks, Chromic Luvisols developed from limestone, Humic Andosols and Vitric Andosols from subrecent volcanic deposits, and Eutric Nitosols from old intermediate volcanic materials. Eutric Fluvisols and Dystric Fluvisols occur along narrow river valleys and in small embayments along the rugged coast.

15f. *Acrisols of Irian Jaya*

Fine-textured, moderately well to poorly drained Ferric Acrisols and medium-textured Plinthic Acrisols with a nearly level to rolling macrorelief occupy a lowland belt between the Maoke mountains and the extensive coastal peat swamps of southern Irian Jaya. These soils are developed from partly reworked

Plio-Pleistocene acid volcanic tuff deposits. Much of the subregion remains under natural rain forest. Anthropic savanna-type vegetation has developed in areas cleared for shifting cultivation.

The main inclusions are Eutric Histosols and Eutric Fluvisols.

15g. *Acrisol-Gleysol association of the Korat plateau*

The Korat plateau of northeastern Thailand is mainly composed of the broad Quaternary terraces of the Mekong and its tributaries, the Mun and Chi rivers. Low, middle and high terrace levels are recognized. Fine-textured, poorly drained Dystric Gleysols are developed on old alluvium of level, low terraces which are inundated during the rainy season. Medium- and coarse-textured, poorly to somewhat poorly drained Gleyic Acrisols and moderately well-drained Ferric Acrisols are developed on old alluvium of middle terraces and have a predominantly undulating macrorelief. Fine-textured, well-drained Orthic Ferralsols occur on older high terrace remnants.

The main inclusions are Orthic Acrisols on the steeply dissected slopes of scattered hills and bordering scarps.

The Korat plateau has been largely cleared of its original dipterocarp forest vegetation.

Rice is cultivated during the rainy season on low-lying level Dystric Gleysols and Gleyic Acrisols, and kenaf is widely grown on predominantly undulating terrain.

15h. *Acrisol-Nitosol association of Java*

The dominant soils on the Neogene peneplain of western Java are fine- and medium-textured, well-drained Orthic Acrisols developed from non-calcareous consolidated clastic sediments and low-grade metamorphic rocks. The macrorelief is undulating to rolling. Fine-textured, well-drained Dystric Nitosols are developed on lahar complexes bordering the coastal plain of northwestern Java and have a nearly level to undulating macrorelief.

The main inclusions are Humic Andosols, Orthic Andosols and Vitric Andosols developed on subrecent unconsolidated volcanic deposits.

The subregion's natural rain forest vegetation has been almost entirely removed.

Dystric Nitosols are intensively planted to rice and a variety of annual food crops. Orthic Acrisols are planted extensively to rubber and, to a lesser extent, tea. In places, alang-alang (*Imperata cylindrica*) vegetation has developed as a fire disclimax.

15i. *Acrisol-Cambisol association of the Moluccas*

Ceram and Buru are the principal non-volcanic islands of the Moluccas. Fine- and medium-textured, well-drained Orthic Acrisols and medium-textured Dystric Cambisols are developed from strongly folded Triassic sandstone, crystalline schist and gneiss. Orthic Acrisols have an undulating to hilly macrorelief, while Dystric Cambisols occur on steeply dissected to mountainous terrain.

The main inclusions are Dystric Fluvisols in narrow coastal swamps and Rendzinas on uplifted Pliocene and Quaternary coral formations.

Both islands remain under natural monsoon forest vegetation, although the northern part of Buru has a savanna cover.

15j. *Acrisol-Nitosol association of the Philippines*

Fine- and medium-textured, well-drained Orthic Acrisols are the dominant soils of Mindoro, Palawan, Samar, Leyte, Negros and southern and central Mindanao. Their macrorelief is predominantly steeply dissected to mountainous. The Orthic Acrisols of the subregion are developed from micaschist, phyllite and quartzite in Mindoro; Mesozoic and Plio-Pleistocene clastic sediments in Negros; Mio-Pliocene molasse deposits and tuffaceous sedimentary rocks in Samar and Leyte; Tertiary sandstone, shale and conglomerate in eastern central Mindanao; and peridotite and gabbro in Palawan. Dystric Nitosols, the secondary component of the association, are developed from pyroclastics, basalt and dacitic or andesitic plugs. The macrorelief of Dystric Nitosols is generally rolling to hilly.

The main inclusions are Gleyic Cambisols and Orthic Luvisols developed on recent alluvial deposits and Pliocene-Miocene marine clastic sediments, respectively.

A large proportion of the subregion remains under dipterocarp forest, evergreen forest and anthropic savanna. Maize and upland rice are grown in areas where shifting cultivation is practised. Permanent agriculture is largely restricted to fruit crops, rubber, abaca and coconuts.

16. NITOSOLS OF THAILAND AND LAO

Nitosols are developed mainly from basalt, diorite and andesite, or biotite-rich granite and gneiss. Their macrorelief ranges from undulating to hilly. These soils occur in areas with an annual rainfall of 1 000 to 3 000 mm, a dry season of less than four months, and an annual temperature above 22°C.

In continental Southeast Asia Nitosols rarely occur over extensive areas and are mainly restricted to local basalt plateaus. Two main occurrences are in the central highlands of Thailand and the Plateau des Bolovens in Lao. Here fine-textured, deep, well-drained Dystric Nitosols are developed on basaltic lava flows.

The main inclusions are Lithosols, lithic Orthic Acrisols, Ferric Acrisols and, in Thailand, Pellic Vertisols.

The Nitosols of the Plateau des Bolovens are extremely degraded owing to repeated burning of the vegetation. The form of shifting cultivation practised in the area includes coffee and vegetables in the rotation. In the central highlands of Thailand Nitosols have recently been extensively cleared of natural dipterocarp forest vegetation and are widely planted to maize and sorghum.

17. NITOSOL-ACRISOL ASSOCIATION OF THE PHILIPPINES

Nitosols are the dominant soils of northern and southern Luzon, Panay, Cebu, Bohol, and western and eastern Mindanao. Their macrorelief ranges from rolling to steeply dissected or mountainous. Acrisols form the secondary component of the association occurring on steeply dissected to mountainous terrain.

The climate of the region is influenced by altitude and ranges from ever-humid semihot equatorial to humid tierra templada. Annual rainfall ranges from 1 000 to over 3 000 mm, and the dry season is most pronounced along the west coast of northern Luzon. Elevations range from sea level to nearly 3 000 m.

Medium- and fine-textured, deep, well-drained Dystric Nitosols are developed from Cretaceous and Paleogene spilite, basalt, keratophyre and andesite. Fine-textured, deep, well-drained Eutric Nitosols are less extensive and are developed on Pliocene and Quaternary volcanics in the southern peninsula of Luzon and in Mindanao. Medium- and fine-textured, well-drained Orthic Acrisols are developed from non-calcareous consolidated clastic sediments and metamorphic and igneous rocks.

The main inclusions are Gleyic Cambisols and Pellic Vertisols developed on recent alluvial deposits, Orthic Luvisols on Pliocene-Miocene marine clastic sediments, and Orthic Andosols on subrecent volcanic materials.

Much of the region remains under natural forest. Anthropic savanna occurs in deforested areas, usually as a consequence of shifting cultivation. Permanent cultivation of fruit crops, coconuts, abaca and rubber is largely restricted to the more gently sloping and accessible Nitosols.

18. FERRALSOLS

Ferralsols occur mainly in Viet Nam, Democratic Kampuchea, Borneo, Irian Jaya and Sulawesi. The macrorelief ranges from undulating to steeply dissected or mountainous, while elevations range from 100 to over 3 000 m. These soils are mainly fossil formations occurring under present climates ranging from ever-humid semihot equatorial in Borneo and Irian Jaya, through moist monsoon hot tropical in Democratic Kampuchea, to humid tierra templada in Sulawesi, Irian Jaya and Viet Nam.

In Democratic Kampuchea and Viet Nam Rhodic Ferralsols are developed on old basalt plateaus with an undulating to rolling macrorelief. Main inclusions are Ferric Acrisols and lithic-phase Orthic Acrisols. Rhodic Ferralsols are extensively used for shifting cultivation and rubber, tea and coffee plantations.

In Borneo Ferralsols are developed on igneous rocks of old complexes in the Schwaner and Meratus mountain ranges. Petroferric or petric Humic Ferralsols are most extensive on rolling and steeply dissected terrain. Petroferric Orthic Ferralsols and petric Rhodic and Xanthic Ferralsols are less extensive, occurring on areas with an undulating to rolling macrorelief. The main inclusions are lithic Orthic and Humic Acrisols, petric Ferric Acrisols and Albic Arenosols. Most Humic Ferralsols are under natural rain forest vegetation. Shifting cultivation is practised on gentler slopes of the more accessible Orthic Ferralsols, Rhodic Ferralsols and Xanthic Ferralsols.

Petroferric Humic and Rhodic Ferralsols are developed from old basic and ultrabasic rocks in central and southeastern Sulawesi. Their macrorelief is steeply dissected to mountainous. Most of these soils remain under natural forest cover. The main inclusions are Orthic Acrisols and Humic Acrisols and petric Ferric Acrisols.

In Irian Jaya petroferric Humic and Rhodic Ferralsols are developed from old basic to intermediate volcanic rocks in the Doberai (Vogelkop) Peninsula. Their macrorelief is steeply dissected to mountainous and the soils have a dense forest cover. The main inclusions are Orthic Acrisols, Chromic Luvisols and Humic Cambisols.

19. HISTOSOLS

The Histosols of Southeast Asia are estimated to cover some 23 million ha. The majority are found in the vast coastal peat bogs of Sumatra, Borneo, Irian Jaya, and to a lesser extent the Malay Peninsula. Inland occurrences are comparatively rare.

The development of lowland peat in the area is estimated to have started 4 000 to 5 000 years ago when a slowing in the rise of the sea level led to the formation of extensive coastal plains and deltas. Initially a topogenous or ground water bog nucleus would develop in a slightly depressed and concave environment. This gradually became ombrogenous (entirely rain-dependent) as the bog extended radially to cover the entire basin, with the surface rising over the former ground water level to form a body of domed peat often more than 15 m thick at the centre.

Most Histosols in the region occur on rain-dependent, nutrient-poor ombrogenous bogs. Topogenous ground water peat bogs cover a relatively small area and their soils vary widely owing to local differences in environmental factors, such as the chemical quality of the ground water. Most Histosols are permanently wet, with the water table close to or above the soil surface. Associated soils are Fluvisols and Gleysols occurring along natural levees, in bog fringes, and on young marine deposits along the coast. The deep soils of the central dome areas are under a light degraded forest composed of relatively few species, while soils of the peripheral zones are under mixed swamp forest.

Dystric Histosols are the dominant soils of the coastal swamps of Sumatra, Borneo, central Irian Jaya and the Malay Peninsula. Thionic Fluvisols and Dystric Fluvisols occur on recent fluvial and marine deposits on narrow levees and in coastal fringes. Humic Gleysols are developed on subrecent alluvium along transitional zones between the levees and the elevated peat domes. A saline phase of Eutric Gleysols occurs along the west coast of the Malay Peninsula.

Eutric Histosols are dominant in the extensive tidal swamps along the south coast of Irian Jaya, where they occur in association with Eutric Fluvisols developed on recent fluvial and marine deposits on evees and in the narrow littoral zone.

References

ANDRIESSE, J.P. *Tropical lowland peats in Southeast Asia.*
1974 Amsterdam, Royal Tropical Institute. Communication No. 63.

BREEMEN VAN, N. Soil forming processes in acid sulphate
1973 soils. In *Proceedings of the International Symposium on Acid Sulphate Soils.* Wageningen. ILRI Publication 18, Vol. 1.

CROCKER, C.D. *Reconnaissance survey of the soils of Cambodia.*
1962 Phnom Penh, Royal Cambodian Government Soil Commission/USAID.

DE JONGH, P.L.J. *Soils of Indonesia.* Bogor, FAO/Soil
1973 Research Institute. Working Paper No. 4.

DENT, F.J. *Reconnaissance soil survey of peninsular Thailand.*
1972 Bangkok, Department of Land Development. Report SSR No. 94.

DENT, F.J., DESAUNETTES, J.R. & MALINGREAU, J.P. *Detailed*
1977 *reconnaissance land resources survey. Cimanuk watershed area (west Java).* Bogor, FAO/Soil Research Institute. Working Paper No. 14.

DRIESSEN, P.M. & SOEPRAPTOHARDJO, M. *Soils for agricultural*
1974 *expansion in Indonesia.* Bogor, Soil Research Institute. Bulletin No. 1.

DUDAL, R. & MOORMANN, F.R. Major soils of Southeast
1964 Asia. *J. trop. Geog.,* 18.

DUDAL, R., MOORMANN, F.R. & RIQUIER, J. Soils of humid
1974 tropical Asia. In *Natural resources of humid tropical Asia,* p. 159-178. Paris, Unesco.

MOORMANN, F.R. *The soils of the Republic of Viet Nam.*
1961 Saigon, Ministry of Agriculture.

MOORMANN, F.R. Acid sulphate soils (cat-clays) of the tropics.
1963 *Soil Sci.,* 95(4).

MOORMANN, F.R. & ROJANASOONTHON, S. *The soils of the*
1972 *Kingdom of Thailand.* Bangkok, Department of Land Development. Report SSR No. 72A.

PONS, L.J. & VAN DER KEVIE, W. *Acid sulphate soils in*
1969 *Thailand.* Bangkok, Department of Land Development. Report SSR No. 81.

VAN DER KEVIE, W. Physiography, classification and mapping
1973 of acid sulphate soils. In *Proceedings of the International Symposium on Acid Sulphate Soils.* Wageningen. ILRI Publication 18, Vol. 1.

WONG, I.F.T. *The present land use of West Malaysia.* Kuala
1966 Lumpur, Ministry of Agriculture, Co-operatives and Lands.

6. LAND USE AND SOIL SUITABILITY

The land use of an area depends on interactions between soil, climate, hydrological characteristics and prevailing socio-economic conditions. Soil is only one of the factors that influence land use. Ecological conditions, and hence land use, vary considerably, but one feature common to all countries within the region is the predominance of rice growing, paddy accounting for over 70 percent of the total cereal production.

Over 80 percent of the region's work force is engaged in an agriculture in which rice and plantation crops are predominant. Subsistence agriculture is prevalent in large areas of Southeast Asia, with arable land being divided into small holdings owned or tenanted by farmers.

Nucleated village settlements are more common than isolated homesteads. The pattern of land utilization in agricultural areas is complicated, as can be expected on land where crops have been raised continuously for over 40 centuries. In the following, land use is discussed briefly for each of the territories in the region, in alphabetical order.[1]

Brunei. About 75 percent of the land area remains under forest. Rubber is the only cash crop of importance. Coconut, rice and sago are grown as subsistence crops.

Democratic Kampuchea. Rice growing dominates the agricultural economy. Citrus, banana and coconut growing are essentially subsistence activities, with 90 percent of the products being consumed on the farms. Vegetable growing, market gardening and cultivation of various cash and industrial crops including maize, tobacco and cotton are carried out on riverine land. Vegetables are mainly consumed by the grower except for dry beans and soybeans, which are sold on the home market or exported. Rubber growing is an important industry. Other crops for export or industrial use are brown maize and green beans.

Indonesia. Subsistence farm agriculture is based on food crops including rice, maize, cassava and other root crops, pulses, groundnuts and soybeans. However, rice must be imported to supplement national production. Cash crops, usually grown in home gardens, include coconut, rubber, coffee, tea, kapok, areca nut, pepper, cloves, nutmeg, sugar cane, tobacco, cinchona, cocoa and oil palm. Of these, only rubber, copra, tea, coffee, sugar, tobacco, oil palm, pepper, kapok and tapioca products enter the world market. Commercial plantations are mainly of rubber, coffee, tea, coconut, sugar cane, cinchona, oil palm, kapok, cocoa and tobacco. In addition, considerable foreign exchange is derived from forest exploitation.

Lao. Paddy, the main crop in the lowlands during the rainy season, is followed by dry-season tobacco and vegetables. Elsewhere, the shifting cultivation of upland rice intercropped with maize, gourds or sweet potato is essentially a subsistence activity. Cotton is grown as a single crop, and so-called industrial crops of coffee and poppies are grown almost entirely by the mountain people.

Peninsular Malaysia and Singapore. Some 19 percent of the land area is under cultivation. Rubber, which occupies about 67 percent of all agricultural land, is followed in order of magnitude by rice, coconut and oil palm. Agriculture is dominated by commercial crops, and 35 to 45 percent of the total rice requirements are imported.

The Philippines. About 49 percent of the land area remains under forest, 31 percent is arable land, and 20 percent is under rough grazing. Some 40 percent of the total farm land is devoted to rice growing. Other crops in order of importance are coconut, maize and sugar cane, the Philippines being the world's leading source of copra. Natural rubber has recently become an important domestic product, and forest products constitute a large share of industrial production.

Sabah. About 80 percent of the land area is under forest which is exploited for timber and exported

---

[1] Land-use data are from the Istituto Geografico De Agostini, *World atlas of agriculture,* Vol. 2, 1973.

in log form, and 12 percent is under shifting cultivation. Rice, rubber and coconut are grown as subsistence crops, and about 35 percent of the total rice requirements must be imported. Rubber, coconut, oil palm, cocoa and abaca are grown commercially.

Sarawak. About 73 percent of the land area remains under forest, and 20 percent is under shifting cultivation. Timber exports are increasing, and the main cash crops are rubber, pepper, sago, coconut and oil palm. Rice, grown as a subsistence crop, meets about half of the total rice requirements.

Thailand. Rice is the dominant crop, and Thailand is one of the world's leading rice suppliers. Rubber is second to rice as a foreign exchange earner. Other major commercial crops are sugar cane, tobacco and cotton for domestic processing industries, and maize and kenaf for export. The production of cassava, soybeans, groundnuts and castor seed is increasing significantly. Fruit and truck crops are grown for local consumption. Forests are lightly but unevenly exploited, with teak forests being seriously overcut.

Viet Nam. A large proportion of the land area consists of uncultivable terrain. Permanent agriculture is largely restricted to the coastal lowlands and deltas where the monocultural production of paddy is the main activity. Other crops include maize, sweet potato, cassava, soybeans, groundnuts, haricot beans, sugar cane, tobacco, cotton, jute, coconut, banana and a variety of fruit trees. Tea and rubber are the main plantation crops.

Land use by soil units is discussed in more detail as follows. The soil units are arranged in alphabetical order of symbols.

A. Acrisols

Af. FERRIC ACRISOLS

Use. Ferric Acrisols are found in the more humid parts of continental Southeast Asia and Indonesia. Important concentrations occur in central Democratic Kampuchea and Viet Nam, southern Thailand, Malaysia, and Kalimantan and Sumatra in Indonesia. The macrorelief is undulating to rolling. The natural vegetation is tropical lowland evergreen rain forest. Large tracts of land have been brought under shifting cultivation of upland rice and cassava, with poor results, leading to the development of anthropic savanna dominated by *Imperata cylindrica*.

Suitability. Ferric Acrisols are acid, have a low organic matter content, and are low in bases and phosphate. Although these soils at present are moderately well to well drained, they have suffered from impeded drainage at some stage in their development. In consequence, hard iron concretions of variable size, or distinct semihard nodules have accumulated in the argillic B horizon. The presence of hard concretions and somewhat cemented or indurated nodules within rooting depth is a limiting factor for plant growth, depending on the relative intensity and depth of occurrence. In addition, natural fertility and productivity are low. Continuous cultivation requires heavy applications of phosphate, potassium and nitrogen fertilizers. Rubber, under careful management, is probably the best tree crop for these soils. However, no satisfactory growth of any crop can be expected where large concretions are abundant at shallow depth.

Ag. GLEYIC ACRISOLS

Use. Gleyic Acrisols occur mainly in northeastern Thailand and adjacent areas of Democratic Kampuchea and Lao. Their macrorelief ranges from nearly level to rolling. The natural vegetation is tropical dry deciduous forest. In low-lying and level areas one crop of rice is grown annually during the rainy season, and crop failures may occur in years with low or poorly distributed rainfall. Rice yields are generally low, ranging from 1 350 to 1 650 kg per ha. Kenaf is grown as a monoculture for up to five years on undulating to rolling areas which are subsequently abandoned to low-intensity grazing. Fruits, vegetables and mulberries are grown locally on the slightly better soils of levelled termite mounds.

Suitability. These highly leached soils are physically and chemically very poor. They have a low natural fertility, a low organic matter content, low pH, and are low in bases. The water economy of these soils is also poor, for although they are described as being poorly to somewhat poorly drained, they dry out very quickly and a drought of one or two weeks during the rainy season may result in crop failure. In addition, salt-affected spots may occur in low-rainfall years. Complex technical problems need to be solved before continuous cultivation can be established on these soils. Irrigation, where feasible, may safeguard crops from failure through drought. The introduction of green manuring crops in a rotation and heavy fertilizer application (possibly including micro-elements) are also required. However, any or all of these measures are only rarely economically justifiable under present conditions. Rice appears to be the most suitable crop on low-lying level terrain where supplementary irrigation water can be provided. The recent development of improved pasture seems to provide a partial economic answer for soils on undulating to rolling terrain.

Ah. HUMIC ACRISOLS

Use. Humic Acrisols are the typical non-volcanic mountain soils of the more humid parts of Southeast Asia. They occur mainly on mountain slopes and in montane valleys of Borneo, Sumatra and Sulawesi. The macrorelief is steeply dissected to mountainous. The natural vegetation, tropical montane rain forest, has been cleared in more accessible areas and planted to tea, coffee and cinchona, or replaced by secondary forest where shifting cultivation is the dominant land use.

Suitability. These soils vary considerably in thickness, and shallow lithic phases are common on upper slopes. They have a moderate natural fertility due largely to their relatively high organic matter content, but are acid and low in bases. They have good physical characteristics and are mainly well drained, but erosion hazard is great if slopes are exposed.

Tea (*Camellia sinensis, Thea sinensis*) is well suited for deep, well-drained soils of mountain slopes above 800 m, with optimum elevations between 1 000 and 1 500 m near the equator, provided that rainfall exceeds the crop moisture requirement. Conservation of sufficient organic matter in the topsoil is essential, and hence mulching and open shading of exposed slopes are considered prudent. Coffee and cinchona are grown with moderate success, but both require a higher level of mineral reserves and base saturation for optimal growth and quality. The same holds for *Aleurites montana*, a tung oil producing tree, and a number of fruit crops, notably soursop and cherimoya.

On lower slopes food crops such as cassava, sweet potato, upland rice, a variety of beans, groundnuts and maize can be grown satisfactorily. However, continuous cultivation is dependent on a high standard of management involving soil conservation measures and a rational use of fertilizers, without which rapid soil deterioration and erosion will occur.

Ao. ORTHIC ACRISOLS

Use. These soils, the most common of Southeast Asia, cover about one third of the region. They are developed from sedimentary rocks, old alluvial deposits, and acid and intermediate igneous and metamorphic rocks. The majority are found on more or less well-drained gently undulating to rolling uplands, hilly land and mountain slopes of low and intermediate elevations, and on well-drained old alluvial terraces. A lithic phase is common on steeply dissected and mountainous slopes. The natural vegetation ranges from tropical evergreen rain forest in the Philippines, Indonesia, Malaysia, southern Thailand and southern parts of Democratic Kampuchea and Viet Nam to tropical deciduous and montane laurel forest in northern Viet Nam, northern Thailand and Lao. Shifting cultivation has been practised over wide areas since ancient times, often resulting in the development of a fire climax of anthropic savanna. During the last century, however, important areas have been brought under permanent crops, of which rubber and oil palm are the most important.

Suitability. Except for lithic phases, most Orthic Acrisols are physically in fairly good condition. They are chemically poor, being acid, low in organic matter content and bases, and lacking in natural fertility if weatherable minerals are exhausted. Although these soils' natural fertility is generally low, it varies considerably, as they are developed from such a wide range of parent materials. Most soils are moderately well to well drained, but compactness of the argillic B horizon makes them susceptible to erosion if exposed on slopes under a torrential rainfall regime.

Rubber (*Hevea brasiliensis*) requires deep, well-drained, acid, medium-to-heavy-textured soils with ample moisture throughout the year, and gives good results on the Orthic Acrisols of the hot, humid parts of the region. Best results are obtained on well-drained uplands between latitudes 15°N and 10°S at elevations below 500 m. Phosphate and nitrogen applications are required in the early years of growth. Rubber also affords good protection against erosion of sloping lands provided that contour or bench terracing measures are applied, giving a solid permanent basis for rural development in areas otherwise unsuited for permanent cropping.

Oil palm (*Elaeis guineensis*) is more stringent in its soil requirements than rubber, but performs reasonably on the more fertile, deep, moderately well to well-drained Orthic Acrisols that have a good moisture retention capacity and adequate soil moisture availability throughout the year. Regular applications of phosphate, potassium and nitrogen fertilizers are essential, and moisture requirements restrict growth to the more humid parts of the region.

Food and cash crops including maize, cassava, groundnuts, soybeans and pineapple can be grown to some extent, but in general natural fertility limitations and erosion hazard on exposed slopes introduce a risk element if these soils are used intensively for the production of annual crops on a large scale.

Successful utilization for annual food or cash crops requires a relatively high standard of management involving soil conservation measures, a rotation including nitrogen-fixing legumes, and regular applications of complete fertilizers (possibly including micro-elements) and lime. The costs involved may not be economically justifiable, and attempts to utilize these soils for permanent annual crop production without adequate management inputs will lead to rapid soil degradation.

Steeper slopes should be reserved for forestry. However, erosion hazard is severe if slopes are exposed, so logging operations should be kept to a minimum.

Ap. PLINTHIC ACRISOLS

Use. Plinthic Acrisols are not extensive, occurring mainly in southern Sumatra and southern Irian Jaya. They are develop from Neogene acid liparitic and dacitic tuff deposits and Plio-Pleistocene alluvial deposits on flat, poorly drained surfaces of dissected peneplains, and have a nearly level to undulating macrorelief. The natural vegetation is tropical lowland evergreen rain forest. Shifting cultivation and rough grazing, the main forms of land use, have led to the development of *Imperata cylindrica*-dominated anthropic savanna or poor scrub forest.

Suitability. Plinthic Acrisols suffer from impeded drainage and are physically and chemically poor. They are acid, low in organic matter content and bases, and have a low natural fertility. A continuous plinthic horizon occurs within 125 cm of the soil surface, which is compact and relatively impermeable. Hard iron concretions may also occur at or near the surface. These soils are generally not suitable for agriculture owing to a combination of limiting factors including low fertility, impeded drainage and rooting limitations. Drainage amendments are impracticable, as plinthite will harden irreversibly on drying to form ironstone. These soils are best left under permanent vegetation.

B. Cambisols

Bd. DYSTRIC CAMBISOLS

Use. Dystric Cambisols are found in all countries of the region, but are most extensive in Sumatra, Irian Jaya, the Moluccas, the Lesser Sunda Islands, Aru and Ewab. They occur on a variety of landforms and acid to intermediate parent rocks. Their macrorelief is predominantly steeply dissected to mountainous, but ranges through rolling to undulating. These soils occur over a wide elevation range under a humid climate where soil leaching is almost continuous and where geological erosion constantly renews the surface. Large tracts remain under tropical evergreen rain forest containing valuable hard woods. Shifting cultivation is practised on more accessible slopes, and locally they are planted to tea, highland coffee, rubber, oil palm, bananas, fruit trees and tobacco.

Suitability. Dystric Cambisols are medium to fine textured, well drained, and have good physical properties. They are slightly acid to acid, and their content of organic matter and bases is low to medium. Their natural fertility is low, but they respond well to applications of potassium, nitrogen, lime and phosphate fertilizers, and to other good management practices. Soil depth is variable, and many of the soils in mountainous areas of Irian Jaya, Sumatra and the Moluccas are relatively shallow. However, deep to very deep soils occur in the flat lowlands of Sumatra and Aru. Low natural fertility, the main limitation of all Dystric Cambisols, may be corrected through rational fertilizer application. Soils on sloping terrain are subject to severe erosion when exposed unless properly terraced.

Sloping soils are best planted to perennial tree crops for sustained production. Tea gives excellent results above 1 000 m if its moisture requirement can be met. Highland coffee demands higher management inputs owing to its more stringent nutrient requirements. In humid lowlands below about 400 m, rubber, oil palm, cloves, bananas and a variety of fruit trees give satisfactory results. Maize, cocoa, sugar cane, tobacco and a variety of fruit crops thrive under a monsoon climate. Rice can also be grown up to 2 000 m with irrigation from springs. However, successful continuous cultivation requires proper bench and contour terrace construction, good cultivation practices, and the regular application of fertilizers in order to combat erosion and maintain and improve soil fertility.

Shallow soils in mountainous areas should be left under natural forest for watershed protection and as a forest reserve.

Be. EUTRIC CAMBISOLS

Use. Eutric Cambisols are not extensive in the region, occurring mainly in Java, Sumatra, Sulawesi and the Lesser Sunda Islands. They are developed from basic to intermediate parent materials of volcanic origin and are usually found on mid-slopes of volcanoes. Their macrorelief is steeply sloping, but individual slopes are long. Natural vegetation is tropical montane evergreen rain forest. In Java and Bali, however, the majority of these soils are terraced and intensively cultivated to irrigated rice or " tega-lan " rainfed crops including cassava, maize, tobacoc, beans, potato, cabbage and occasionally upland rice, while home gardens support fruit trees, vegetables and coffee.

Suitability. Eutric Cambisols are generally deep and medium textured, and have good physical prop-erties. They are slightly acid to neutral in reaction. Their organic matter content is usually sufficient and they have a moderate supply of bases, and hence are quite fertile. Initially, only nitrogen and phospho-rus are required to give good yields, although potas-sium should be added after a number of years' continuous use. The soils are easily worked to a good tilth. Their main limitations are susceptibility to water erosion on unprotected slopes, and occasional moisture shortage due to inadequate rainfall. Soil conservation measures are a prerequisite to utilization.

Tea and highland coffee are well suited on upper slopes above approximately 1 000 m. Permanent agriculture should be limited to deep soils with moderate slopes. Terraced rainfed food and cash crops give satisfactory results, especially if nitrogen-fixing legumes are introduced into the rotation, but phosphate application is necessary for sustained production of groundnuts and other legumes. Terraced continuous rice cultivation is also successful where spring water irrigation is feasible. However, as these soils are usually situated within catchment areas, it may be better to combine one crop of rice during the rainy season with a summer legume crop with less demanding water requirements than rice in order to release water resources for downstream irrigation. Steep land with shallow soils should remain under forest or be allowed to revert to forest.

Bf.   FERRALIC CAMBISOLS

Use. Ferralic Cambisols occur in association with Humic Acrisols and Orthic Ferralsols in limited areas in Sarawak and Kalimantan. They are devel-oped from acid tuff deposits and Paleogene sand-stone on foot slopes bordering river plains, and have a rolling to hilly macrorelief. The majority of these soils remain under tropical lowland evergreen rain forest which is locally cleared for shifting cultivation.

Suitability. Ferralic Cambisols are deep, fine to medium textured, and well drained. They have good physical properties and a medium organic matter content. They are strongly acid, low in bases, and have a low cation exchange capacity. The main limitations to permanent agriculture are low natural

fertility and susceptibility to water erosion. These soils are best suited for the production of perennial crops such as rubber, oil palm, banana, abaca and coconut. However, sustained agricultural produc-tion requires regular fertilizer application, at least during the early years of growth for tree crops, and adequate protection against erosion on sloping land.

Bg.   GLEYIC CAMBISOLS

Use. Gleyic Cambisols occur mainly in the Philip-pines and to a lesser extent in Java. They are developed on subrecent alluvial deposits derived from intermediate to basic parent materials, and occupy broad, slightly dissected low continental river terraces. Their macrorelief is nearly level to gently undulating, and ground water is at or near the surface during the peak of the rainy season. The natural vegetation is tropical lowland evergreen rain forest, but little of this remains as most of these soils are under intensive permanent agriculture. In the Philippines they are planted to irrigated rice, maize, tomatoes, cabbage, beans, cucumbers and melons. In Java they support irrigated rice rotated every three years with sugar cane (Glebagan system) which is not ratooned.

Suitability. Gleyic Cambisols are deep, medium to fine textured, and poorly to somewhat poorly drained. They are slightly acid to neutral in reaction, and have a moderate supply of bases and a moderate to high cation exchange capacity. The physical and chemical properties of these soils are highly favour-able for the sustained cultivation of a wide range of crops. They are considered best suited to irrigated rice and to short-season vegetables and cash crops of relatively high value which can pay the cost of irrigation and fertilizer inputs. The main limitation is occasional flooding. However, high yields can be expected with good management, good cultural methods, moisture control, improved crop varieties and adjustment of planting time to minimize the flooding hazard.

Bh.   HUMIC CAMBISOLS

Use. Humic Cambisols are not extensive in the region, occurring mainly in Sumatra and Irian Jaya. They are developed from acid to intermediate parent rocks and occupy upper slopes of the Barisan range in Sumatra and the Maoke and Van Rees mountains of Irian Jaya. Their macrorelief is predominantly steeply dissected to mountainous, although areas of hilly to rolling terrain occur in Sumatra. The natural vegetation is tropical montane evergreen rain forest.

Shifting cultivation is practised on some accessible lower slopes, and tea and highland coffee are grown locally in Sumatra.

Suitability. These are deep, medium-textured, well-drained soils. They are slightly acid in reaction and have a moderate to high organic matter content, but are relatively low in bases. They have good physical properties and a moderate natural fertility due largely to their high organic matter content. However, they are highly susceptible to erosion when exposed on slopes subject to frequent torrential rains. Consequently, perennial crops offer the best possibilities for permanent agriculture on gentler slopes, and steeply dissected land should remain under forest. Tea and cinchona give satisfactory results at elevations above 1 000 m, but highland coffee demands higher management inputs owing to its more stringent nutrient requirements. Regular phosphate, potassium and nitrogen fertilizer applications and bench or contour terracing protection against erosion are mandatory for sustained cultivation on gentler slopes.

Bv. VERTIC CAMBISOLS

Use. Vertic Cambisols are mainly restricted to small areas of central Java. They are developed on fine-textured subrecent fluvial and colluvial deposits derived from intermediate to basic rocks, and have a nearly level to gently undulating macrorelief. Most of the natural vegetation (tropical moist deciduous forest) has been removed. The soils are planted to rice and sugar cane where irrigation is feasible. Rainfed crops include maize, cassava and a variety of pulses. Many areas are left fallow for low-intensity grazing during the dry season.

Suitability. Vertic Cambisols are moderately deep to deep, fine textured and well drained. They are slightly acid to neutral in reaction, have a moderate organic matter content, and are fairly high in bases. Although these soils are relatively fertile, their physical properties are less favourable for tillage; they crack deeply during the dry season when moisture deficiency limits plant growth. The availability of sufficient moisture during the dry season is the key to productivity on these soils. Where irrigation water is available, rice and sugar cane are well suited under good management including rational fertilizer application to maintain fertility. If irrigation is not feasible, a rotation of maize or rainfed rice with pulses such as Javanese soybeans (" kedele ") or chick-peas is fairly successful. Certain varieties of mango, guava, papaya and pineapple may be considered provided that the dry season is not too pro-

nounced. Where this is the case, dry-season utilization is limited to low-intensity grazing.

E. Rendzinas

Use. Rendzinas are not widespread in the region. They are mainly found in parts of Irian Jaya, Aru, Ewab, the Lesser Sunda Islands, the Moluccas, Sulawesi and Sumatra, where they occur in association with Lithosols, Chromic Luvisols and Regosols. In Irian Jaya, Sulawesi and Sumatra, Rendzinas are developed from Tertiary or older limestone rocks, while those of the Moluccas and Lesser Sunda Islands are developed from Quaternary coral limestone. Their macrorelief is variable, ranging from gently undulating to steeply dissected. Elevations range from near sea level to over 1 000 m. The natural vegetation is a poor tropical evergreen rain forest in Sumatra, Irian Jaya and Sulawesi, and tropical dry deciduous forest elsewhere. Only calciophile species survive and thrive well in a limestone habitat. Rendzinas are not extensively cultivated. Fruit crops are grown locally and cloves are successful in Ambon. Where these soils have been used for pasture, serious overgrazing has occurred.

Suitability. Rendzinas are shallow to moderately deep, fine-textured, well to somewhat excessively drained soils. They are chemically rich and well provided with plant nutrients, and have a near-neutral to slightly alkaline soil reaction. However, their productive capacity is determined by their water-retention capacity, which varies widely depending on the combination of depth and organic matter content of the mollic topsoil, and physical factors including depth and the hardness or brittleness of the underlying limestone. In addition, soils on exposed slopes are highly susceptible to erosion.

In general, tropical Rendzinas are better suited for perennial or permanent crops than for annual food crops. On gently sloping moderately deep soils where sufficient moisture is available, cloves, mango, papaya, avocado, cashew nut and a variety of fruit crops give good-quality products. Elsewhere, these soils are best left under forest.

F. Ferralsols

Fa. ACRIC FERRALSOLS

Use. Acric Ferralsols occur only in the Pleiku-Kontum region of Viet Nam. They are developed from basaltic parent material and have an undulating to rolling macrorelief. Most of the natural vegetation (tropical dry deciduous forest) has been cleared for shifting rice cultivation, which has led to the development of anthropic short-grass pseudo-steppe vegetation. Tea is also grown on a limited scale.

Suitability. Acric Ferralsols are deep, fine-textured, well-drained soils. They have a strongly acid soil reaction, are low in bases and organic matter content, and have a low cation exchange capacity. They have a poor water-retention capacity and dry out deeply during the dry season, which is pronounced even though annual rainfall exceeds 2 000 mm. Low fertility and poor moisture-retention capacity leading to moisture deficiency during the dry season are the main limitations. Heavy use of phosphate and nitrogen fertilizers (possibly micro-elements), liming and irrigation are required if these soils are to be continuously cultivated. Tree crops stand a better chance of success than annual food or cash crops. Tea has given satisfactory yields where sprinkler irrigation has been applied. In general, however, regeneration of forest should be encouraged where better soils are available for agriculture.

Fh. HUMIC FERRALSOLS

Use. Humic Ferralsols are mainly restricted to parts of Sumatra, Kalimantan, Sulawesi and Irian Jaya. They occur as petroferric and petric phases, and are developed from old complex volcanic deposits and acid to intermediate igneous rocks. Their macrorelief is predominantly steeply dissected to mountainous, although a rolling to hilly petric phase occurs in Kalimantan. Elevations range from 200 to over 1 000 m. The natural vegetation is tropical montane evergreen rain forest. These soils are rarely exploited for agricultural purposes and remain largely under dense forest.

Suitability. Humic Ferralsols are moderately deep to deep, medium-to-fine-textured, well-drained soils. They have a strongly acid soil reaction and low cation exchange capacity and are low in bases, but have a moderate to high organic matter content. A petroferric horizon consisting of a more or less continuous layer of indurated material or a layer of hard ironstone concretions occurs within the rooting zone, causing limitations to plant growth. The combination of limitations within the rooting zone, low soil fertility and high susceptibility to erosion on exposed slopes generally precludes these soils from permanent cultivation. Rubber is a possible crop on the rolling petric phase of Humic Ferralsols in Kalimantan, but the high management inputs required to overcome the limitations may not be

economically justifiable under present conditions. Hence these soils are best left under forest, and any exploitation for timber should be carried out in a cautious and conservative manner.

Fo. ORTHIC FERRALSOLS

Use. Orthic Ferralsols occur in association with Humic Ferralsols in Thailand and Viet Nam, and a petroferric phase is found in Kalimantan, Sulawesi, Sumatra and the Moluccas. In Viet Nam they are developed on ancient basalt plateaus, and in Thailand on old alluvial terrace remnants. Orthic Ferralsols in Indonesia are developed on highly weathered, acid to intermediate old volcanic rock complexes. Their macrorelief is generally undulating to rolling. The natural vegetation ranges from tropical lowland evergreen forest in Indonesia to tropical dry deciduous forest in Thailand and Viet Nam. The majority of Indonesian Orthic Ferralsols remain under dense forest, but locally an *Imperata cylindrica*-dominated anthropic savanna has developed where shifting cultivation has long been practised. In Thailand and Viet Nam most of these soils have been subjected to shifting cultivation and are often abandoned to anthropic savanna. However, in Viet Nam tea and coffee are grown locally.

Suitability. These soils are medium to fine textured, moderately deep to deep, and well drained. They have a strongly acid soil reaction, a low content of organic matter and bases, and a low cation exchange capacity. Consequently, their natural fertility is low. In Viet Nam and Thailand they are fine textured and rather impervious, and superficial waterlogging is a common feature during the rainy season when they are sticky and difficult to work. In the dry season they dry out deeply and moisture deficiency becomes a limiting factor. In Indonesia Orthic Ferralsols are characterized by the presence of a more or less continuous petroferric horizon in the rooting zone which limits plant growth. In addition, all these soils are susceptible to erosion on unprotected slopes. Regular applications of phosphate and nitrogen fertilizers (possibly micro-elements) and liming are required for successful cultivation. Sprinkler irrigation is beneficial, where feasible, in Thailand and Viet Nam. Sloping land also requires protective measures to guard against erosion.

Tree crops offer better possibilities for continuous use than annual crops. In Indonesia rubber and a variety of fruit trees, including durian, give satisfactory results under good management. Tea and coffee have proved satisfactory crops in Viet Nam. In Thailand a more pronounced dry season and lack of irrigation water have resulted in most of these soils being abandoned to low-intensity grazing as the high management inputs required to bring them under permanent cultivation are not economically justifiable under present conditions. Here, recent developments in improved pasture offer the best possibilities for future use.

Fr. RHODIC FERRALSOLS

Use. Rhodic Ferralsols are not extensive in the region, occurring mainly in Kalimantan, Irian Jaya, Sulawesi and the Lesser Sunda Islands where petroferric and petric phases are dominant; and in Peninsular Malaysia, Viet Nam and Democratic Kampuchea. In Indonesia and Peninsular Malaysia they are developed from highly weathered basic to intermediate igneous rocks and, to a lesser extent, acid extrusive volcanic rocks. In Viet Nam and Democratic Kampuchea they are developed on ancient basalt plateaus. Their macrorelief ranges from undulating to steeply dissected. The natural vegetation in Indonesia and Peninsular Malaysia is tropical evergreen rain forest, most of which remains, except where lower slopes have been subjected to shifting cultivation or planted to rubber. In Viet Nam and Democratic Kampuchea little natural forest remains, as most of these soils are under shifting rice cultivation, rubber or coffee, and secondary forest and anthropic savanna are the dominant vegetation types. In the coastal regions of Viet Nam Rhodic Ferralsols are used for intensive cultivation of a wide variety of food crops.

Suitability. These soils are deep to moderately deep (petroferric phase), medium to fine textured, and well drained. Soil reaction varies from slightly to strongly acid, organic matter content is moderate, bases are generally low, and cation exchange capacity is low. Natural soil fertility is generally low, but soils with slightly higher pH tend to have a more favourable nutrient status. The physical properties of Rhodic Ferralsols are generally good; the soil structure in upper layers is typically crumb, which enables rain water to infiltrate rapidly and consequently makes them fairly resistant to erosion. In Indonesia the presence of a petroferric horizon or a layer of hard iron concretions within rooting depth limits plant growth. Moisture deficiency is usually not serious, as these soils do not appear to have developed in areas with a distinct dry season.

Under good management, including regular phosphate and nitrogen fertilizer application, gently sloping soils have a high agricultural potential for plantation crops (rubber, coffee), fruit trees, pepper and industrial crops (fibres, tobacco). Good possibilities exist for dryland food crops (maize, groundnuts,

soybeans) and vegetables, and terraced rice gives satisfactory results where irrigation is feasible. Steeply sloping petroferric phases require greater management inputs and should be restricted to tree crops (rubber and fruit trees below 800 m, highland coffee and tea above 1 000 m), or reserved for forestry.

Fx. XANTHIC FERRALSOLS

Use. These soils occur only as a petric phase in western parts of Kalimantan and the Sumatran islands of Bangka, Belitung and Riau, where they are found in association with Ferralic Arenosols. They are developed from acid igneous and metamorphic rocks and on Neogene coastal sand deposits. Their macrorelief is generally undulating to rolling, although they also occur on steeply dissected terrain in Kalimantan. The natural vegetation is a poor tropical evergreen rain forest which has degraded to *Imperata cylindrica*-dominated savanna over wide areas. Shifting cultivation is the main land use. White pepper is cultivated locally.

Suitability. Depth is variable, being shallow to moderately deep on steeply dissected slopes, and moderately deep to deep on undulating to rolling terrain. Xanthic Ferralsols are medium textured and well to excessively drained. Soil reaction is strongly to extremely acid. Organic matter content is medium to low. They are low in bases and have a low cation exchange capacity. The presence of a layer of hard iron concretions within rooting depth limits plant growth, the degree of limitation depending on the depth of occurrence and abundance of concretions. Low natural fertility and the presence of a petric layer within rooting depth are the main limitations to permanent cultivation, while steeper members are susceptible to erosion on unprotected slopes. Heavy regular applications of phosphate, nitrogen and potassium fertilizers (possibly micro-elements) are required, the cost of which may not be economically justifiable under present conditions. Under good management, coconuts, rubber, pepper, cashew nuts and pineapples deserve consideration. Annual food and cash crops are generally not economically viable, and the agricultural potential of these soils is low. Steeply sloping members should remain under, or be allowed to revert to, natural forest.

G. Gleysols

Gd. DYSTRIC GLEYSOLS

Use. Dystric Gleysols occur mainly in Thailand, Malaysia, Lao, Viet Nam and Kalimantan. They are developed on subrecent marine and riverine alluvium and occupy positions on raised coastal flats and low river terraces. Their macrorelief is predominantly flat. They are waterlogged and inundated during the rainy season, but dry out to some depth during the dry season. The natural vegetation (mixed swamp forest) has been largely cleared for rice cultivation. Most areas produce one crop of rainfed rice a year, or two crops a year where irrigation is possible. Yields are generally low (1 350 to 1 650 kg per ha in Thailand), and where irrigation is not feasible the soils are left in fallow for low-intensity grazing during the dry season.

Suitability. Dystric Gleysols are strongly leached, fine-textured kaolinitic clay soils with poor to very poor drainage. Soil reaction is strongly to slightly acid, and they have a low to moderate organic matter content and are low in bases. Poor drainage and regular inundation generally preclude the cultivation of dryland crops or tree crops. Natural conditions are best suited to paddy cultivation, especially where irrigation water is available during the dry season. However, drainage measures may be necessary in areas where flash flooding endangers crop growth during the rainy season. Under irrigation, two crops of rice or one crop of rice followed by a summer legume crop can be grown in most years. These soils have low natural fertility, and in northeastern Thailand potential or actual salinity is a limiting factor in dry years. In addition, aluminium toxicity in strongly acid soils may depress yields. Consequently, good management involving regular phosphate, nitrogen and potassium fertilizer applications, careful cultural practices, and water control is essential for successful continuous cultivation.

Ge. Eutric Gleysols

Use. Eutric Gleysols occur in parts of Lao, Viet Nam, Democratic Kampuchea, Thailand, Peninsular Malaysia, Java, Kalimantan and the Philippines. They occupy raised coastal flats and low river terraces, but, unlike Dystric Gleysols, are developed on subrecent alluvium derived from more basic parent material. They have been largely cleared of the original mixed swamp forest and are intensively used for continuously irrigated rice, or rice in rotation with vegetables, pulses, tobacco and occasionally sugar cane. Saline-phase soils occurring on the coastal flats of Thailand, Peninsular Malaysia and Viet Nam are used for salt pans.

Suitability. Eutric Gleysols are mainly fine textured, although medium- and coarse-textured soils

occur in the Philippines. They are poorly to very poorly drained, being waterlogged and inundated during the rainy season, but dry out to some depth during dry periods. Soil reaction is generally slightly acid to neutral, organic matter content is moderate to low, and they have a moderate supply of bases and a moderate to high cation exchange capacity. Consequently, these soils are fairly fertile. Their agricultural potential depends on the degree of water control feasible. A combination of irrigation during the dry season and drainage during the rainy season to restrict flooding allows for intensive use under good management, especially as irrigation water is usually of good quality. Continuous rice cultivation gives good results, with yields of between 4 000 and 5 000 kg per ha being recorded with regular fertilizer application. Rice in rotation with vegetables, pulses and tobacco is a satisfactory use in drier areas, while sugar cane is worth while where good drainage works are feasible. The saline phases are unsuited for agriculture, but provide a livelihood from salt extraction.

Gh. Humic Gleysols

Use. Humic Gleysols occur mainly in Sumatra, Kalimantan, Irian Jaya and Sulawesi, where they occupy peripheral zones of coastal peat swamps. They are developed on acid subrecent alluvium overlain by partially decomposed organic material. Their macrorelief is flat and they are waterlogged and inundated for long periods, although they dry out to some depth during dry spells. Original mixed swamp forest remains over wide areas. The principal land use is shifting rice cultivation.

Suitability. These soils are fine textured and poorly to very poorly drained. Soil reaction is generally strongly acid. Organic matter content is high owing to the presence of dystric histic material in surface layers not exceeding 40 cm in depth. They are low in bases and have a low natural fertility. Rainfed paddy is grown with some success under good management, but where the level of management is low and without regular fertilizer application and liming, a shifting pattern develops with land being abandoned after two or three years' cultivation. Pineapples, cassava and even rubber are grown where elementary drainage can be installed. In general, however, these soils can only support poor subsistence cultivation without high management inputs, which are rarely economically justifiable under present conditions.

I. Lithosols

Use. Lithosol associations occur in all countries of the region. Associated soils are mainly Rendzinas, Calcic Luvisols and Cambisols, Chromic Luvisols, Orthic Acrisols and Ferric Acrisols. Small occurrences of Lithosols are found on a wide variety of parent rocks, but they are most extensive on limestone. Their macrorelief is generally steeply dissected to mountainous. The landscape is of a very rugged character. Forest cover is patchy with many virtually bare rock outcrops. Cultivation is generally not practicable and land use is restricted to shifting cultivation on associated deeper soils.

Suitability. Lithosols are shallow, poor soils with little agricultural potential. They are highly susceptible to erosion, and stoniness, rock outcrops and steep slopes generally make them unsuitable for plough cultivation or irrigation. In some areas terrace construction might allow for arable crop cultivation, or tree crop cultivation where the underlying rock is sufficiently broken to afford deep root penetration, but the costs and labour required would rarely be economically justifiable. These soils are best left or put under forest.

J. Fluvisols

Jd. DYSTRIC FLUVISOLS

Use. Dystric Fluvisols occur mainly in Sumatra, Java, Kalimantan, Irian Jaya, Sulawesi and the Moluccas. They are developed on recent fluviatile, marine and lacustrine deposits and occupy positions on river levees, present flood plains, deltas and lake shores where alluvium is derived from predominantly acid parent rocks. Their macrorelief is generally flat, although levees often have an undulating microrelief. Soils subject to deep flooding remain under mixed swamp forest. Along coasts, soils which are periodically inundated by sea water are mainly under mangrove vegetation, which is intensively used in places for charcoal making. Where flooding is not too deep, or where flood protection and drainage works have been constructed, these soils are intensively used for paddy cultivation. Levee soils are traditionally used for settlement sites with home gardens, orchards and banana plantations. The better-drained Dystric Fluvisols of northern Sumatra produce Deli wrapper tobacco, and rubber and oil palm give very high yields.

Suitability. Most Dystric Fluvisols are stratified, medium to fine textured, and poorly to very poorly drained, although better-drained soils occur on levees.

Soil reaction is slightly to strongly acid. Organic matter content is variable, but generally moderate to high. These soils are low in bases, but respond well to moderate applications of nitrogen and phosphate fertilizers. Water control presents the main problem for the successful utilization of these soils. A combination of irrigation during the dry season and flood protection and drainage during the rainy season is required on poorly drained soils. Where this is feasible, two crops of rice a year can be achieved, giving high yields under good management involving the use of high-yielding varieties, regular fertilizer application, and the use of insecticides and pesticides. In drier areas where irrigation water is limited, rainfed rice followed by a summer legume crop or tobacco gives satisfactory results under good management. Rubber, oil palm and sugar cane thrive where drainage is adequate. Where no drainage or flood control is required, these soils may be cultivated under a wide range of food, fruit and industrial crops with moderate applications of fertilizers. Where flood control is not feasible, recent developments in the breeding of floating rice varieties seem promising. The better-drained levee soils are generally fully utilized for settlement sites, home gardens, orchards and banana plantations.

Je. EUTRIC FLUVISOLS

Use. Eutric Fluvisols occur in all countries of the region, although their combined area is less than that of Dystric Fluvisols. In Indonesia they are found on virtually all of the Greater and Lesser Sunda Islands, the Moluccas and Irian Jaya. In the Philippines they are dominant in the fertile alluvial plains of Pangasinan and Nueva Ecija on Luzon. They occur in the alluvial plains of the Chao Phraya, Mekong and Red rivers upstream of the deltas and are dominant in the coastal plains of southern Thailand, Peninsular Malaysia and Viet Nam. Landforms, macrorelief and natural vegetation are similar to those described for Dystric Fluvisols. However, unlike Dystric Fluvisols, these soils are developed on recent alluvium derived mostly from intermediate to basic parent rocks. Extensive areas of Eutric Fluvisols are under annual crops. Rice, the dominant crop, can be grown twice a year if sufficient irrigation water is available and the soils are afforded flood protection. On better-drained levee soils a great number of fruit and vegetable crops are grown together with industrial crops such as abaca, coconuts and cocoa.

Suitability. Like Dystric Fluvisols, these soils are more or less stratified, and are generally medium-to-fine-textured. Most are poorly to very poorly drained, although better-drained members are found on levees. Organic matter content is moderate to high, and soil reaction is neutral to slightly acid. Unlike Dystric Fluvisols, these soils have a moderate base status. Their agricultural potential is generally high, but is again dependent on water control for poorly to very poorly drained soils, while in drier areas moisture deficiency may be experienced on better-drained members during the dry season if insufficient irrigation water is available. Under good management excellent rice yields may be obtained, with two crops possible with irrigation. A wide range of annual and perennial crops can be grown on the better-drained soils and the need for fertilizer application is less than on Dystric Fluvisols. Specific crops respond well to fertilizers where the moisture factor is not a limitation.

Jt. THIONIC FLUVISOLS

Use. Thionic Fluvisols occur mainly in the Chao Phraya and Mekong deltas, and to a lesser extent in tidal swamps along the coasts of Viet Nam, Democratic Kampuchea, Thailand, Peninsular Malaysia, Sumatra and Sulawesi. A saline phase occurs in Kalimantan, Sarawak and Sabah. They are developed on brackish water alluvium containing considerable amounts of sulphides, mainly pyrites. Potential acid sulphate soils occur where the parent material remains totally reduced. However, developed acid sulphate soils occur after drainage and aeration of originally waterlogged and reduced parent material. The oxidation of the sulphides produces acid sulphates. These are partly neutralized by neutralizing components and possibly partly by leaching, but the remaining acid attacks the clay minerals, causing the liberation of aluminium ions in amounts toxic for plant roots and micro-organisms. The natural vegetation consists mainly of *Avicennia* and *Rhizophora* mangroves. There are also dense stands of *Melaleuca leucadendron* which are a good source of firewood and cajeput oil. Attempts to grow rice, including floating varieties, have produced poor results. Oil palm has given satisfactory yields in Malaysia under careful reclamation on soils where the toxic layer occurs below 75 cm and where the water table is controlled to minimize oxidation of the sulphidic horizon.

Suitability. These soils are characterized by the presence of a sulphuric horizon or of sulphidic materials within a depth of 125 cm. The limitations generally ascribed to these soils are due partly to the physiographic setting and partly to their inherent dynamic instability. Environmental problems are either poor external drainability and permanent flooding, or large seasonal fluctuations in ground water levels. Correction by drainage produces catastrophic acidification and toxic concentrations of Al^{+++}, Fe^{++} and often Mn^{++}, poor microbiological activity, and deficiencies in macronutrients and micronutrients. Subsequent flooding only partly reverses the acidification and its side effects, and introduces risks of Fe^{++} and H_2S toxicity and salinity. At present it is not possible to suggest generally applicable techniques for improved agriculture on Thionic Fluvisols. Ground water control and leaching are possibilities, but it takes ten or more years to remove most of the pyrite and there is the problem of utilizing the soils during this period, as intense acidity develops during the leaching process. Experiments with liming have been reported, but calculations of the amounts required to neutralize the potential acidity show as much as 150 tons/ha, which is uneconomic. The agricultural potential of Thionic Fluvisols, therefore, is generally very low, even though they occur over large areas of flat land which could be supplied with irrigation.

L. Luvisols

Lc. CHROMIC LUVISOLS

Use. Chromic Luvisols occur over small areas of Thailand, Viet Nam, Sumatra, Java, Kalimantan, Sulawesi, the Lesser Sunda Islands and Irian Jaya. A stony phase is found in Java, Sulawesi, the Lesser Sunda Islands and Irian Jaya, and a lithic phase in Viet Nam. They are developed from the weathering products of olivine basalt, intermediate volcanic tuff and lahar, and from limestone, marl and claystone. Their macrorelief is predominantly steeply dissected, although they also occur on rolling terrain in Viet Nam, Sumatra and the Lesser Sunda Islands. Steep, stony and shallow members remain under tropical evergreen rain forest or tropical deciduous forest. On gentler slopes many of these soils have been used for shifting cultivation and are often abandoned to scrub and anthropic savanna following excessive erosion. In Thailand maize, sorghum, cotton, vegetables and a variety of fruit crops are grown on Chromic Luvisols, and in Indonesia deeper soils are terraced for intensive rainfed annual food crop production and to a lesser extent irrigated rice and sugar cane.

Suitability. These soils are fine textured and well to excessively drained. Soil reaction is slightly acid to neutral, and they have a moderate to high supply of bases and cation exchange capacity. Organic matter content is variable, but is usually moderate to low. Soil depth ranges from shallow (lithic phase) to deep, and the presence of stones (stony phase) is often sufficient to preclude plough cultivation or necessitate extensive stone clearing operations. Chromic Luvisols are highly susceptible to erosion on unprotected slopes, and moisture deficiency is experienced in areas with a marked dry season. Chemically, they are fairly rich, but intensive use is restricted by shallowness, stoniness, erosion hazard and moisture limitations. Deeper, gently sloping members have a good potential for agricultural development under good management involving phosphate, nitrogen and some potassium fertilizer applications, stringent weed control, and adequate protection against erosion. Where feasible, supplementary irrigation is profitable and increases the choice of crops. Satisfactory results can be obtained from fruits and vegetables, groundnuts, maize, sorghum, pulses and oilseeds. Sugar cane and rice perform well under irrigation. Rubber and oil palm are feasible under more humid conditions, and coconuts are favoured in coastal areas. Tea, coffee, spices and other high-value crops may offset the cost of bench terracing on steep slopes, but generally these are better left or put under permanent vegetation. Good management is essential for the continuous use of these soils, for they will degenerate rapidly without intensive soil conservation measures, fertilizer applications and weeding.

Lf. FERRIC LUVISOLS

Use. Ferric Luvisols are restricted to a minor occurrence of a petric phase in northern Lao. These soils are developed from weathering products of limestone plateaus, and have a rolling to steeply dissected macrorelief. The natural vegetation is mixed moist deciduous forest, and land use is restricted to a form of shifting cultivation practised by mountain people. Upland rice, maize, gourds and sweet potatoes are intercropped, together with the opium poppy.

Suitability. These soils are fine textured and well drained. Soil reaction is slightly acid to neutral. Organic matter content is moderate, and the cation exchange capacity and content of bases are low. They are high in aluminium oxides and have severe deficiencies of phosphate, potassium, calcium and magnesium. The presence of a layer of hard iron concretions within rooting depth also limits plant growth, and they are susceptible to erosion on unprotected slopes. Potential for agricultural development is rather low. Continuous production of adapted annual crops or tree crops such as tea or coffee requires high management inputs which are

rarely economically justifiable under present conditions. Consequently, these soils are best left or put under permanent vegetation.

Lg. GLEYIC LUVISOLS

Use. Gleyic Luvisols are not extensive, occurring mainly in parts of Lao, Thailand and Democratic Kampuchea. They are developed on old terrace alluvium in intermontane basins in northern Thailand and Lao, while in Democratic Kampuchea they occur on outwash plains developed from old colluvial materials from mixed basic and acid sources. Their macrorelief is nearly level to rolling. The original vegetation (dry deciduous forest) has been largely cleared for rainfed rice cultivation, with steeper slopes being terraced. Tobacco is also important on somewhat poorly drained higher members, and rice is followed by a summer vegetable or pulse crop where supplementary irrigation is possible.

Suitability. Gleyic Luvisols are fine textured and poorly to somewhat poorly drained. Soil reaction ranges from slightly acid to mildly alkaline and increases with depth. Organic matter content is generally low, while base status and cation exchange capacity are moderate to high. Physical and chemical properties are generally good. These soils are quite fertile and crops respond well to phosphate and nitrogen fertilizer applications. The ground water level fluctuates, standing at or near the surface during the peak of the rainy season, and falling rapidly at the onset of the marked dry season when moisture deficiency occurs. Consequently, the agricultural potential of these soils is largely dependent on the availability of irrigation water during the pronounced dry season. Under rainfed conditions and good management one crop of rice a year is possible, with average yields of between 2 000 and 2 600 kg per ha. If sufficient irrigation water is available, two crops of rice would be feasible; otherwise supplementary irrigation could support a short-season summer vegetable crop utilizing a ridge-and-furrow cultivation system. Other cropping possibilities capable of giving satisfactory results are pulses including soybeans, vegetable crops, tobacco, cotton, sweet potato, coconut and mango. Irish potato and wheat could be cultivated in northern Thailand and Lao during the cool season from November to February.

Lk. CALCIC LUVISOLS

Use. Calcic Luvisols occur only along the northwest coast of Sabah. They are found on gently sloping coastal terraces and are developed from weathering products of coral limestone. The natural vegetation is tropical lowland evergreen rain forest, but an *Imperata cylindrica*-dominated anthropic savanna has developed where this has been cleared for shifting cultivation. Coconut, oil palm, maize, and recently cocoa are the main crops.

Suitability. Calcic Luvisols are moderately deep to deep, fine-to-medium-textured, well-drained soils. Organic matter content is moderate, and base status and cation exchange capacity are high. Soil reaction is mildly alkaline. Under good management, including the use of complete fertilizers and soil conservation measures, these soils are excellent for a wide range of crops and have a high agricultural potential.

Lo. ORTHIC LUVISOLS

Use. Orthic Luvisols occur mainly in parts of Sumatra, Java, Kalimantan, Sulawesi, the Moluccas, the Lesser Sunda Islands, Sabah and the Philippines. They are developed from weathering products of limestone, basic and intermediate volcanic rocks, and basic and intermediate volcanic ash and lahar deposits. Their macrorelief ranges from rolling to steeply dissected. Tropical evergreen rain forest and, in drier areas, tropical dry deciduous forest remain on steeper slopes, but most of the rolling terrain occupied by these soils has been cleared for cultivation. Where irrigation is feasible, they are used intensively for terraced rice, and to a lesser extent sugar cane. Rainfed crops include rice, pulses, maize, cassava and vegetables. In the Philippines these soils are important for coconut production. Fruit crops thrive in home gardens and orchards, and rubber, oil palm and cocoa are grown in Sabah.

Suitability. Orthic Luvisols are medium-to-fine-textured, well-drained soils. The majority are deep, although shallow members occur in association with Lithosols. Soil reaction is slightly acid to neutral and organic matter content is generally moderate to low. Base status and cation exchange capacity are moderate to high. These soils have a good structure and are easily worked. They are fairly fertile and respond well to applications of phosphate, nitrogen and some potassium fertilizers. The main limitations to continuous cultivation are high susceptibility to erosion and moisture deficiency in drier areas. However, under good management they are suitable for the cultivation of a wide range of crops, especially if supplemental irrigation is feasible. Irrigated rice, sugar cane, groundnuts, maize, sorghum, pulses, oilseeds and vegetables give satisfactory results. Fruit crops such as banana and mango, coconut, rubber, oil palm, cocoa and spices are profitable if moisture requirements can be met. On steeper slopes these soils are better left or put under permanent vegetation, unless bench terracing is done at high cost to grow high-value crops such as tea, coffee, fruits and vegetables.

Lv. VERTIC LUVISOLS

Use. Vertic Luvisols occur only in parts of Java and the Lesser Sunda Islands. They are developed from intermediate to basic volcanic ash, tuff and lahar deposits, and from limestone, marl and claystone. Their macrorelief is predominantly rolling to hilly and they occupy positions on footslopes of volcanoes and, to a lesser extent, on karstic plateaus where they occur in association with Lithosols. Little natural forest vegetation remains on these soils, which have long been intensively cultivated for irrigated rice and sugar cane, and a wide variety of rainfed annual crops including maize, sorghum, cassava, pulses and vegetables. Fruit trees are found in home gardens and orchards, and highland coffee and tea are the main plantation crops above 1 000 m elevation. Where moisture deficiency occurs in areas with a marked dry season, these soils are left in fallow and used for low-intensity grazing.

Suitability. Vertic Luvisols are fine-textured, well-drained soils. Their depth varies, but most are deep. Soil reaction is slightly acid to neutral. Organic matter content is low, and base status and cation exchange capacity are moderate to high. These soils are relatively fertile, but physical properties are less favourable for tillage; they crack deeply during the dry season when moisture deficiency limits plant growth. Agricultural potential is dependent on the availability of sufficient moisture during the dry season. Where irrigation water is available, rice and sugar cane are well suited under good management involving rational fertilizer application to maintain fertility and terracing to provide adequate protection against erosion. If irrigation is not feasible, maize, sorghum or rainfed rice in rotation with short-season pulses or chick-peas is fairly successful. Mango, guava, papaya and pineapple give good results, provided that the dry season is not too pronounced. Steep slopes are erosion-prone and are best left or put under permanent vegetation, unless bench terracing is done at high cost to grow high-value crops such as highland coffee, tea, fruits and vegetables.

N. Nitosols

Nd. DYSTRIC NITOSOLS

Use. Dystric Nitosols occur in parts of Lao, Democratic Kampuchea, Thailand, Malaysia and

Indonesia, and are extensive in the Philippines. They are developed on a wide variety of highly weathered rocks and sediments and have a nearly level to hilly macrorelief. The natural vegetation is mainly tropical evergreen rain forest, but wide areas have been cleared for both shifting and permanent cultivation. They are terraced for irrigated rice in Java and support annual crops such as groundnuts, sweet potato, beans and cassava. Fruit crops are grown together with sisal and kapok in home gardens and orchards. Main plantation crops are rubber, oil palm, coffee and cocoa. In the Philippines these soils are mainly used for a shifting cultivation of maize and upland rice which does not appear to cause appreciable degradation. Permanent agricultural use is directed toward fruit crops, rubber, abaca and coconut.

Suitability. Dystric Nitosols are predominantly fine-textured, deep, well-drained soils. Soil reaction is slightly to strongly acid. Organic matter content is moderate to low, and base status and cation exchange capacity are low. Although chemically poor, these soils respond well to combined dressings of phosphate and nitrogen fertilizers, but occasionally require trace elements. They have excellent physical properties for tillage and are erosion-resistant. Consequently, they have a fairly high agricultural potential. Under good management involving regular fertilizer application, sound cultural practices and adequate conservation measures, good results can be expected from terraced irrigated rice; annual crops such as maize, groundnuts, pulses, oilseeds, sweet potato and cassava; fruit crops such as papaya, citrus, jackfruit, banana and pineapple; and plantation crops such as rubber, oil palm, coffee, cocoa, coconut and abaca.

Ne. EUTRIC NITOSOLS

Use. Eutric Nitosols are extensive in the Philippines and occur over smaller areas in parts of Democratic Kampuchea, Java and Sulawesi. They are developed from highly weathered intermediate to basic volcanic rocks and have a rolling to steeply dissected macrorelief. Most steeply sloping areas remain under original tropical evergreen rain forest. In Java they have long been cleared for intensive cultivation including terraced irrigated rice and rainfed annual crops, and fruit trees are commonly grown in home gardens. The main plantation crops are coffee and cocoa. In Sulawesi and the Philippines shifting cultivation of upland rice, maize and cassava is the main land use, and fruits, coconut, abaca and rubber are the dominant permanent crops.

Suitability. These deep, fine-textured, well-drained soils have good physical properties for tillage, and

are erosion-resistant. Soil reaction is slightly acid to neutral, organic matter content is moderate, and base status and cation exchange capacity are moderate to high. They have a higher level of natural fertility than Dystric Nitosols, and have a high agricultural potential. Under good management involving moderate fertilizer inputs, good cultural practices and adequate conservation measures, these soils are suitable for the cultivation of a wide range of annual and perennial crops as described for Dystric Nitosols. Soils on steep slopes, however, should be kept under permanent vegetation, or bench-terraced at high cost for growing high-value crops such as coffee, fruits and vegetables.

Nh. HUMIC NITOSOLS

Use. Humic Nitosols occur only in small parts of Sumatra and Kalimantan. They are developed from deeply weathered acid to intermediate volcanic tuff and lahar deposits and have a nearly level to rolling macrorelief. They occupy volcanic plains and footslopes, and are mainly under original tropical evergreen rain forest, although in western Sumatra they are used for terraced irrigated rice cultivation, and support fruit trees in home gardens.

Suitability. These deep, well-drained, fine-textured soils have good physical properties for tillage and are erosion-resistant. Soil reaction is strongly to slightly acid, organic matter content is medium to high, and base status and cation exchange capacity are generally low. They respond well to phosphate and nitrogen fertilizer applications, and under good management have a fairly high agricultural potential. Good results can be expected from terraced irrigated rice, groundnuts, pulses and vegetables, fruit crops, rubber, oil palm, coffee and cocoa.

O. Histosols

Od. DYSTRIC HISTOSOLS

Use. These soils are extensive in low coastal areas of Sumatra, Borneo and Irian Jaya, and occur over smaller areas near the coasts of Peninsular Malaysia, Thailand and Viet Nam. They have developed over subrecent coastal swamps with a flat to slightly depressed concave environment where conditions are favourable for the accumulation of organic matter and plant debris. The majority of Dystric Histosols occur in rain-dependent, nutrient-poor ombrogenous peat bogs which are more or less domed. Most remain under tropical inundation bog forest. Land use is mainly restricted to the gathering of useful natural products, which are plentiful in certain areas. In Borneo and Sumatra many palms provide thatching, notably the nipa palm (*Nypa fruticans*), which also yields palm sugar. In Irian Jaya sago palms (*Metroxylon* sp.) are cut to harvest sago, producing as much as 125 kg per tree trunk. Elsewhere rattan palms (*Calamos* sp.) and locally raffia palms (*Raphia* sp.) are gathered for fibre and furniture making. Valuable hardwoods are exploited for timber, although extraction is difficult under permanently waterlogged conditions. In locally reclaimed areas, mainly on shallow peat, oil palm, rubber, coconuts, pineapples, root crops, ramie fibre and vegetable crops are grown. Shifting cultivation of paddy is also carried out on bog fringes, but yields are generally poor and the crop fails completely on deeper peats.

Suitability. The reclamation of Dystric Histosols is hindered by a number of serious limitations. They are chemically poor, and oligotrophic peats with ash contents of 1 percent or less occur over wide areas. In addition, physical properties are only marginal, even after reclamation. Main problems are:

— high subsidence after drainage and stripping of vegetation;

— locally, extremely rapid horizontal hydraulic conductivity or extremely slow vertical conductivity;

— high heat capacity and low thermal conductivity;

— locally, slight decomposition of organic material and/or a high wood content;

— low bearing capacity (transportation of produce is difficult) and poor rooting capacity (trees and top-heavy plants topple over);

— rapid oxidation/decomposition of organic material after drainage; and

— irreversible shrinkage resulting in adverse water retention characteristics and increased sensitivity to erosion.

Many of these problems would not occur if the soils could be kept permanently inundated and used for paddy. Unfortunately, the generative growth of rice on stagnant peat " sawahs " has proved a complete failure, possibly owing to certain organic compounds, notably polyphenolic lignin degradation products, which hinder directly or indirectly (through copper fixation) one or more essential enzyme-catalyzed carbohydrate formations.

The agricultural potential of these soils will remain low until ways are found to suitably reclaim and utilize them.

Oe. EUTRIC HISTOSOLS

Use. Eutric Histosols occur extensively in tidal swamps along the south coast of Irian Jaya, over smaller areas in the Greater Sunda Islands of Indonesia, and locally in Malaysia. They are developed in tidal swamps accumulated behind beach bars of recent origin and have a slightly convex surface. The saline Eutric Histosols of Aru and Irian Jaya occur in association with Gleyic Solonchaks in unique wildlife areas where the gathering of useful natural products is the only form of land use. The bark of many *Rhizophora* and *Avicennia* spp. contains good-quality tannin and the wood makes good charcoal. Further inland, where conditions are less saline, palms dominate the vegetation pattern, providing thatching, palm sugar and sago. Several screwpines (*Pandanus* sp.) also occur, providing edible seeds and very tough leaves used in basket, mat and hat making, and for thatching. Little or no permanent agriculture is practised on these soils.

Suitability. The natural fertility of Eutric Histosols is greater than that of Dystric Histosols, provided that the level of soil salinity does not interfere with crop growth. The diagnostic difference between Eutric Histosols and Dystric Histosols is in the pH of the solum, the former having pH values above 5.5 and thus excluding the presence of sulphidic material. However, under the influence of brackish water many Eutric Histosols are slightly to strongly saline, notably those in the tidal swamps of Irian Jaya. The more or less decomposed plant debris from which these soils originated is largely the same as that of Dystric Histosols, although in the tidal swamp environment there is a dominance of material from typical mangrove vegetation, giving a less fibrous peat than the accumulated debris of palms. Natural drainage is very poor and the occurrence of water lenses in the peat is common in tidal swamps, and diagnosis of the extent and depth of such hydric layers is required before any attempt is made at reclamation. The non-saline Eutric Histosols have considerable productive potential when the water table is effectively under control. Problems after reclamation are similar to those described for Dystric Histosols, but are thought to be less severe. However, under cautious drainage to minimize subsidence, and with specialized cultural practices, oil palm, rubber, liberica coffee, pineapple, ramie fibre, and a variety of tuber and root crops could be grown on non-saline Eutric Histosols. Sugar cane and rice could be considered only if sufficient mineral soil material were present at shallow depth or incorporated in histic layers.

P. Podzols

Pg. GLEYIC PODZOLS

Use. Gleyic Podzols occur mainly in Kalimantan and Sarawak. They are developed on Neogene sand deposits probably derived from Mio-Pliocene coastal sediments, and have a nearly level to undulating macrorelief lying at an elevation of about 25 m. The natural vegetation is " kerangas " forest, characteristic species being *Dacrydium elatim, Casuarina sumatrana, Agathis dammara, A. alba,* and *Whiteodendron moultanian.* Orchids and mosses are abundant, both on trees and on the ground. Land use is restricted to subsistence crops and vegetables around settlements, and some farmers rear pigs.

Suitability. Gleyic Podzols are deep, coarse-textured, very poor wet soils with a slowly permeable layer impeding drainage. Soil reaction is strongly acid. Organic matter is moderate to high. The carbon: nitrogen ratio ranges from 15 to 20 in surface horizons to a maximum of 100 in the B horizon. Base status is generally very low. The chemical and physical properties of these soils are poor and their agricultural potential is low. Regrowth after removal of natural vegetation is very slow. Possible uses are vegetables on night soil, pineapples, cashews and coconuts, although yields are generally low. These soils are better left under permanent vegetation or reforested with casuarina or *Pinus caribaea.*

Ph. HUMIC PODZOLS

Use. Humic Podzols occur mainly in parts of Kalimantan and Irian Jaya, where they are developed on Neogene sand deposits. Their macrorelief is undulating to rolling, and altitude ranges from 25 to 75 m. The natural vegetation is kerangas forest which, where degraded, is replaced by padang vegetation consisting of scattered groups of stunted trees and patches of ground mosses. Land use is confined to cultivation of coconuts, subsistence agriculture around settlements, and pig rearing by some farmers in Kalimantan.

Suitability. Humic Podzols are deep, coarse-textured, well to excessively drained soils, although impeded drainage conditions probably occurred at some stage of their development. Dispersed organic matter occurs in the spodic B horizon which has a high carbon: nitrogen ratio. Soil reaction is strongly acid and base status is very low. They are physically and chemically poor and suffer from moisture deficiency during dry spells owing to excessive drainage. Consequently, their agricultural potential is low. Coconuts, cashews and pineapples may be

grown, but generally give low yields. These soils are better left under permanent vegetation or reforested with casuarina or *Pinus caribaea.*

Po. ORTHIC PODZOLS

Use. Orthic Podzols occur in small areas west of Lake Toba in northern Sumatra and on the islands of Bangka, Belitung and Riau. They are developed from liparitic tuff and Triassic sandstone, marl and slate, and have a nearly level to undulating macrorelief. The natural vegetation comprises kerangas forest on the islands east of Sumatra where white pepper growing is the main form of permanent agriculture, and *Pinus merkusii* forest in northern Sumatra.

Suitability. Orthic Podzols are deep, coarse-to-medium-textured, well to excessively drained soils. Soil reaction is strongly acid and base status is very low. They have a characteristic albic E horizon which overlies a dark-coloured spodic B horizon containing organic matter with iron or aluminium, or both. They are physically and chemically poor and suffer from moisture deficiency during dry spells owing to excessive drainage. Their agricultural potential is low, although satisfactory yields of white pepper are obtained under good management. In general, however, these soils are best left under permanent vegetation or reforested with casuarina or pines.

Q. Arenosols

Qa. ALBIC ARENOSOLS

Use. Albic Arenosols occur in association with Orthic Podzols in parts of western Kalimantan and Sarawak. Developed on reworked Mio-Pliocene coastal deposits, they occupy positions on nearly level to undulating plains. The natural vegetation is kerangas forest or poor tropical lowland evergreen rain forest. Anthropic savanna has developed in areas utilized for shifting cultivation, and permanent agriculture is restricted to pepper and rubber.

Suitability. Albic Arenosols are deep, coarse-to-medium-textured, excessively drained to well-drained soils. Soil reaction is strongly acid and base status and cation exchange capacity are low. These soils are characterized by the presence of a thick albic E horizon. They are physically and chemically poor and coarser members suffer from moisture deficiency during dry spells. Their agricultural potential is generally low, but under good management involving complete fertilizer applications and good cultural practices pepper, rubber and coconuts give fairly satisfactory results. In general, however, these soils are better left or put under permanent vegetation. Improved pasture under low-intensity grazing is a possible alternative.

Qc. CAMBIC ARENOSOLS

Use. Cambic Arenosols occur in association with Dystric Cambisols, mainly in Sumatra, Kalimantan and the Philippines. They are developed from slightly consolidated Miocene sandstone and have a nearly level to rolling macrorelief. Much of the original tropical lowland evergreen rain forest has been replaced by *Imperata cylindrica*-dominated anthropic savanna as a result of shifting cultivation and irresponsible burning by hunters. Rubber and pepper growing are the main forms of permanent agriculture in Indonesia, and coconuts in the Philippines.

Suitability. Cambic Arenosols are deep, coarse-textured, excessively drained soils showing colouring or alteration characteristics of a cambic B horizon immediately below the A horizon. Soil reaction is strongly acid, and base status, cation exchange capacity and organic matter content are low. These soils are physically and chemically poor and suffer from moisture deficiency owing to excessive drainage. Their agricultural potential is low, and permanent cultivation of annual crops would involve high management inputs to correct fertility and moisture limitations which in general are not economically justifiable under present conditions. Pepper and plantation crops such as rubber and coconut can be grown under good management practices, among which complete fertilizer applications are essential. In general, however, these soils are best left or put under permanent vegetation. Improved pasture under low-intensity grazing is a possible alternative.

Qf. FERRALIC ARENOSOLS

Use. Ferralic Arenosols occur in association with Ferric Acrisols over limited areas of the Moluccas and are secondary components of Eutric Regosol associations in Viet Nam, Thailand and Peninsular Malaysia. In the Moluccas they are developed on old acid igneous deposits and Triassic sandstone and have a predominantly rolling macrorelief. Most remain under poor tropical lowland evergreen rain forest. Land use is largely limited to shifting cultivation of upland rice and cassava.

Suitability. Ferralic Arenosols are deep, coarse-textured, excessively drained soils. Soil reaction is strongly acid, organic matter content is low, and base status and cation exchange capacity are very low. They are physically and chemically poor and have low moisture- and nutrient-retention capacities. Consequently, their agricultural potential is low, and permanent cultivation of annual crops would require high management inputs which are not economically justifiable under present conditions. Rubber, coconut and pepper offer possibilities under good management providing moisture requirements can be met. Improved pasture under low-intensity grazing is another alternative. In general, however, these soils are best kept under permanent vegetation.

R. Regosols

Rc. CALCARIC REGOSOLS

Use. Calcaric Regosols occur only over minor areas of southeastern Sulawesi. They are developed on calcareous Neogene coastal sand deposits and have an undulating to rolling macrorelief. Mangroves occur along the littoral fringe, but most of these soils are under a poor tropical lowland evergreen rain forest dominated by calciophile species. Land use is restricted to shifting cultivation of upland rice and cassava, which has resulted in the development of tracts of *Imperata cylindrica*-dominated anthropic savanna. Coconut growing is the main form of permanent agriculture.

Suitability. These soils are deep and coarse textured. In general they are excessively drained, but along the coast they are poorly drained. Soil reaction is neutral at the surface and the subsoil is calcareous. Organic matter content is generally low, but base status is high. These soils are chemically fairly rich, but they have a low moisture-retention capacity and suffer from moisture deficiency during dry spells owing to excessive drainage. Their agricultural potential depends on the availability of supplemental irrigation water. Where irrigation is feasible tobacco, soybeans, groundnuts, sweet potato and maize are possible annual crops under good management, and coconut can be expected to give good results where the water table is not too deep.

Rd. DYSTRIC REGOSOLS

Use. Dystric Regosols occur in association with Dystric Gleysols and Histosols in parts of Kalimantan and Irian Jaya. They are developed on leached sandy coastal sediments and dunes with a nearly level to gently undulating macrorelief. The vegetation is generally sparse and scrub-like, grading to mixed swamp forest along transitions with Dystric Gleysols and Histosols, and mangroves occur on the littora fringe. These soils are not exploited to any great extent and coconut growing is the only form of permanent agriculture.

Suitability. Dystric Regosols are deep, coarse-textured, excessively drained soils. Soil reaction is strongly to slightly acid, organic matter content is low to medium, and base status is low. These soils are physically and chemically poor, having low moisture- and nutrient-retention capacities. They have a low agricultural potential and are generally not cultivated, except for coconut plantations where the water table is not too deep. With adequate rainfall pineapple may be grown, or reforestation with casuarina or pines may be considered.

Re. EUTRIC REGOSOLS

Use. Eutric Regosols occur on recent sandy coastal sediments and dunes along the shores of Viet Nam, Thailand, Peninsular Malaysia and the Lesser Sunda Islands. In addition, a stony phase developed on intermediate to basic volcanic tuff, ashes and lahar deposits occurs in Java and the Lesser Sunda Islands. Eutric Regosols on recent beach and dune deposits have a nearly level to rolling macrorelief, and those on volcano slopes occupy hilly to steeply dissected terrain. Vegetation on the coastal sandy members is sparse and scrub-like, and the main land uses are coconut and casuarina plantations and recreation. Stony phases in the Lesser Sunda Islands largely remain under original forest, but in Java many areas have been cleared and planted to vegetables, groundnuts, pulses, and root and tuber crops. Where sufficient spring irrigation water is available, they are terraced for paddy cultivation.

Suitability. The sandy Eutric Regosols of beaches and dunes are coarse textured, deep, and excessively drained. Soil reaction is slightly acid, organic matter content is low, and base status is moderate. The moisture- and nutrient-retention capacities of these soils are generally low, and so is their agricultural potential. Coconut and casuarina or pine plantations offer the best possibilities for permanent agriculture. They also provide attractive recreation sites.

The stony Eutric Regosols of volcano slopes are coarse-to-medium-textured, well to excessively drained, and vary considerably in depth. Soil reaction is slightly acid, organic matter content is moderate to low, and base status is moderate. Their moisture- and nutrient-retention capacities are better than those of sandy Regosols. Their main limitations are stoni-ness and depth, which may be sufficient to hinder

tillage and produce moisture deficiency and erosion hazard on unprotected slopes. Under good management involving phosphate and nitrogen fertilizer applications, careful cultural practices, terracing and water control, satisfactory results can be expected from spring irrigated rice on less stony and deep soils below approximately 1 000 m. Where spring irrigation is insufficient for rice, good results are obtained from tobacco, soybeans, groundnuts, sweet potato and maize. Above 1 000 m permanent forest should be maintained unless bench terraces are constructed at high cost for growing high-value crops such as highland coffee, tea, fruit and vegetables. Shallow and very stony soils should be kept under permanent vegetation.

T. Andosols

Th. HUMIC ANDOSOLS

Use. Humic Andosols occur in the vicinity of young volcanoes on the Greater and Lesser Sunda Islands of Indonesia. They are developed on recent pyroclastic sediments mainly of andesitic nature and occur at elevations ranging from lowland to over 1 500 m. These soils commonly occur on long smooth slopes of volcanic mountain complexes which are only slightly sloping in the lowlands but become gradually steeper in the mountains and are frequently dissected by deep gullies and incised valleys. The original vegetation is tropical evergreen rain forest, but extensive areas of Humic Andosols are under permanent cultivation or some form of shifting cultivation with intermittent secondary forest fallow. Common crops are upland rice, groundnuts, soybeans, tobacco, pulses, root and tuber crops, fruits, vegetables and spices. Tea is the main crop in the highlands.

Suitability. Humic Andosols are deep, medium-textured, well-drained soils. They generally have a low bulk density and a texture dominated by the silt fraction. The exchange complex is dominated by amorphous materials (allophane and related minerals) of high exchange capacity which are capable of fixing large amounts of phosphate. They normally have a considerable reserve of weatherable minerals in the silt and sand fraction which supplies elements for plant growth. Although well drained and permeable, these soils have a high moisture-retention capacity, and physical conditions are excellent for plant growth. Steeply sloping soils are subject to erosion when exposed to heavy rains, but this is not a major problem on gentler slopes. Chemical conditions are sometimes more limiting, as some Humic Andosols may have considerable exchangeable aluminium in the exchange complex. Exchangeable Al^{+++} is apparent only in soils with a pH below 5.2, and is toxic to a number of plants. In addition, some soils may have certain micro-element deficiencies, notably boron.

In general these soils have a high agricultural potential, and virtually any crop requiring deep, well-drained, medium-textured soils under a nearly continuous high moisture regime will grow well on non-acid Humic Andosols. Recommended lowland crops include tobacco, nutmeg, sugar cane, rubber, oil palm, coconut and a wide variety of fruits and vegetables. Tea is an excellent crop for highland acid Humic Andosols, as it is an aluminium accumulator and a calcifuge. Lowland acid Humic Andosols give disappointing yields of crops susceptible to aluminium toxicity, such as upland rice, groundnuts, soybeans and pulses. All Humic Andosols have a slight phosphate deficiency seconded by a low potash status, but under good management involving fertilizer amendments, good cultural practices, conservation measures and water control, these soils are highly productive.

Tm. Mollic Andosols

Use. Mollic Andosols occur only in parts of Java, the Lesser Sunda Islands and the Moluccas having a more or less pronounced dry season. They are developed from recent pyroclastic sediments which are andesitic or basaltic in nature, and are found on long slopes of recent volcanoes. Upper slopes are moderately steep to steep, while lower slopes are nearly level and are frequently dissected by deep gullies and incised valleys. The natural vegetation is tropical deciduous forest and is stratified according to elevation. Extensive areas have long been cleared for cultivation. Where irrigation water is available, terraced rice is grown during the rainy season followed by pulses and other short-season crops if rainfall permits. Filler tobacco and sugar cane are also grown, although the latter crop performs better on heavier soils. Fruit trees, coffee and cocoa are also grown extensively. On the slopes of the more active volcanoes soils are often under a pioneer vegetation, as existing vegetation is periodically destroyed by repeated volcanic eruptions and ash falls.

Suitability. Mollic Andosols are deep, medium-textured, well to somewhat excessively drained soils, and their water-retention capacity relates to their organic matter content and its distribution throughout the solum. Under prevailing climatic conditions the amount of leaching is insufficient to cause deep desaturation and acidification. Consequently, their base status and pH are higher than those of Humic

Andosols. Mollic Andosols generally have a somewhat coarser texture than Humic Andosols. Their internal physical and chemical characteristics are good, and they have a high productive capacity where available moisture, slope and elevation are not limiting factors. Where irrigation water is available, terraced rice followed by short-season crops gives satisfactory returns. Under rainfed conditions filler tobacco, a variety of fruit trees and annual or biennial fruits requiring a certain dry season give good results. Coffee and cocoa grow well, with coffee being particularly well suited for higher Mollic Andosols. Soil moisture deficiency, slope and erosion hazard are the main limitations. However, many of these soils have a high agricultural potential under good management, and generally respond well to generous applications of phosphate and, to a lesser extent, potassium and nitrogen fertilizers.

To. Ochric Andosols

Use. These are the most widespread Andosols of the region, occurring in Java, the Lesser Sunda Islands and the Moluccas in Indonesia, and on Luzon, Mindanao and smaller volcanic islands in the Philippines, where they occur in association with Nitosols. They are developed from recent andesitic pyroclastic material. Landforms are virtually the same as for other Andosols, the soils occurring on long slopes of young andesitic volcanoes at elevations ranging from near sea level to over 1 500 m. Slopes are smooth and increase regularly in gradient with increasing elevation. The original vegetation consists of tropical evergreen or deciduous forest stratified according to elevation. Extensive areas have long been cleared for shifting cultivation and are planted intermittently or permanently to food crops. Terraced rice cultivation is common where irrigation water is available. Clove trees are extensively planted on many smaller volcanic islands, while coffee, tea and cinchona are the main highland crops.

Suitability. Ochric Andosols are medium-textured, moderately permeable, well-drained soils with a good structure. They are generally deep, although steeply sloping members are shallow and occur in association with Lithosols. They have a low bulk density and have a typical smeary consistence when moist owing to the dominance of allophane in the clay fraction. Erosion is a hazard on slopes where soils are exposed under a torrential rainfall regime. The natural productivity of these soils is moderate to high, but is dependent on pH and levels of exchangeable aluminium, soil texture, organic matter content, and mineral soil reserves. Acid lowland Ochric Andosols produce poor yields from crops susceptible to aluminium toxicity (e.g. rice, groundnuts, soybeans and pulses), and the planting of adaptable crops or crop varieties is recommended rather than utilizing corrective soil amendments. Non-acid lowland Ochric Andosols are well suited to a variety of crops including paddy and upland rice, pulses, cassava, filler tobacco, sugar cane, banana, cocoa, cloves, nutmeg and fruits. Acid highland Ochric Andosols are well suited for tea if they are deep enough and not too coarse in texture. Coffee and cinchona require non-acid soils and are better suited for Mollic Andosols. Good management including liberal applications of nitrogen, phosphate and potassium fertilizers is required for optimal crop production, with special attention being directed to problems of pH and phosphate fixation. Ochric Andosols on high, steep slopes where shallow and lithic soils appear are better left under protective natural vegetation as a measure of watershed conservation.

Tv. VITRIC ANDOSOLS

Use. These soils are of local importance on volcanic slopes in Java, Sulawesi, the Moluccas, the Lesser Sunda Islands and Sumatra, where they are mapped as a stony phase. They are developed from recent andesitic volcanic ejecta occupying the slopes of young volcanoes and mudflows derived from them, and have a rolling to steeply dissected or mountainous macrorelief. Many Vitric Andosols are barren or under a pioneer vegetation of ferns and shrubs creeping up the volcanic slopes. Lowland Vitric Andosols and those formed on mudflows are usually under forest.

Agricultural exploitation is generally restricted to shifting cultivation.

Suitability. Vitric Andosols are coarse textured and somewhat excessively drained, and have a poor water-retention capacity. The coarse fraction consists of pumice, gravel or stones and boulders. They are chemically rich and have an abundant mineral reserve, but lack sufficient capacity to retain cations. The clay mineral that is first formed from pumice and volcanic glass is amorphous gel-like allophane, which is by no means constant in chemical composition. Cations are easily released from Vitric Andosols, but phosphate is retained. The natural productivity of these soils is mainly dependent on texture, degree of stoniness, and abundance of boulders. If texture and stone and boulder content permit, coffee, cocoa and cinchona can be grown on non-acid members, and tea is a possibility on acid members. Intensive cultivation of annual crops is generally not recommended, but a variety of biennial or perennial fruit crops could be considered. In general, however,

Vitric Andosols are best left under natural vegetation or brought under forest for conservation purposes.

V. Vertisols

Vc. CHROMIC VERTISOLS

Use. Chromic Vertisols are found mainly in Java and Luzon, and occur elsewhere in the region as secondary components in Pellic Vertisol associations. They are developed from a variety of parent materials, but are commonly found near footslopes of old alluvial areas, on calcareous sedimentary claystones and marl, or on old volcanic materials in areas with a pronounced dry season. Their macrorelief is nearly level to gently undulating, and a distinctive gilgai microrelief is common. Most Chromic Vertisols are under a savanna vegetation comprising hard grasses, drought-tolerant shrubs and low trees. Where irrigation water is available, these soils have been cleared and put under paddy. Sugar cane and a variety of fruit crops are extensively cultivated where the dry season is not too marked and the soils are not waterlogged during the rainy season.

Suitability. Chromic Vertisols are deep, fine-textured soils. They are imperfectly to poorly drained, during the rainy season but dry out rapidly and crack deeply in the dry season. This recurring drying and wetting cycle results in the formation of slickensides in deeper layers and gilgai microrelief at the surface owing to the presence of expandable clay minerals. The occurrence of large wedge-shaped structural aggregates is common in the lower solum where accumulations of soluble salts or gypsum may be found. These soils are chemically rich, are well saturated with exchangeable bases, and have a relatively high cation exchange capacity. Their main limitations are adverse physical properties and poor workability. Their use for paddy cultivation is largely dependent on the availability of sufficient irrigation water. Where irrigation is possible, a rotation of rice with Javanese soybeans or chick-peas gives satisfactory results. In areas with a short dry season sugar cane, mango, guava, papaya and pineapple grow well if the soils are not waterlogged in the rainy season. These soils are capable of sustaining continuous cropping and do not require a rest period for recovery, but where no source of irrigation water is available, the overall productivity remains low and dry-season utilization is limited to low-intensity grazing.

Vp. PELLIC VERTISOLS

Use. These are the most widespread Vertisols of the region, occurring in parts of Java, the Lesser

Sunda Islands, Luzon, Lao, Viet Nam, Democratic Kampuchea and Thailand where a pronounced monsoon climate prevails. They are developed from a variety of parent materials including old clay terrace alluvium, old basic volcanic rocks, and limestone-clay sediments. Their macrorelief is nearly level to gently undulating and is sometimes dissected by erosion gullies and crevices, and a distinctive gilgai microrelief is common. Most Pellic Vertisols are under some form of cultivation. If sufficient irrigation water is available, one or two paddy crops are grown yearly. Where the supply of irrigation water is limited, as in parts of Java and the Lesser Sunda Islands, pulses and food crops are grown in rotation with rice. Where no source of irrigation water is available, the soils are left for low-intensity grazing.

Suitability. Pellic Vertisols are deep clay soils distinguished by a dark topsoil which is a result of clay-organic matter complex formation and is no direct indication of organic matter content. Drainage is imperfect to poor during the rainy season. These soils crack deeply when drying out and swell when moistened owing to dominant expandable clay minerals in the solum. Pellic Vertisols with strong biological activity in the topsoil may develop a fine granular structure, but many have a strong coarse blocky structure and are much more difficult to work. Their permeability is very slow and they are susceptible to water erosion in the rainy season if no protective measures are taken. Most Pellic Vertisols are chemically rich, are well provided with exchangeable bases, and have a relatively high cation exchange capacity. Their physical conditions are often more favourable than those of Chromic Vertisols, and consequently their productive capacity is generally higher. Moisture availability and distribution are the main problems limiting the agricultural potential of these soils. If climatic conditions are favourable, or if sufficient irrigation water can be supplied, Pellic Vertisols are adaptable to a wide variety of annual or perennial crops including continuous rice, rice in rotation with pulses or short-season food crops, filler tobacco, sugar cane, maize, sweet potato, cassava, a variety of peas or beans, bananas, cocoa and fibre crops. In general, permanent types of utilization such as paddy, sugar cane or adapted perennial crops are more desirable than repeated cycles of annual crops that require frequent tillage of the land.

Conclusions

A remarkable feature of the soils of Southeast Asia is the predominance of Acrisols, which cover some 51 percent of the total land area. Orthic Acrisols alone account for about 35 percent of the region's area. The majority of the steeply sloping, lithic, stony and petric members of Acrisols have severe physical limitations due to continuous cultivation which, when combined with their inherent low fertility, results in a low to very low agricultural potential. Deep, gently sloping Acrisols without physical limitations within rooting depth have a low natural fertility and are susceptible to erosion on exposed slopes. Their use for permanent agriculture is entirely dependent on the level of management feasible. Under good management involving regular fertilizer application, adapted crops or varieties of crops, adequate erosion protection, good cultural practices and careful water control, satisfactory results can be expected from a number of annual and perennial food and commercial crops. However, these soils are easier to manage and maintain under commercial tree crops such as rubber and oil palm. Expansion of permanent agriculture on these soils is practicable only if the essential high management inputs are economically justifiable under prevailing socio-economic conditions. Attempts to expand agricultural production on these soils without essential management inputs will introduce a high risk element which may lead to serious and widespread soil degradation.

Nitosols, Luvisols and Cambisols, each covering approximately 5 percent of the total land area of the region, have moderate to high agricultural potential, except for members with strongly dissected slopes or adverse physical properties. Although their natural fertility is low to moderate, they respond well to phosphate and nitrogen fertilizer applications. Under good management satisfactory production can be expected from a variety of annual and perennial food and commercial crops, and from commercial tree crops. Luvisols have a moderate to high natural fertility and perform well under good management if crop moisture requirements can be met. In drier areas their intensive use is dependent on the availability of irrigation water, while adequate protection against erosion is essential if soil degradation is to be avoided. The natural fertility of Cambisols varies considerably. Poorer members require heavy fertilizer treatment if under sustained agricultural production. However, their physical properties are usually good, and under good management satisfactory production can be expected from a variety of irrigated and rainfed food and commercial crops on gently sloping members.

Ferralsols cover approximately 4 percent of the region's total land area. Petric and petroferric phases of these soils, which have severe physical limitations to plant growth in the rooting zone and a low natural fertility, are usually not suitable for sustained agricultural production. However, deep, gently sloping members have good physical properties which somewhat offset their poor natural fertility, and have a moderate agricultural potential under good management.

Fluvisols and Gleysols, covering approximately 8 and 5 percent of the total area, respectively, are the main paddy-growing soils of the region. However, Thionic Fluvisols and saline phases of Eutric Fluvisols and Eutric Gleysols have severe actual or potential limitations to sustained cultivation. Other Fluvisols and Gleysols are moderately to highly productive under water control involving drainage and flood protection in the rainy season and irrigation in the dry season.

Histosols cover approximately 6 percent of the total land area of the region. At first sight their environmental properties appear to favour paddy cultivation, but to date attempts to grow rice on these soils have proved complete failures. Reclamation for dryland cultivation also introduces a number of physical limitations to sustained agriculture. Their overall potential will remain low until continued research provides answers to utilization problems.

Andosols and Vertisols cover approximately 2 and 1 percent of the region, respectively. Andosols in general have a high agricultural potential, and under good management support intensive cultivation of a wide variety of annual, perennial and tree crops. Acid Andosols support a narrower range of crops owing to aluminium toxicity and phosphate fixation, but give satisfactory results when planted to adaptable crops or varieties. Vitric Andosols are generally unsuitable for permanent cultivation owing to stoniness and poor nutrient- and moisture-retention capacities, and are best left under permanent vegetation. Vertisols are chemically rich, but are difficult to work and suffer from moisture deficiency during the dry season. However, these soils have a high agricultural potential if supplemental irrigation water is available, and high yields can be expected from a variety of annual and perennial food and commercial crops and a number of fruit trees provided that good management is maintained.

Podzols and Arenosols each cover approximately 2 percent of the region, and Regosols occur over less than 1 percent. Most of these soils are not suitable for sustained cultivation owing to their coarse texture and poor water- and nutrient-retention capacities. They are best left under permanent vegetation or planted to casuarinas or pines. Pepper has given good results under good management on some Podzols and Arenosols, while sustained intensive cultivation of a wide variety of crops has been achieved on finer-textured Regosols developed on recent volcanic materials. In general, however, these soils have a low agricultural potential.

Lithosols and Rendzinas cover approximately 3 and 1 percent of the total area of the region, respectively. Their shallowness and the presence of stones and rock outcrops generally preclude permanent cultivation. Consequently, these soils are best left under permanent vegetation.

References

ANDRIESSE, J.P. *The soils of west Sarawak*. Kuching, Soil
1972 Survey Division, Department of Agriculture.

ANDRIESSE, J.P. *Tropical lowland peats in Southeast Asia*.
1974 Amsterdam, Royal Tropical Institute. Communication No. 63.

BUSNAWI, I. *Reconnaissance soil survey of southeast Sumatra*.
1973 Palembang. Working Paper, FAO/UNDP Project INS/69/518.

COMPY, E.Z. & REIMER, A.H. *Soils of An Giang province*,
1969 *Viet Nam*. Washington, D.C., Department of the Army, Engineer Agency for Resource Inventories. EARI Development Research Series, Report No. 1.

COULTER, J.K. The management of acid sulphate and pseudo-
1973 acid sulphate soils for agriculture and other uses. In *Proceedings of the International Symposium on Acid Sulphate Soils*. Wageningen. ILRI Publication 18, Vol. 1.

CROCKER, C.D. *Reconnaissance survey of the soils of Cam-
1963 bodia*. Phnom Penh, Royal Cambodian Government Soil Commission/USAID.

DE JONGH, P.L.J. *Soils of Indonesia*. Bogor, FAO/Soil
1973 Research Institute. Working Paper No. 4.

DENT, F.J. *Final Report of the Technical Officer (Soil Survey)*.
1968 Hat Yai. FAO/UNDP Rubber Development Project No. 176.

DENT, F.J. *General land suitability for crop diversification in
1969 peninsular Thailand*. Bangkok, Department of Land Development. Report SSR No. 76.

DENT, F.J. *Reconnaissance soil survey of peninsular Thailand*.
1972 Bangkok, Department of Land Development. Report SSR No. 94.

DENT, F.J. *Land capability of southeast Sumatra*. Palem-
1974 bang. Working Paper, FAO/UNDP Project INS/69/518.

DENT, F.J., DESAUNETTES, J.R. & MALINGREAU, J.P. *Detailed
1977 reconnaissance land resources survey. Cimanuk watershed area (west Java)*. Bogor, FAO/Soil Research Institute. Working Paper No. 14.

DRIESSEN, P.M. & SOEPRAPTOHARDJO, M. *Soils for agricultural
1974 expansion in Indonesia*. Bogor, Soil Research Institute. Bulletin No. 1.

DRIESSEN, P.M. & SUHARDJO, H. On the defective grain
1976 formation of sawah rice on peat. In *Peat and podzolic soils and their potential for agriculture in Indonesia*. Bogor, Soil Research Institute. Bulletin No. 3.

DUDAL, R. *Dark clay soils of tropical and subtropical regions*.
1965 Rome, FAO, 161 p. FAO Agricultural Development Paper No. 83.

DUDAL, R. & MOORMANN, F.R. Major soils of Southeast
1964 Asia. *J. trop. Geog.*, 18.

DUDAL, R., MOORMANN, F.R. & RIQUIER, J. Soils of humid
1974 tropical Asia. In *Natural resources of humid tropical Asia*, p. 159-178. Paris, Unesco.

Istituto Geografico De Agostini. *World atlas of agri-
1973 culture.* Vol. 2. Novara.

Mariano, J.A. & Valmidiano, A.T. *Classification of Philip-
1972 pines soils in the higher categories.* Manila, Bureau of
Soils.

Moormann, F.R. *The soils of the Republic of Viet Nam.*
1961 Saigon, Ministry of Agriculture.

Moormann, F.R. Acid sulphate soils (cat-clays) of the tropics.
1963 *Soil Sci.,* 95(4).

Moormann, F.R. & Rojanasoonthon, S. *The soils of the
1972 Kingdom of Thailand.* Bangkok, Department of Land
Development. Report SSR No. 72A.

Nguyen Van-Hoai. *Inventory and nomenclature of Viet Nam
1962 soils.* Ithaca, N.Y., Cornell University. (Thesis)

Pons, L.J. Outline of genesis, characteristics, classification
1973 and improvement of acid sulphate soils. In *Proceedings of the International Symposium on Acid Sulphate
Soils.* Wageningen. ILRI Publication 18, Vol. 1.

Pons, L.J. & van der Kevie, W. *Acid sulphate soils in Thailand.*
1969 Bangkok, Department of Land Development. Report
SSR No. 81.

Rojanasoonthon, S. *Morphology and genesis of grey podzolic
1972 soils in Thailand.* Corvallis, Oregon State University.
(Thesis)

Scholten, J.J. & Boonyawat, W. *Detailed reconnaissance
1972 soil survey of Nan province.* Bangkok, Department of
Land Development. Report SSR No. 90.

Soepraptohardjo, M. & Driessen, P.M. The lowland peats
1976 of Indonesia, a challenge for the future. In *Peat and
podzolic soils and their potential for agriculture in Indonesia.* Bogor, Soil Research Institute. Bulletin No. 3.

Thomas, P., Lo, F.K.C. & Hepburn, A.J. *The land classifica-
1976 tion of Sabah.* Surbiton, Surrey, Land Resources
Division, Ministry of Overseas Development. Land
Resource Study 25.

Tour guides for the pre- and post-Conference tours. Conference
1977 on Classification and Management of Tropical Soils,
Kuala Lumpur.

van Breemen, N. Soil forming processes in acid sulphate
1973 soils. In *Proceedings of the International Symposium
on Acid Sulphate Soils.* Wageningen. ILRI Publication 18, Vol. 1.

van der Kevie, W. Physiography, classification and mapping
1973 of acid sulphate soils. In *Proceedings of the International
Symposium on Acid Sulphate Soils.* Wageningen.
ILRI Publication 18, Vol. 1.

van der Kevie, W. & Yenmanas, B. *Detailed reconnaissance
1972 soil survey of southern central plain.* Bangkok, Department of Land Development. Report SSR No. 89.

van der Kevie, W. & Yenmanas, B. *Semi-detailed survey of
1972 a part of the central plain.* Bangkok, Department of
Land Development. Report SSR No. 88.

Wong, I.F.T. *The present land use of West Malaysia.* Kuala
1966 Lumpur, Ministry of Agriculture, Co-operatives and
Lands.

MORPHOLOGICAL, CHEMICAL AND PHYSICAL PROPERTIES OF SOUTHEAST ASIAN SOILS: DATA FROM SELECTED PROFILES

In this Appendix data are presented on typical profiles representing several of the major soil units that occur as dominant or associated soils on the Soil Map of Southeast Asia.

The profiles were selected from published and unpublished material available to the project. Sources of data are listed, by country, in the References section.

The purpose of including these descriptions and tables is to help define more clearly the nature of the soil units used in the map. Naturally, the description and analyses of one or two profiles will not show the range of characteristics within such broad units but, combined with the definitions in Volume I and with the descriptions and analyses of other volumes, they should help at least to establish the concepts on which the legend is based.

For most of the soil units only one profile is described. However, for some of the more extensive units up to three profiles are presented to give some impression of the range that can be expected.

The data have been set out systematically to include most of the items generally available in survey reports. With such a variety of sources there is of course considerable diversity in the information supplied. However, an attempt has been made to present it as uniformly as possible so that valid comparisons can be made. Where established standards such as the U.S. Department of Agriculture *Soil survey manual* (Soil Survey Staff, 1951) have been used, there is no difficulty. In other places there may be some uncertainty in the definition of terms, and care in interpretation is needed.

Presentation of data

Whenever possible the data have been taken from the original documents without alteration. However, some changes have been made for the sake of brevity or uniformity of presentation.

SITE DESCRIPTION

The information used to describe the site is as follows:

Location: An attempt was made to locate the site of each profile by the distance and direction from the main town. In many reports insufficient information was given to determine accurate siting.

Altitude: The altitude is given in metres above mean sea level.

Physiography: Where possible, the nature of the landscape is given.

Drainage: The drainage description is usually given, as in the U.S. Department of Agriculture *Soil survey manual* (Soil Survey Staff, 1951), as a synthesis of runoff, permeability, and internal soil drainage.

Parent material: Where possible, the nature of the parent material or parent rock is given.

Vegetation: Only general terms are used to describe the kind of natural plant cover or present land use.

Climate: The climatic type is described in general terms. Where possible, annual rainfall and time and duration of the rainy season are indicated.

PROFILE DESCRIPTION

Only minor, if any, changes have been made in the profile descriptions. The pattern outlined in *Guidelines for soil profile description* (FAO, 1977) is followed in most cases. Horizon designations have been altered to conform with the definitions given in Volume I. Where they were not included in the original description, they have been added on the basis of the descriptive and analytical information available.

ANALYSES

When considering analyses, it is important to know the methods that have been used. In most reports these are described or at least outlined, and a reference is given.

Figures have sometimes been rounded for the sake of uniformity.

pH: This is usually measured on saturated soil paste, but 1 : 1 and 1 : 2.5 soil/water ratios are also used. Measurements in N KCl are given where they are available.

Particle size analysis: Unless otherwise specified, the international system is used to determine the size limits of soil separates.

Cation exchange capacity (CEC): Methods used to determine CEC vary from country to country, but in general ammonium acetate, 1N, pH 7.0 are used in accordance with soil laboratory methods and procedures outlined in *Soil survey laboratory methods and procedures for collecting soil samples* (Soil Conservation Service, 1972).

Exchangeable cations: In general Ca-Mg-K-Na are determined by extracting with normal ammonium acetate. Ca and Mg are measured by atomic absorption spectroscopy and K and Na by flame photometry.

Organic matter: The Walkley-Black method is used, with or without modification.

Nitrogen: The Kjeldahl or semi-micro Kjeldahl method using a selenium-copper catalyst is generally applied.

Calcium carbonate: The calcimeter method with HCl is generally used.

Soluble salts are quoted as electrical conductivity (EC) in mmhos/cm at 25°C of a saturated soil paste or saturation extract.

Other analyses are explained in the tables where necessary.

Discussion

Because of the limited number of profiles presented, it is not possible to discuss the properties of the soil units in any detail. Furthermore, profiles were not sampled specifically to characterize the particular soil units, but rather were selected as satisfactory representatives of the various units within the limits of the data available.

The variations may be viewed in two ways. First, there are the variations in properties from unit to unit, and second, there are the variations within each unit.

Despite the scarcity of samples in a sequence such as Fluvisols-Cambisols-Acrisols-Ferralsols, the falling pH, falling bases and phosphorus, and increasing clay content are examples of the trends present. Some of the differences, of course, follow from the use of such factors as cation exchange capacity, percent base saturation and percent clay in the definitions, but the overall pattern is consistent with our concepts of these soils. The very low levels of potassium and phosphorus in the more developed soils is a notable feature that will be of particular importance in their agricultural development and use.

Soil profiles are the result of the operation of a complex array of factors. Changes in any given factor do not necessarily show up in clear differences in properties. However, the site information and the morphological, physical and chemical data do give a useful overall picture of each unit. They also help us to understand how the soils were formed, how they are related, how they may be classified and how they may be used.

References

GENERAL

FAO. *Guidelines for soil profile description.* 2nd ed. Rome. 1977

SOIL CONSERVATION SERVICE. *Soil survey laboratory methods*
1972 *and procedures for collecting soil samples.* Washington, D.C., U.S. Department of Agriculture. Soil Survey Investigations Report No. 1.

SOIL SURVEY STAFF. *Soil survey manual.* Washington, D.C.,
1951 U.S. Department of Agriculture. Agriculture Handbook No. 18.

INDONESIA

BUSNAWI, I. *Reconnaissance soil survey of southeast Sumatra.*
1973 Palembang. Working Paper, FAO/UNDP INS 18 Project.

INDONESIA. MINISTRY OF AGRICULTURE. *Field trip guide*
1972 *book, Second ASEAN Soil Conference, July 22-29, 1972.* Bogor.

INDONESIA. SOIL RESEARCH INSTITUTE. *Peat and podzolic*
1976 *soils and their potential for agriculture in Indonesia.* Bogor.

MALAYSIA

Tour guides for the pre- and post-Conference tours. Conference
1977 on Classification and Management of Tropical Soils, Kuala Lumpur.

PHILIPPINES

MARIANO, J.A. & VALMIDIANO, A.T. *Classification of Philip-*
1972 *pines soils in the higher categories.* Manila, Bureau of Soils.

SARAWAK

ANDRIESSE, J.P. *The soils of west Sarawak*. Kuching, Soil
1972 Survey Division, Department of Agriculture.

THAILAND

DENT, F.J. *Final report of the technical officer (Soil Survey)*.
1968 Hat Yai. FAO/UNDP Rubber Development Project
     No. 176.

ROJANASOONTHON, S. *Morphology and genesis of gray podzolic*
1972 *soils in Thailand*. Corvallis, Oregon State University.
     (Thesis)

SCHOLTEN, J.J. & BOONYAWAT, W. *Detailed reconnaissance*
1972 *soil survey of Nan province*. Bangkok, Department of
     Land Development. Report SSR No. 90.

VAN DER KEVIE, W. & YENMANAS, B. *Detailed reconnaissance*
1972 *soil survey of southern central plain*. Bangkok, Depart-
     ment of Land Development. Report SSR No. 89.

VAN DER KEVIE, W. & YENMANAS, B. *Semi-detailed soil survey*
1972 *of a part of the central plain*. Bangkok, Department
     of Land Development. Report SSR No. 88.

VIET NAM

COMPY, E.Z. & REIMER, A.H. *Soils of An Giang province*,
1969 *Viet Nam*. Washington, D.C., Department of the
     Army, Engineer Agency for Resources Inventories.
     EARI Development Research Series, Report No. 1.

MOORMANN, F.R. Unpublished field notes.
1960–61

NGUYEN, VAN-HOAI. *Inventory and nomenclature of Vietnam*
1962 *soils*. Ithaca, N.Y., Cornell University. (Thesis)

LIST OF SOIL PROFILES

Symbol	Unit		Country	Page	Symbol	Unit		Country	Page
Af	ACRISOL	Ferric	Thailand	80	Jc	FLUVISOL	Calcaric	Thailand	116
Af		Ferric	Sabah	82	Jt		Thionic	Viet Nam	118
Ag		Gleyic	Thailand	84	Jt		Thionic	Thailand	120
Ah		Humic	Thailand	86					
Ah		Humic	Indonesia	88	Lf	LUVISOL	Ferric	Sabah	122
Ao		Orthic	Sarawak	90	Lg		Gleyic	Thailand	124
Ao		Orthic	Thailand	92	Lk		Calcic	Thailand	126
Ao		Orthic	Thailand	94	Lo		Orthic	Thailand	128
Ap		Plinthic	Thailand	96	Lp		Plinthic	Viet Nam	130
					Nd	NITOSOL	Dystric	Thailand	132
Be	CAMBISOL	Eutric	Thailand	98	Ne		Eutric	Viet Nam	134
Bf		Ferralic	Malaysia	100					
Bk		Calcic	Thailand	102	Ph	PODZOL	Humic	Sarawak	136
					Po		Orthic	Malaysia	138
Fa	FERRALSOL	Acric	Malaysia	104					
Fo		Orthic	Viet Nam	106	Qc	ARENOSOL	Cambic	Thailand	140
Fo		Orthic	Thailand	108					
Fr		Rhodic	Viet Nam	110	Th	ANDOSOL	Humic	Philippines	142
					Tm		Mollic	Indonesia	144
Ge	GLEYSOL	Eutric	Malaysia	112	Vc	VERTISOL	Chromic	Thailand	146
Ge		Eutric	Viet Nam	114	Vp		Pellic	Philippines	148

FERRIC ACRISOL   Af

Location	Nakhon Phanom station, Amphoe Muang, Thailand
Altitude	150 m (approximately)
Physiography	Undulating low terrace
Drainage	Well drained
Parent material	Old alluvial deposit
Vegetation	Annual crops
Climate	Monsoon tropical; rainfall 2 150 mm (approx.); rainy season from May through November.

Profile description

Ap   **0-8/12 cm**   Dark brown (10YR 3/3) and light brownish grey (10YR 6/2 dry) sandy loam; moderate common fine granular structure but on the lower portion strong medium platy structure; hard, dry, particularly in plough sole; slightly sticky and slightly plastic; common very fine vesicular and interstitial pores; few fine root pores; common mixing of dark and light spots by ploughing; many fine roots; clear wavy boundary; pH 5.0.

E   **8/12-40 cm**   Dark brown (10YR 4/3) and greyish brown (10YR 5/2 dry) sandy loam; weak fine subangular blocky structure; firm, slightly sticky and slightly plastic; few very fine vesicular and interstitial pores; few fine root pores; common bleached sand grains; few fine roots; compact pan-like; clear smooth boundary; pH 6.0.

EB   **40-53 cm**   Strong brown (7.5YR 5/6-5/8) sandy loam; weak fine subangular blocky structure; very firm, slightly sticky and plastic; patchy thin cutans in root pores; common very fine to fine vesicular and interstitial pores; few fine animal pores; few fine roots; gradual smooth boundary; pH 4.5.

BE   **53-72 cm**   Yellowish red (6YR 5/6) sandy clay loam; weak medium subangular blocky structure; firm, sticky and plastic; broken thin cutans in pores and some patchy cutans on peds; common very fine vesicular pores, few very fine to fine tubular pores; few fine roots; gradual smooth boundary; pH 4.5.

Bt   **72-119 cm**   Yellowish red (5YR 5/6) sandy clay loam; few fine, very faint mottles; moderate medium subangular blocky structure; friable, sticky and plastic; continuous moderately thick clay skins in larger pores; patchy thin cutans around peds; common very fine to fine tubular and vesicular pores; few fine roots; gradual smooth boundary; pH 4.5.

Btg1   **119-147 cm**   Yellowish brown (10YR 5/4) matrix and common fine faint mottles with strong brown (7.5YR 5/6) colour; sandy clay loam; weak fine subangular blocky structure; friable, sticky and plastic; clay skins similar to above horizon; common very fine to fine tubular and vesicular pores; very fine roots; gradual smooth boundary; pH 4.5.

BCg   **147-153+ cm**   Light yellowish brown (10YR 6/4) matrix, mottled colour (7.5YR 5/8), common fine distinct mottles; fine sandy clay; weak fine subangular blocky structure; friable, sticky and plastic; patchy thin cutans in pores and around peds; common very fine to fine tubular and vesicular pores; very few roots; pH 4.5.

FERRIC ACRISOL

Thailand

Horizon	Depth cm	pH		Cation exchange me %									CaCO$_3$ %
		H$_2$O 1:1	KCl 1:1	CEC	TEB	% BS	Ca	Mg	K	Na	Al	H	
Ap	0–8/12	5.4	4.6	5.7	1.6	28	1.0	0.3	0.1	0.2		4.1	
E	8/12–40	6.4	5.1	6.4	2.3	36	1.7	0.3	0.1	0.2		4.1	
EB	40–53	5.7	5.0	4.8	1.6	33	1.0	0.4	0.04	0.2		3.2	
BE	53–72	5.2	4.5	5.8	1.0	17	0.5	0.2	0.1	0.2		4.8	
Bt	72–119	5.2	4.7	5.2	0.5	10	0.2	0.1	0.04	0.2		4.7	
Btg	119–147	5.0	4.7	6.0	0.6	8	0.2	0.1	0.1	0.2		5.4	
BCg	147–153+												

Horizon	Sol. salts		Organic matter				Particle size analysis %						Flocc. index
			% C	% N	C/N	% OM	Stones	C. sand	F. sand	Silt	Clay	Texture	
Ap			1.07	0.08	13			59.1		28.0	12.9	sl	
E			0.63	0.06	10			10.3	45.7	28.0	16.0	sl	
EB			0.36	0.05	7			55.0		27.3	17.6	sl	
BE			0.29	0.04	7			10.6	41.8	25.7	21.9	scl	
Bt			0.26	0.03	9			52.7		26.9	20.4	scl	
Btg			0.22	0.03	7			10.1	40.3	27.4	22.2	scl	
BCg													

FERRIC ACRISOL   Af

Location	Manusi division, Tawau, Sabah
Altitude	20 m (approximately)
Physiography	Weakly dissected low coastal plain
Drainage	Well drained
Parent material	Old colluvial volcanic ash
Vegetation	Oil palm plantation
Climate	Humid tropical; rainfall 1 800 mm (approx.) with weak maximum from May to August

---

Profile description

Ah	**0-2 cm**	Dark greyish brown (10YR 4/2) loam; moderate to strong medium granular; very hard; very common roots; clear smooth boundary to
E	**2-10 cm**	Yellowish brown (10YR 5/4) and dark greyish brown (10YR 4/2) due to worm-cast, loam to sandy clay loam; moderate to strong fine to medium subangular blocky and coarse granular; hard (dry); many roots; gradual smooth boundary to
EB	**10-20 cm**	Dark yellowish brown (10YR 4/4) sandy clay loam; strong medium subangular blocky; very hard; many roots; few fine fragments of decomposing moderately hard rock; common moderately thick humus staining along cracks and pores; common roots; diffuse smooth boundary to
BE	**20-30 cm**	Yellowish brown (10YR 5/6) clay loam; structure as above; rock fragments as above; common roots; common moderately thick humus staining along cracks and pores; diffuse smooth boundary.
Bt1	**30-45 cm**	Brown to dark brown (7.5YR 4/4) sandy clay to clay loam; structure similar to above; hard; common decomposed rock fragments as above; common roots; diffuse boundary to
Bt2	**45-60 cm**	Brown to strong brown (7.5YR 4/4) sandy clay with few fine distinct light olive grey (5Y 6/2) mottles; structure as above; hard; broken thin clay cutans on ped surfaces and pore channel; decomposed rock fragments as above; common roots; diffuse boundary to
Bt3	**60-87 cm**	Reddish brown (5YR 5/4) clay with common fine distinct light olive brown (2.5Y 5/4) mottles; structure as above; firm (moist); decomposed rock as above; few fine reddish concretions; few roots; broken thin cutans on ped surfaces; diffuse boundary to
Bt4	**87-120 cm**	Yellowish red (5YR 5/6) clay with common medium to coarse distinct light yellowish brown (2.5Y 6/4) mottles; strong coarse subangular blocky; firm; decomposed rock fragments as above; iron concretions as above; few roots; broken thick cutans on ped surfaces; abrupt wavy boundary to
Ccs1	**120-153 cm**	Yellowish red (5YR 4/8) clay with common coarse distinct light yellowish brown (2.5Y 6/4) mottles; abundant (± 80%) (2-10 mm diam.) hard subangular dusky red iron concretions; common rounded stones (25 mm diam.); decomposed rock fragments as above; slightly firm; abrupt wavy boundary to
Ccs2	**153-210 cm**	Red (2.5YR 5/6) clay with common to many coarse light yellowish brown (2.5Y 6/4) mottles; moderately medium subangular blocky; many iron concretions (size as above), but decreasing in depth; few decomposed rock fragments; friable to firm.

FERRIC ACRISOL
Sabah

Horizon	Depth cm	pH		Cation exchange me %										Ext. Al KCl IN ppm
		H₂O	KCl	CEC	TEB	% BS	Ca	Mg	K	Na	Al	H	
E	2–10	4.0	3.5	6.41		21	0.82	0.43	0.06	0.02		0.51	139
BE	20–30	3.8	3.5	4.95		6	0.14	0.09	0.03	0.02		0.40	225
Bt1	30–45	4.0	3.5	5.10		6	0.08	0.07	0.03	0.02		0.51	231
Bt2	45–60	3.8	3.5	6.17		3	0.06	0.04	0.03	0.01		0.41	224
Bt3	60–87	3.8	3.5	6.99		2	0.03	0.02	0.03	0.02		0.41	291
Bt4	87–120	3.8	3.5	7.85		1	0.06	0.01	0.03	0.02		0.41	283
Ccs1	120–153	3.8	3.7	6.02		2	0.03	0.01	0.04	0.02		0.51	249

Horizon	Sol. salts		Organic matter				Particle size analysis %						Flocc. index
			% C	% N	C/N	% OM	Stones	C. sand	F. sand	Silt	Clay	Texture	
E			1.93	0.13				19.5	44.1	10.4	20.0		
BE			0.47	0.05				17.3	41.3	11.2	27.8		
Bt1			0.39	0.04				18.5	38.3	10.5	29.5		
Bt2			0.30	0.04				14.8	31.8	9.7	41.6		
Bt3			0.28	0.04				12.6	26.7	0.7	56.2		
Bt4			0.26	0.03				10.8	19.9	7.5	57.0		
Ccs1			0.23	0.03				36.5	19.0	6.9	34.3		

GLEYIC ACRISOL   Ag

Location	Amphoe Paktho, Ratchaburi province, Thailand
Altitude	7 to 10 m
Physiography	Flat low terrace
Drainage	Poorly drained; flooded four months a year
Parent material	Old alluvial deposit
Vegetation	Transplanted rice
Climate	Monsoon tropical; rainfall 1 200 mm (approx.) from May through October

Profile description

Ap   **0-17 cm**   Light yellowish brown (10YR 6/4 moist) and very pale brown (10YR 8/3 dry) loam with many fine to coarse distinct yellowish brown mottles; weak coarse subangular blocky; hard dry, firm moist, sticky and plastic wet; common fine and medium vesicular, common very fine interstitial and few fine and very fine tubular pores; very few fine subrounded hard iron and manganese concretions; many fine and common very fine roots; clear smooth boundary; pH 5.5.

AEg   **17-26 cm**   Light grey (10YR 7/2 moist and 10YR 8/2 dry) loam with many medium distinct strong brown mottles; weak coarse subangular blocky, breaking to moderate medium blocky; hard dry, firm moist, sticky and plastic wet; thin broken silt coatings on ped faces; common fine soft subrounded iron concretions and common fine and medium soft manganese concretions; fine interstitial, few fine tubular and vesicular pores; many fine, common very fine and few medium roots; gradual smooth boundary; pH 5.0.

Btg1   **26-51 cm**   Pale brown (10YR 6/3) silty clay with many fine distinct yellowish brown mottles; moderate coarse subangular blocky; hard dry, firm moist, sticky and plastic wet; thin continuous clay coatings in pores, thick broken silt coatings on ped faces; few fine subrounded hard iron and manganese concretions; many very fine and fine interstitial, common fine vesicular pores; few fine, very fine and medium roots; clear smooth boundary; pH 5.0.

Btg2   **51-67 cm**   Yellowish brown (10YR 5/4) silty clay with common very fine strong brown and common medium red mottles; moderate medium and coarse subangular blocky, breaking to moderate fine blocky; firm moist, sticky and plastic wet; thick broken clay coatings on ped faces and thick continuous coatings in pores; few fine subrounded hard iron and manganese concretions; many very fine and fine interstitial, few fine and very fine tubular pores; few very fine roots; clear smooth boundary; pH 4.5.

Btg3   **67-90+ cm**   Light brownish grey (10YR 6/2) clay with many medium distinct yellowish red and few very fine red mottles; moderate coarse subangular blocky, breaking to strong medium blocky; firm moist, sticky and plastic wet; thick broken clay coatings on ped faces, thick continuous coatings in pores; very few fine subrounded hard iron and manganese concretions; many very fine and fine interstitial, few fine and very fine tubular pores; no roots; pH 4.5.

GLEYIC ACRISOL

Thailand

Horizon	Depth cm	pH H₂O 1:1	pH KCl 1:1	CEC	TEB	% BS	Ca	Mg	K	Na	Extr. acidity	K ppm ammon. acetate	P ppm Bray
Ap	0–17	4.7	4.0	8.3	2.7	30	1.4	0.8	0.2	0.3	6.4	96	7
Eg	17–26	5.6	4.3	8.8	4.2	42	2.2	1.4	0.2	0.4	5.9	73	5
Btg1	26–51	5.6	3.8	9.3	2.9	25	1.2	1.0	0.2	0.5	8.8	64	4
Btg2	51–67	5.6	3.7	12.9	2.9	21	0.6	1.3	0.2	0.8	10.9	70	6
Btg3	67–90	5.5	3.5	17.1	5.1	29	0.9	2.6	0.2	1.4	12.6	88	5

The pH column header spans "H₂O 1:1" and "KCl 1:1" under "pH"; columns CEC through Extr. acidity are under "Cation exchange me %".

Horizon	Sol. salts		% C	% N	C/N	% OM	Stones		Sand	Silt	Clay	Texture	Conductivity 1:5
Ap			0.81						10	61	29		130
Eg			0.60						9	61	30		86
Btg1			0.11						9	49	42		66
Btg2			0.58						10	43	47		63
Btg3			0.35						9	37	54		63

Columns % C, % N, C/N, % OM are under "Organic matter"; Stones, Sand, Silt, Clay, Texture are under "Particle size analysis %".

HUMIC ACRISOL   Ah

Location	Khao Yai National Park, Korat province, Thailand

Altitude	800 m (approximately)
Physiography	Rolling high plateau
Drainage	Well drained
Parent material	Residual deposit from weathering of granites
Vegetation	Fallow with *Imperata cylindrica* after shifting cultivation
Climate	Monsoon tropical; high rainfall, estimated at 3 000 mm from May through October

Profile description

Ap	0-15 cm	Very dark greyish brown (10YR 3/2 moist) clay loam; fine and medium crumb structure; very friable; common very fine tubular and many very fine interstitial pores; many roots; clear smooth boundary; pH 5.5.
A	15-22 cm	Dark brown (8YR 3/3 moist) clay loam; moderate fine subangular blocky structure, fine to medium crumb structure in spots; very friable; common very fine tubular, many very fine interstitial pores; many roots; clear smooth boundary; pH 5.5.
BA	22-36 cm	Reddish brown (5YR 4/4 moist) light clay; moderate fine to medium subangular blocky; friable; broken, moderately thick clay cutans; common, very fine tubular, many very fine interstitial pores; common roots; gradual smooth boundary; pH 5.0.
Bt1	36-55 cm	Yellowish red (4YR 4/6 moist) clay; moderate to strong fine and medium subangular blocky structure; friable; broken, moderately thick clay cutans; many very fine tubular, many very fine interstitial pores; common roots; gradual smooth boundary; pH 5.0.
Bt2	55-100 cm	Red (2.5YR 4/6 moist) clay; moderate to strong fine and medium subangular blocky; friable; broken, moderately thick clay cutans; many very fine tubular, common very fine interstitial pores; common roots; gradual smooth boundary; pH 5.0.
BC	100+ cm	Red (2.5YR 4/6 moist) and yellowish red (4YR 4/6 moist) clay; moderate to strong, fine and medium subangular blocky; friable; broken, moderately thick clay cutans; common very fine tubular, common very fine interstitial pores; few fine lateritic concretions; pieces of brownish yellow (10YR 6/8) weathering granite; few roots; pH 5.0.

HUMIC ACRISOL
Thailand

| Horizon | Depth cm | pH | | Cation exchange me % | | | | | | | | | CaCO₃ % |
		H₂O 1:1	KCl 1:1	CEC	TEB	% BS	Ca	Mg	K	Na	Al	H	
Ap	0–15	4.3	3.9	28.68	2.33	8.1	1.55	0.30	0.48	—			
A	15–22	4.9	4.1	22.34	0.84	3.8	0.51	0.07	0.26	—			
BA	22–36	5.1	3.9	15.13	1.79	11.8	1.53	0.10	0.16	—			
Bt1	36–55	5 0	3.9	13.34	2.33	17.5	2.04	0.13	0.16	—			
Bt2	55–100												
BC	100+	5.1	3.9	12.45	1.28	10.3	1.02	0.10	0.16	—			

| Horizon | Sol. salts | | Organic matter | | | | Particle size analysis % | | | | | | Flocc. index |
			% C	% N	C/N	% OM	Stones	C. sand	F. sand	Silt	Clay	Texture	
Ap			4.6	0.30	15.4			9.0	20.9	23.5	46.6		
A			3.3	0.24	13.9			7.0	20.7	33.8	48.5		
BA			1.3	0.10	12.8			6.3	19.2	22 8	51.7		
Bt1			0.6	0.6	10.5			9.2	10.9	26.2	53.7		
Bt2													
BC			0.3	0.03	9.3			7.4	16.2	32.2	44.2		

HUMIC ACRISOL   **Ah**

Location	Waspada, Garut, western Java, Indonesia
Altitude	1 400 m (approximately)
Physiography	Slope of Mount Tjikuraj
Drainage	Well drained
Parent material	Colluvial andesitic volcanic materials
Vegetation	Annual crops
Climate	Humid tropical; rainfall 2 470 mm

Profile description

Ah1   **0-13 cm**   Black (10YR 2/1) clay loam; weak medium crumb; very friable; diffuse smooth boundary.

Ah2   **13-32 cm**   Black (7.5YR 2/0) clay loam; weak medium crumb to subangular blocky; very friable; abrupt smooth boundary.

Bt   **32-55 cm**   Dark brown (7.5YR 3/2) sandy clay; moderate medium to coarse subangular blocky; friable; gradual smooth boundary.

2Bt   **55-120 cm**   Brown to dark brown (7.5YR 4/4) heavy clay; strong medium to coarse angular blocky; firm; diffuse smooth boundary.

2BC   **120+ cm**   Dark brown to brown (7.5YR 4/4-5/4) silty clay; moderate medium angular blocky; firm.

Horizon	Depth cm	pH		Cation exchange me %									CaCO, %
		H₂O	KCl	CEC	TEB	% BS	Ca	Mg	K	Na	Al	H	
Ahl	0–13	6.0	4.9	36.0	14.7	41							
Ah2	13–32	6.0	4.9	42.0	15.3	36							
Bt	32–55	6.7	5.2	33.8	18.4	54							
2Bt	55–120	6.8	5.1	34.4	15.1	44							
2BC	120+	6.6	5.3	38.4	14.4	38							

Horizon	Sol. salts		Organic matter				Particle size analysis %						Flocc. index
			% C	% N	C/N	% OM	Stones	C. sand	F. sand	Silt	Clay	Texture	
Ahl			4.29	0.39	11			42.4		29.4	28.2		
Ah2			5.46	0.40	14			38.2		33.4	28.4		
Bt			1.10	0.16	7			47.8		18.2	34.0		
2Bt			1.07	0.08	13			5.5		22.5	72.0		
2BC			1.24	0.09	14			8.3		43.6	48.1		

ORTHIC ACRISOL   **Ao**

Location	Bau district, Sarawak

Altitude	70 m (approximately)
Physiography	Strongly dissected hilly; slope 15 percent
Drainage	Well drained
Parent material	Weathering material from shales
Vegetation	Secondary forest
Climate	Humid tropical; annual rainfall 3 250 mm (approx.)

Profile description

A	0-5 cm	Brown (10YR 5/3) loam; many medium to fine slightly decomposed roots; many worm holes; moist; friable; clear smooth boundary.
E	5-30 cm	Brownish yellow (10YR 6/6) clay loam with few coarse to fine roots; infiltration of organic matter from above; no mottles; slightly friable; weak angular blocky structure; gradual wavy boundary.
BE	30-55 cm	Reddish yellow (7.5YR 7/8) clay with few roots; very weak clayskins developed along cracks; massive in profile; slightly firm; angular blocky structure; diffuse wavy boundary.
Bt	55-87 cm	Yellow (10YR 7/8) clay with common distinct reddish yellow (5YR 7/8) mottles; few fine dead roots; massive in profile; slightly firm; strong angular blocky structure; weak clayskins along cracks; diffuse wavy boundary.
BC	87-135 cm	Yellow (10YR 7/8) 50 percent and reddish yellow (7.5YR 7/8) 50 percent clay; common pale yellow (2.5Y 8/4) and yellowish red (5YR 5/6) mottles; firm; strong blocky structure; less clayskin development than Bt; clear wavy boundary.
C	135+ cm	Yellow (10YR 7/8) gritty clay with accumulation of red (2.5YR 4/6) weathered shale; few white quartz pebbles; prominent strong brown (7.5YR 5/8) iron-coated shale; firm.

ORTHIC ACRISOL
Sarawak

Horizon	Depth cm	pH		Cation exchange me %										CaCO₃ %
		H₂O 1:2.5	KCl	CEC	TEB	% BS	Ca	Mg	K	Na	Al	H	
A	0–5	4 6		27.27		13.57	1.50	1.76	0 36	0 08	12 58	0 23	
E	5–30	4 7		21.60		2 78	0.01	0 44	0 11	0 05	13.52	0 08	
BE	30–55	5.0		20.86		1 92	0 01	0.24	0.09	0.07	12.67	0.05	
Bt	55–87	4 9		41.34		0.90	0.01	0.20	0.09	0.08	12.06	0 02	
BC	87–135	5.0		22.29		2.47	0 15	0.22	0 10	0 08	10.36	0 02	
C	135+	5.0		18.33		7.91	1 15	0.16	0 09	0 05	9.42	0.03	

Horizon	Sol. salts		Organic matter				Particle size analysis %						Flocc. index
			% C	% N	C/N	% OM	Stones	C. sand	F. sand	Silt	Clay	Texture	
A			3 93	0 31	12 52			2 14	24 59	24.91	40.49		
E			1.07	0 11	10 00			1.30	27.96	23 13	47.29		
BE			0 47	0 06	7.34			0.86	26.44	19.49	53.05		
Bt			0 30	0 06	5.26			0.85	22.25	18.02	58.07		
BC			0.34	0 04	8 10			0.79	17.51	18.62	60 68		
C			0 29	0 05	5 27			20 33	15.58	16.38	47 38		

ORTHIC ACRISOL   **Ao**

Location	Along the track from Fang Min to Huai Lot villages, Nan province, Thailand
Altitude	400 m (approximately)
Physiography	Colluvial footslope in hilly landscape
Drainage	Well drained
Parent material	Mixed colluvial deposit from quartzites and shales; gravel content increases with depth
Vegetation	Mixed deciduous forest with *Dipterocarpus* species
Climate	Monsoon tropical; rainfall 1 400 mm (approx.); rainy season from May through mid-October

Profile description

A   **0-10 cm**   Very dark greyish brown (10YR 3/2 moist) and grey (10YR 6/1 dry) loam with a discernible gravel fraction of angular fine quartz fragments; moderate medium and fine subangular blocky and some granular structure; slightly sticky and slightly plastic; firm; slightly hard; many fine and very fine interstitial pores; few small animal holes; common very fine and medium roots; clear smooth boundary; pH 6.0.

AB   **10-22 cm**   Dark brown to brown (7.5YR 4/4 moist) and light yellowish brown (10YR 6/4 dry) clay loam; moderate coarse breaking to medium and fine subangular blocky; slightly sticky and plastic; firm; hard; many fine and very fine interstitial pores; few scattered angular and subangular medium quartz fragments; few large and medium animal holes; many fine and few medium roots; gradual smooth boundary; pH 5.0.

BA   **22-36 cm**   Brown (7.5YR 4-5/4 moist) and light brown (7.5YR 6/4 dry) clay loam with higher clay content; moderate coarse breaking to medium and some fine subangular blocky; slightly sticky and plastic; firm; hard; patchy thin clay coatings in pores and on some ped faces; many fine and few medium interstitial pores; few fine tubular pores; few medium and large subangular quartz fragments; common fine and medium and few large roots; gradual smooth boundary; pH 5.0.

Bt   **36-75 cm**   Yellowish red (5YR 4/6 moist and 5YR 5/6 dry) clay; moderate coarse breaking to medium and fine subangular blocky; sticky and plastic; slightly firm; hard; broken moderately thick clay coatings on ped faces and in pores; common fine and medium interstitial pores; few fine tubular pores; few fine and medium subangular quartz and shale fragments; few medium animal holes; few fine and large and common medium roots; gradual smooth boundary; pH 5.0.

BC   **75-160+ cm**   Yellowish red (5YR 4/6 moist and 5YR 5/6 dry) very gravelly clay with about 50 percent gravel by volume increasing to 70 percent with depth; massive; sticky and plastic between gravel; slightly firm; slightly hard; broken moderately thick clay coatings on gravel faces; gravel consists of quartz, phyllite and shale fragments; common fine and few large roots; pH 5.0.

ORTHIC ACRISOL

Thailand

Horizon	Depth cm	pH		Cation exchange me %								P ppm Bray	K ppm ammon. acetate
		H₂O 1:1	KCl 1:1	CEC	TEB	% BS	Ca	Mg	K	Na	Extr. acidity		
A	0–10	7.1	5.4	18.4	10.3	58	7.1	2.8	0.3	0.1	7.6	7.0	137
AB	10–22	6.2	4.4	12.3	3.9	31	2.1	1.5	0.2	0.1	8.8	5.2	79
BA	22–36	5.9	4.1	11.6	1.8	16	0.6	0 9	0.2	0.1	9.4	4.4	88
Bt	36–75	5.5	3.8	11.4	1.5	14	0.5	0.7	0.2	0.1	9.6	2.3	85
BC	75–160+	5.5	3.6	10.9	2.5	21	1.1	1.1	0.2	0.1	9.6	2.2	82

Horizon	Sol. salts		Organic matter				Particle size analysis %					Conduc- tivity 1:5 EC×10⁶	Flocc. index
			% C	% N	C/N	% OM	Stones	C. sand	F. sand	Silt	Clay		
A			2.29					35.0		50.5	14.5	0.02	
AB			1.13					34.5		44.5	21.0	0.02	
BA			0.72					31.0		39.5	29.5	0.01	
Bt			0.47					27.0		32.0	41.0	0.01	
BC			0.62					31.0		29.0	40.0	0.01	

ORTHIC ACRISOL   **Ao**

Location	Khlong Thom, Thailand
Altitude	50 m (approximately)
Physiography	Undulating to rolling
Drainage	Moderately well drained
Parent material	Old terrace alluvial deposit
Vegetation	Young rubber plantation
Climate	Monsoon tropical; rainfall 2 200 mm (approx.), mainly from November to mid-March.

Profile description

Ap   **0-7/13 cm**   Dark greyish brown (10YR 4/2) fine sandy loam; fine subangular blocky structure breaking to moderate crumb; consistence when wet non-sticky and non-plastic, moist friable, dry soft; patchy thin cutans confined to root and pore channels; common discontinuous tubular pores; ant nests and worm casts; frequent varied roots; pH 5.5.; clear wavy boundary.

E   **7/13-23 cm**   Reddish yellow (7.5YR 6/6) fine sandy loam to fine sandy clay loam; fine to medium subangular blocky structure breaking to moderate crumb; consistence when wet slightly sticky and slightly plastic, moist friable, dry slightly hard; cutans as in Ap horizon; common discontinuous tubular and interstitial pores; frequent varied roots; pH 5.0; gradual wavy boundary.

EB   **23-40 cm**   Strong brown (7.5YR 5/6) fine sandy clay loam; medium subangular blocky structure breaking to very fine prismatic; consistence when wet slightly sticky and slightly plastic, moist friable, dry slightly hard; cutans as in Ap horizon; pores as in E horizon; frequent fine and very fine roots, few coarse roots; pH 4.8; gradual wavy boundary.

Bt1   **40-78 cm**   Yellowish red (5YR 5/6) fine sandy clay loam; medium subangular blocky structure; consistence when wet slightly sticky and slightly plastic, moist friable, dry slightly hard; patchy thin cutans mainly confined to root and pore channels, some along vertical and horizontal ped faces; pores as in E horizon; common, fine and very fine roots; pH 4.8; gradual wavy boundary.

Bt2   **78-110 cm**   Yellowish red to red (5YR 5/6 to 2.5YR 5/6) clay loam; medium subangular blocky structure; consistence when wet sticky and plastic, moist firm, dry slightly hard; cutans, pores and roots as above; pH 4.7; clear wavy boundary.

C   **110+ cm**   Red (2.5YR 5/8) gravelly clay; medium subangular blocky structure; consistence when wet sticky and plastic, moist firm, dry slightly hard; patchy thin cutans along vertical and horizontal ped faces; pores as above; few very fine roots; frequent angular, strongly weathered red and purple shale and sandstone fragments, and few small hard angular laterite concretions; pH 4.5.

ORTHIC ACRISOL

Thailand

Horizon	Depth cm	pH		Cation exchange me%										CaCO₃ %
		H₂O	KCl	CEC	TEB	% BS	Ca	Mg	K	Na	Al	H	
Ap	0–7/13												
E	7/13–23												
EB	23–40												
Bt1	40–78												
Bt2	78–100												
C	110+												

Horizon	Sol. salts		Organic matter				Particle size analysis %						Flocc. index
			% C	% N	C/N	% OM	Stones	C. sand	F. sand	Silt	Clay	Texture	
Ap								4.0	57.0	18.0	17.0		
E								3.6	54.4	19.0	20.0		
EB								3.4	52.8	17.0	23.0		
Bt1								2.7	49.7	15.0	28.0		
Bt2								2.3	44.1	17.0	38.0		
C								3.0	39.6	16.0	39.0		

PLINTHIC ACRISOL   Ap

Location	Chiang Mai, Thailand
Altitude	325 m (approximately)
Physiography	Undulating lower terrace
Drainage	Moderately well drained
Parent material	Old alluvial deposit
Vegetation	Open *Dipterocarpus* forest
Climate	Monsoon tropical; rainfall 1 250 mm; rainy season from May to mid-November.

Profile description

A   **0-5 cm**   Very dark grey (10YR 3/1) and grey (10YR 5/1 dry) sandy loam; weak fine subangular blocky structure; hard; slightly sticky, slightly plastic; common very fine vesicular pores; fine to very fine animal holes in peds; many fine roots; pH 5.5; clear wavy boundary.

E   **5-11 cm**   Brown (10YR 5/3) and light grey (10YR 7/2 dry) sandy loam; moderate fine subangular blocky structure; very hard, non-sticky and non-plastic; common fine to very fine vesicular and interstitial pores; common bleached sand grains; common fine roots; pH 5.0; gradual smooth boundary.

BE   **11-40 cm**   Light yellowish brown (10YR 6/4) sandy loam; moderate medium subangular blocky structure; firm, slightly sticky and slightly plastic; common very fine vesicular and interstitial pores; thin, patchy cutans in pores; few medium roots and common fine roots; pH 5.0; gradual wavy boundary.

Bt   **40-73 cm**   Light yellowish brown (10YR 6/4) matrix; few fine distinct mottles of strong brown colour (7.5YR 5/6); sandy clay loam; moderate medium subangular blocky structure; friable, sticky and plastic; common very fine vesicular pores, few fine tubular pores; patchy bridging cutans with common moderately thick cutans in pores; sparse medium roots; pH 5.0; gradual smooth boundary.

BCgs   **73-122+ cm**   Light brownish grey (10YR 6/2) matrix; many medium prominent mottles with variegated colour of red and brown (10R 4/6 and 7.5YR 5/6) plinthite; clay; weak medium subangular blocky structure; firm, very sticky and very plastic; common very fine vesicular pores with few fine to very fine tubular pores; moderately thick, continuous cutans in pores and on peds; sparse medium roots; pH 5.5.

PLINTHIC ACRISOL

Thailand

Horizon	Depth cm	pH		Cation exchange me %									CaCO₃ %
		H₂O 1:1	KCl 1:1	CEC	TEB	% BS	Ca	Mg	K	Na	Al	H	
A	0–5	5.9	5.0	7.6	2.8	37	2.1	0.4	0.1	0.2		4.8	
E	5–11	5.8	4.5	3.1	1.0	32	0.6	0.2	0.1	0.2		2.1	
BE	11–40	5.4	4.3	3.6	0.7	37	0.2	0.2	0.1	0.2		1.2	
Bt	40–73	5.7	4.4	3.0	0.7	30	0.2	0.2	0.1	0.2		1.6	
BCgs	73–122	5.4	4.2	5.2	1.7	26	0.7	0.5	0.3	0.2		4.8	

Horizon	Sol. salts		Organic matter				Particle size analysis %						Flocc. index
			% C	% N	C/N	% OM	Stones	C. sand	F. sand	Silt	Clay	Texture	
A			0.93	0.06	16			24.9	36.6	29.4	9.1	sl	
E			0.25	0.04	6			61.47		30.2	8.3	sl	
BE			0.03	0.02	2			27.7	33.4	27.3	11.6	sl	
Bt			0.04	0.02	2			59.03		26.8	14.2	sl	
BCgs			0.08	0.03	3			22.7	19.6	22.5	37.2	cl	

EUTRIC CAMBISOL   **Be**

Location	Nam Song village, Sa district, Nan province, Thailand
Altitude	220 m
Physiography	Dissected erosion landscape; steep slopes
Drainage	Well drained
Parent material	Residual deposit and slope colluvium derived from shales and phyllites
Vegetation	Shifting cultivation of upland rice and other annual crops
Climate	Monsoon tropical; rainfall 1 150 mm (approx.); rainy season from May to mid-October.

Profile description

Ap   **0-15 cm**   Dark brown to brown (10YR 4/3 moist) and pale brown (10YR 6/3 dry) slightly gravelly loam with about 10 percent fine and medium angular weathering shale fragments; weak coarse subangular blocky breaking to moderate fine and medium granular structure; slightly sticky and slightly plastic; slightly firm; slightly hard; many fine and very fine and common medium interstitial pores; common very fine and few fine roots; abrupt smooth boundary; pH 6.

Bw   **15-60 cm**   Dark yellowish brown (10YR 3/4 moist) and brown (10YR 5/3 dry) gravelly clay loam with about 30 percent fine and medium angular weathering shale fragments; moderate medium breaking to fine subangular blocky; slightly sticky and plastic; friable; slightly hard; patchy thin clay coatings in pores and shining veneers on gravel faces; many very fine and fine and common medium interstitial pores; few fine tubular pores; common fine and few medium roots; gradual irregular boundary; pH 6.5.

C   **60+ cm**   Light olive grey (5Y 6/2), dark brown (7.5YR 4/4) and reddish brown (5YR 4/4) very gravelly clay with about 80 percent olive and olive yellow (5Y 5/6 and 5Y 6/6) weathering shale fragments; there is some evidence of clay illuviation between the shale fragments; pH 6.5.

EUTRIC CAMBISOL

Thailand

Horizon	Depth cm	pH		Cation exchange me %								P ppm Bray	K ppm ammon. acetate
		H₂O 1:1	KCl 1:1	CEC	TEB	% BS	Ca	Mg	K	Na	Extr. acidity		
Ap	0–15	6.7	5.8	33.4	23.4	71	17.2	5.4	0.6	0.2	9.4	4.5	163
Bw	15–60	6.4	4.3	29.2	22.3	74	13.7	8.1	0.2	0.3	8.0	4.1	56
C	60+	6.4	3.7	26.9	22.3	72	13.9	7.7	0.1	0.6	8.9	3.3	50

Horizon	Sol. salts		Organic matter				Particle size analysis %					Conductivity 1:5	CaCO₃ %
			% C	% N	C/N	% OM	Stones	C. sand	F. sand	Silt	Clay		
Ap			2.35					31.0		54.5	14.5	0.07	1.6
Bw			0.39					12.0		60.5	27.5	0.01	1.2
C			0.28					7.5		67.5	25.0	0.01	0.9

FERRALIC CAMBISOL   **Bf**

Location	Experimental station, Ayer Hitam, Johore, Malaysia

Altitude	40 m (approximately)
Physiography	Undulating coastal plain
Drainage	Moderately well drained
Parent material	Argillaceous shale
Vegetation	Secondary jungle
Climate	Humid tropical; rainfall 2 300 mm (approx.)

Profile description

Ap   **0-15 cm**   Light grey to grey (10YR 6/1) clay; moderately strong medium and few coarse subangular and angular blocky and few medium crumbs; moist friable; many pores; many roots; clear boundary.

Bw1   **15-45 cm**   Pale yellow (2.5Y 7/4) clay; strong coarse prismatic and few subangular and angular blocky; moist very firm; common pores; few roots; common fine distinct brownish yellow (10YR 6/8) mottling; few termite channels; diffuse boundary.

Bw2   **45-63 cm**   Pale yellow (2.5Y 8/4) clay; moderate strong coarse and very coarse prismatic; moist very fine; few pores; no roots; many fine medium prominent dark yellowish brown (10YR 4/4) and brownish yellow (10YR 6/8) mottles; clear boundary.

Bcs   **63-75 cm**   Light grey (10YR 8/2) clay; a band of somewhat compact gravelly iron concretions (60-70 percent); many fine medium prominent brownish yellow (10YR 6/3) mottles; clear boundary.

C   **75-138 cm**   Light grey (10YR 8/1) clay; weak coarse and very coarse subangular and angular blocky and few coarse prismatic; moist very firm; few pores; no roots; abundant medium and coarse prominent brownish yellow (10YR 6/8) mottles.

FERRALIC CAMBISOL

Malaysia

Horizon	Depth cm	pH		Cation exchange me %										CaCO₃ %
		H₂O	KCl	CEC	TEB	% BS	Ca	Mg	K	Na	Al	H	
Ap	0–15	4.7	3.8	11.1		11.9	0.31	0.69	0.27	0.05	5.87		
Bw1	15–45	4.6	3.7	9.6		6.8	0.09	0.43	0.09	0.04	8.46		
Bw2	45–63	4.7	3.7	11.6		3.7	0.09	0.23	0.06	0.05	9.44		
Bcs	63–75	5.2	3.8	11.8		4.4	0.11	0.31	0.05	0.05	8.67		
C	75+	5.3	3.9	12.4		2.8	0.10	0.10	0.10	0.05	6.65		

Horizon	Sol. salts		Organic matter				Particle size analysis %						Flocc. index
			% C	% N	C/N	% OM	Stones	C. sand	F. sand	Silt	Clay	Texture	
Ap			1.88	0.19				10.4	11.0	39.3	36.4		
Bw1			0.39	0.09				8.2	10.4	33.6	50.3		
Bw2			0.27	0.07				8.2	9.4	30.2	52.2		
Bcs			0.25	0.06				7.7	9.0	33.4	50.4		
C			0.11	0.04				9.4	15.9	36.6	39.7		

CALCIC CAMBISOL   **Bk**

Location	Lam Narain, Chai Badan district, Lop Buri province, Thailand
Altitude	110 m (approximately)
Physiography	Undulating to rolling; slope 3 to 6 percent
Drainage	Well drained
Parent material	Mixed basic rocks (basalts, limestones, andesite)
Vegetation	Permanent cultivation of upland crops
Climate	Monsoon tropical; rainfall 1 450 mm (approx.); rainy season from May through October

---

Profile description

Ap	**0-29 cm**	Dark brown (7.5YR 3/2) clay; moderate medium subangular blocky; sticky, plastic; slightly firm moist; common very fine interstitial and few fine tubular pores; few fine (diam. ± 2 mm) lime concretions; common very fine and fine roots; clear smooth boundary; pH 8.0.
BA	**29-49 cm**	Dark reddish brown (5YR 3/4) clay; moderate medium subangular blocky; sticky, plastic; friable moist; few very fine interstitial and tubular pores; few fine (diam. ± 2 mm) lime concretions; few very fine roots; gradual wavy boundary; pH 8.0.
Bw	**49-82 cm**	Reddish brown (5YR 4/4) clay; moderate medium subangular blocky; sticky, plastic; slightly firm moist; shiny faces that may be patchy thin cutan or pressure faces; few very fine interstitial and tubular pores; few fine (diam. ± 2 mm) lime concretions and very few fine angular rock fragments; few very fine roots; abrupt wavy boundary; pH 7.5-8.0.
C	**82-150+ cm**	Layer of weathered rock (basalt) containing more than 80 percent lime concretions and some basalt fragments (diam. ± 15 cm); pH 8.0.

CALCIC CAMBISOL

Thailand

Horizon	Depth cm	pH H₂O 1:1	pH KCl 1:1	CEC	TEB	% BS	Ca	Mg	K	Na	Al	H	CaCO₃ %
Ap	0–29	7.8	6.6	84.0	78.8	94	73.6	4.1	0.7	0.4		6.5	8.1
BA	29–49	7.2	6.1	84.1	70.9	84	66.6	3.6	0.4	0.3		9.0	4.8
Bw	49–82	7.3	6.0	79.6	72.7	91	68.5	3.3	0.5	0.4		9.3	4.5
C	82–150+	8.0	6.7	38.0	52.4	138	50.5	1.4	0.2	0.3		1.9	49.9

The cation exchange columns (CEC, TEB, % BS, Ca, Mg, K, Na, Al, H) are grouped under "Cation exchange me %".

Horizon	P ppm Bray 2	K ppm ammon. acetate	% C	% N	C/N	% OM	Stones	C. sand	F. sand	Silt	Clay	Texture	Flocc. index
Ap	24.0	254	1.5						12.0	36.0	52.0		
BA	9.9	166	0.7						11.0	36.0	53.0		
Bw	10.8	181	0.6						13.0	29.0	58.0		
C	38.0	88	0.3						29.0	38.5	32.5		

The columns % C, % N, C/N, % OM are grouped under "Organic matter"; Stones, C. sand, F. sand, Silt, Clay, Texture are grouped under "Particle size analysis %".

ACRIC FERRALSOL   **Fa**

Location	Bukit Goh oil palm scheme, Kuantan district, Pahang, Malaysia

Altitude	30 m (approximately)
Physiography	Gently undulating coastal plain
Drainage	Somewhat excessive
Parent material	Weathering clay from basalt
Vegetation	Oil palm plantation
Climate	Humid tropical; rainfall 2 800 mm (approx.)

Profile description

Ap	**0-18 cm**	Brown to dark brown (10YR 4/3) clay; weak fine subangular blocky and strong crumb; friable to firm; few medium roots; few channels; diffuse boundary.
Bs1	**18-46 cm**	Dark yellowish brown (10YR 4/4) clay; weak, medium subangular blocky; very friable; few fine roots; few channels; thin coatings on ped faces; diffuse boundary.
Bs2	**46-121 cm**	Dark yellowish brown (10YR 4/4) clay; weak, medium and coarse subangular blocky; very friable; few fine roots; thin coatings on ped faces; diffuse boundary.
Bs3	**121-200 cm**	Dark yellowish brown (10YR 4/4) clay; weak, medium and fine subangular blocky; friable; few fine roots; thin coatings on ped faces.

ACRIC FERRALSOL
Malaysia

| Horizon | Depth cm | pH | | Cation exchange me % | | | | | | | | | CEC |
		H$_2$O	KCl	CEC	TEB	% BS	Ca	Mg	K	Na	Al	H	NH4Cl
Ap	0–18	4.3	3.9	9.24	1.17	12.7	0.70	0.32	0.12	0.03		11.7	2.32
Bs1	18–46	4.6	4.1	5.20	0.28	5.4	0.15	0.07	0.04	0.02		9.8	0.90
Bs2	46–121	4.8	4.2	4.08	0.21	5.1	0.12	0.05	0.02	0.02		8.5	0.82
Bs3	121–200	4.8	4.3	3.16	0.25	7.9	0.17	0.04	0.02	0.02		7.5	0.72

| Horizon | Sol. salts | | Organic matter | | | | Particle size analysis % | | | | | | Free iron |
			% C	% N	C/N	% OM	Stones	C. sand	F. sand	Silt	Clay	Texture	%
Ap			1.93	0.29	7			7.3	8.3	24.7	59.8		12.4
Bs1			0.40	0.12	3			4.0	6.7	24.1	65.2		12.5
Bs2			0.30	0.06	5			3.6	10.8	20.3	65.3		13.0
Bs3			0.18	0.06	3			2.9	6.9	21.0	69.1		14.9

ORTHIC FERRALSOL   **Fo**

Location	Pleiku, Viet Nam

Altitude	740 m (approximately)
Physiography	Undulating to rolling plateau
Drainage	Well drained
Parent material	Weathering clay from basalt
Vegetation	Short grass savanna burned yearly
Climate	Monsoon tropical; rainfall 2 500 mm (approx.); rainy season from May through October

---

Profile description

Ah	0-25 cm	Reddish brown (5YR 4/4 dry, 5YR 3/3 moist) sandy clay loam; medium fine crumb structure; very friable to loose; low bulk density; many fine to medium pores; smooth boundary.
Bs	25-150+ cm	Reddish brown (5YR 4/5 moist) clay loam to clay; weak fine subangular blocky, fine crumbs in spots; friable; low bulk density; many fine to medium pores with some larger channels; at 120 cm, very localized spots of a few cm diameter with somewhat firmer consistence.

ORTHIC FERRALSOL
Viet Nam

Horizon	Depth cm	pH H₂O	pH KCl	CEC	TEB	% BS	Ca	Mg	K	Na	Al	H	P ppm
Ah	0–25	5.0	4.3	10.0		24	1.7	0.7	0.02	0.03			10
Bs	40–50	5.5	4.9	4.0		29	1.0	0.1	0.06	0.03			5
Bs	80–100	5.2	5.0	4.0		33	1.0	0.2	0.04	0.08			6
Bs	130–150	5.4	4.9	3.0		58	1.5	0.2	0.02	0.03			8

Horizon	Sol. salts		% C	% N	C/N	% OM	Stones	C. sand	F. sand	Silt	Clay	Texture	Flocc. index
Ah								53	26	21			
Bs								41	22	37			
Bs								33	24	43			
Bs								35	22	43			

ORTHIC FERRALSOL   Fo

Location	Soil and Water Conservation Centre, Sa district, Nan province, Thailand
Altitude	280 m
Physiography	Undulating old alluvial terrace
Drainage	Somewhat excessive
Parent material	Old alluvial deposit
Vegetation	Permanent rainfed agriculture of annual crops (groundnuts, upland rice, soybeans)
Climate	Monsoon tropical; rainfall 1 150 mm (approx.); rainy season from May to mid-October

Profile description

Ap1   **0-5 cm**   Very dark brown (7.5YR 2/2 moist) and (very) dark greyish brown to dark brown (10-7.5YR 3-4/2 dry) sandy loam; weak medium crumb to medium subangular blocky; very friable; slightly hard; powders on crushing; weak surface crust develops on bare or cultivated areas; clear smooth boundary; pH 6-6.3.

Ap2   **5-10 cm**   Very dark brown and brown (7.5YR 2/2 and 7.5YR 4/4 moist) and brown to dark yellowish brown (7.5-10YR 4/4 dry) sandy loam; weak medium subangular blocky to massive; friable; hard; powders on crushing; clear smooth boundary; pH 6.0.

AB   **10-15 cm**   Brown (7.5YR 4/2-4 moist) and brown to dark yellowish brown (10-7.5YR 4/3-4 dry) sandy clay loam; massive; friable; very hard; mixing of soil materials from underlying and overlying horizons by earthworm or termite activity; worm casts can be separated from the soil mass and comprise both A and B horizon materials; clear irregular boundary; pH 6.0.

BA   **15-40 cm**   Reddish brown (5YR 4/4 moist) and yellowish red (5YR 4-5/6 dry) sandy clay loam; massive; friable; very hard; no clayskins except along voids formed by earth worms; some discontinuous clay zones; large oval animal voids (5 × 2 cm); other small termite voids and channels; common roots; gradual wavy boundary; pH 5.5.

Bws1   **40-70 cm**   Yellowish red (5YR 4/8 moist and 5YR 5/8 dry) sandy clay loam; massive; weak medium crumb to medium subangular blocky due to termite activity; nonsticky; subplastic (subplasticity suggests kaolinite plus iron or aluminium as flocculating agent); slightly hard; inclusions of A horizon material due to earthworm activity; gradual wavy boundary; pH 5.2.

Bws2   **70-90 cm**   Yellowish red (5YR 4/8 moist and 5YR 5/8 dry) sandy clay loam; massive; gradual arbitrary boundary; pH 5.

Bws3   **90-140+ cm**   Yellowish red (5YR 4/8 moist and 5YR 5/8 dry) sandy clay loam; massive; gradual boundary; pH 5.2.

ORTHIC FERRALSOL
Thailand

Horizon	Depth cm	pH H₂O 1:1	pH KCl 1:1	CEC	TEB	% BS	Ca	Mg	K	Na	Extr. acidity	P ppm Bray	K ppm ammon. acetate
Ap1	0–5	5.9	5.4	9.6	6.5	59	4.8	1.2	0.3	0.2	4 5	34.5	108
Ap2	5–10	4.9	4.7	6.3	4.1	41	2.8	1.0	0.1	0.2	5.8	16.6	52
AB	10–15	4.7	4.3	6.0	2.3	28	1.3	0.7	0.1	0.2	6.0	4.7	37
BA	15–40	4.2	4.0	4.9	1.1	14	0.5	0.3	0.1	0.2	6.6	2.6	22
Bws1	40–70	4.2	4.0	4.3	0.7	11	0.4	0.1	0.1	0.2	5.7	2 2	16
Bws2	70–90	4.7	4.0	3.9	0.7	12	0.4	0.1	0.1	0.2	5.1	2.0	16
Bws3	90–140+	4.7	4.0	4.0	0.8	12	0.4	0.2	0.1	0 2	5.8	5.3	16

Horizon	Sol. salts		% C	% N	C/N	% OM	Stones	C. sand	F. sand	Silt	Clay	Conductivity 1:5 EC × 10⁶	Flocc. index
Ap1			1.51	0.09				64.0		31.5	4.5	0.05	
Ap2			1.05	0.08				61.0		31.0	8.0	0.03	
AB			0.70	0.06				64.0		28.5	7.5	0.02	
BA			0.47	0.05				61.0		22.5	16.5	0.01	
Bws1			0.25	0.06				55.5		22.5	22.0	0.01	
Bws2			0.19	0.05				52.0		26.0	22.0	0.01	
Bws3			0.15	0.05				47.5		26.5	26.0	0.01	

RHODIC FERRALSOL   **Fr**

Location	Ban Methuot, Pleiku road; Km 445, Viet Nam

Altitude	550 m (approximately)
Physiography	Incised basalt plateau
Drainage	Well drained
Parent material	Residual clay from weathering of basalts
Vegetation	Savanna with scattered trees and *Imperata cylindrica*
Climate	Monsoon tropical; rainfall 1 800 mm (approx.) from May to October

Profile description

A   **0-14 cm**   Dusky red (10R 3/4) clay; strong fine crumb structure; low bulk density; loose consistence; many fine pores; smooth gradual boundary.

AB   **14-30 cm**   Dusky red (10R 3/4) clay; moderate fine crumb structure and weak subangular blocky in spots; loose consistence; many fine pores; smooth clear boundary.

Bws1   **30-90 cm**   Dark red (10R 3/5) clay; moderate fine subangular blocky structure and spots with moderate fine crumb; some discontinuous thin clay coatings in some root channels; low bulk density; soft; many fine pores; smooth gradual boundary.

Bws2   **90+ cm**   Dark red (10R 3/5) clay; moderately strong medium subangular blocky structure; some discontinuous thin clay coatings on peds and in root channels; slightly hard; many fine pores; no change in profile to be observed at depth of approximately 3.50 m.

RHODIC FERRALSOL
Viet Nam

| Horizon | Depth cm | pH | | Cation exchange me % | | | | | | | | | P ppm |
		H$_2$O	KCl	CEC	TEB	% BS	Ca	Mg	K	Na	Al	H	
A	0–14	6.1	5.2	5.93		109	9.00	2.90	0.19	3.57			6
AB	14–30	5.1	4.5	1.72		83	1.70	0.10	0.08	2.82			1
Bws1	30–90	5.0	4.3	2.90		53	1.50	0.10	0.08	2.61			1
Bws2	90+	5.6	4.5	1.59		68	1.00	0.30	0.06	2.75			1

| Horizon | Sol. salts | | Organic matter | | | | Particle size analysis % | | | | | | Flocc. index |
			% C	% N	C/N	% OM	Stones	C. sand	F. sand	Silt	Clay	Texture	
A			3.44		17				37	26	37		
AB			1.00		16				15	20	65		
Bws1			1.68		14				23	20	57		
Bws2			6.92		13				13	20	67		

EUTRIC GLEYSOL   **Ge**

Location	Kampong Tasek, Telok Gong, Malacca, Malaysia
Altitude	17 m
Physiography	Flat river flood plain
Drainage	Imperfect to poor
Parent material	River alluvial deposit
Vegetation	Rubber plantation
Climate	Humid tropical; rainfall 2 200 mm (approx.)

Profile description

Ap   **0-14 cm**   Greyish brown (2.5Y 5/2) clay; strong, coarse angular blocky; sticky; common distinct (5YR 5/6) mottles, predominantly along root channels; many fine roots; few coarse roots; low biological activity; rather sharp boundary.

BAg   **14-31 cm**   Light brownish grey (2.5Y 6/2) clay; weak, coarse angular blocky; sticky; many (5Y 5/8) mottles along root channels and in matrix; few coarse roots; some charcoal fragments; diffuse boundary.

Bg1   **31-62 cm**   Light grey (2.5Y 7/2) clay; moderate, coarse prismatic; sticky; common (5YR 6/8) root streaks adjoining void walls and diffused outward; common large distinct (2.5YR 5/8) mottles on ped faces; few fine roots; diffuse boundary.

Bg2   **62-94 cm**   Light grey (2.5Y 7/2) clay; weak, coarse prismatic; sticky; common large distinct (2.5YR 5/8) mottles on ped faces; no roots; rather sharp boundary.

Cr   **94-110+ cm**   Grey (N 6/0) clay; massive; water table at 110 cm.

EUTRIC GLEYSOL
Malaysia

Horizon	Depth cm	pH		Cation exchange me %									Free iron %
		H₂O	KCl	CEC	TEB	% BS	Ca	Mg	K	Na	Al	H	%
Ap	0–14	4.6	4.2	15.66		64	5.42	4.11	0.30	0.20			1.90
BAg	14–31	4.8	4.2	15.78		50	3.67	3.74	0.15	0.26			2.01
Bg1	31–62	4.7	3.9	16.96		40	1.97	4.11	0.21	0.46			4.04
Bg2	62–94	4.9	4.2	15.81		61	2.98	5.75	0.20	0.73			1.93
Cr	94–110+	5.3	4.5	16.21		60	2.81	5.91	0.20	0.85			1.92

Horizon	Sol. salts		Organic matter				Particle size analysis %						Flocc. index
			% C	% N	C/N	% OM	Stones	C. sand	F. sand	Silt	Clay	Texture	
Ap			1.99					0.3	10.6	34.0	55.1		
BAg			1.12					0.2	10.1	32.3	57.3		
Bg1			0.47					0.2	9.2	28.3	62.3		
Bg2			0.34					0.5	21.7	26.0	51.8		
Cr			0.43					0 2	28.8	25.3	45.8		

EUTRIC GLEYSOL   Ge

Location	Thanh Quoi village, An Giang province, Viet Nam

Altitude	1 m
Physiography	Back swamps and depressions in flat alluvial plain of the Mekong river
Drainage	Very poor to poor; annual floods of 0.8 to 1.5 m for several months
Parent material	Mixed marine and fresh water alluvial clays
Vegetation	Floating rice
Climate	Humid monsoon; rainfall 1 500 mm (approx.) from May to November

Profile description

Ap   **0-20 cm**   Dark grey (5Y 4/1) clay with a few fine brown (7.5YR 4/4) mottles; moderate fine angular blocky; very hard, firm, plastic; mottling occurs in many old rice root channels; strongly acid; abrupt smooth boundary.

Bg   **20-105 cm**   Grey (2.5Y 6/0) clay with common medium brownish yellow (10YR 6/5) mottles; moderate coarse angular blocky; very hard, very firm, plastic; medium acid; diffuse smooth boundary.

Cg   **105-120 cm** Light brownish grey (2.5Y 6/2) clay with brownish stain smearing to impart a brownish colour; massive; plastic; medium acid.

EUTRIC GLEYSOL

Viet Nam

Horizon	Depth cm	pH		Cation exchange me %									V %
		Moist	Dry[1]	CEC	TEB	% BS	Ca	Mg	K	Na	S		
Ap	0–20	5.5	4.6	27.8			12.0	6.2	0.35	0.77	19.32		69
Bg	20–105	6.5	6.0	17.8			7.6	8.8	0.21	0.71	17.32		97
Cg	105–120	7.0	6.6	17.8			7.4	8.2	0.19	0.94	16.73		93

Horizon	Sol. salts		Organic matter				Particle size analysis %						Flocc. index
			% C	% N	C/N	% OM	Stones	C. sand	F. sand	Silt	Clay	Texture	
Ap			3.40	0.28					6	24	70		
Bg			0.64	0.08					6	16	78		
Cg			0.48	0.06					6	22	72		

[1] Determined after soil thoroughly air-dried.

CALCARIC FLUVISOL   Jc

Location	Amphoe Photharam, Ratchaburi province, Thailand

Altitude	3 to 4 m
Physiography	Stream levee
Drainage	Well drained
Parent material	Recent alluvial deposit
Vegetation	Vegetable gardens and orchards
Climate	Monsoon tropical; rainfall 1 200 mm (approx.) from May through October

---

Profile description

A   0-7 cm   Dark greyish brown (10YR 4/2) silty clay loam with many fine to coarse faint brown mottles; weak, medium subangular blocky, breaking to fine blocky; friable moist, slightly sticky and slightly plastic wet; few mica flakes; many very fine interstitial, common very fine and fine tubular pores; fine and very fine roots; clear smooth boundary; pH 7.0.

C1   7-56 cm   Brown (7.5YR 4/2) silty clay loam with many medium and coarse faint dark yellowish brown mottles; friable moist, slightly sticky and slightly plastic wet; mica flakes; many very fine interstitial and tubular, few fine and medium tubular pores; very few fine and very fine roots; clear smooth boundary; pH 7.0.

C2   56-77 cm   Brown (7.5YR 4/4) loam with many medium faint brown mottles; friable, slightly sticky and slightly plastic wet; many mica flakes; many very fine interstitial and tubular, few fine medium and coarse tubular pores; few very fine roots; moderately calcareous; clear smooth boundary; pH 8.0.

C3   77-100+ cm   Yellowish brown (10YR 5/6) sandy loam with few fine faint brown mottles; friable moist, slightly sticky and non-plastic wet; many mica flakes; few very fine soft black manganese concretions; many very fine tubular and interstitial pores; moderately calcareous; pH 8.0.

CALCARIC FLUVISOL

Thailand

Horizon	Depth cm	pH H₂O 1:1	pH KCl 1:1	CEC	TEB	% BS	Ca	Mg	K	Na	Extr. acidity	P ppm Bray	K ppm ammon. acetate
							Cation exchange me %						
A	0–7	6.8	6.1	23.6	23.9	80	19.8	2.8	1.0	0.3	6.1	62	213
C1	7–56	6.9	5.9	20.9	20.3	83	17.9	1.7	0.3	0.4	4.3	22	132
C2	56–77	8.0	7.1	13.4	26.0	98	24.7	0.7	0.2	0.4	0.5	27	88
C3	77–100+	8.2	7.4	7.5	19.1	99	18.2	0.4	0.1	0.4	0.1	31	59

Horizon	Sol. salts		% C	% N	C/N	% OM	Stones	C. sand	F. sand	Silt	Clay	Conductivity 1:5	CaCO₃ %
			Organic matter				**Particle size analysis %**						
A			2.35					19		52	29	77	1.0
C1			0.74					9		50	40	32	1.1
C2			0.48					33		38	29	64	3.2
C3			—					54		30	16	62	3.0

THIONIC FLUVISOL   **Jt**

Location	Vinh Han village, An Giang province, Viet Nam
Altitude	1 m
Physiography	Flat alluvial plain of the Mekong river
Drainage	Poor to very poor; annual floods of 0.5 to 1.5 m for several months
Parent material	Mixed marine and fresh water alluvial clays
Vegetation	Floating rice
Climate	Humid monsoon; rainfall 1 500 mm (approx.) from May to November

---

Profile description

Ap   **0-20 cm**   Light brownish grey (10YR 6/2) clay with many coarse black (2.5Y 2/0) mottles and yellowish brown (10YR 5/8) mottling along old rice root channels; weak fine angular blocky; hard, firm, plastic; many old rice root channels; extremely acid; abrupt smooth boundary.

Bg   **20-80 cm**   Grey (20YR 5/1) clay with common medium brownish yellow (10YR 6/6) mottles; moderate coarse angular blocky; very hard, very firm, plastic; extremely acid; diffuse smooth boundary.

Cg   **80-140 cm**   Light brownish grey (10YR 6/2) clay with common medium brownish yellow (10YR 6/6) mottles; massive; very plastic; extremely acid.

THIONIC FLUVISOL

Viet Nam

Horizon	Depth cm	pH		Cation exchange me %									V %
		Moist	Dry[1]	CEC	TEB	% BS	Ca	Mg	K	Na	S		
Ap	0–20	4.8	3.7	19.1			2.2	1.7	0.19	0.15	4.24		22
Bg	20–80	4.2	3.1	21.2			2.7	1.5	0.13	0.13	4.48		21
Cg	80–140	—	2.2	28.2			6.0	5.6	0.06	0.06	11.88		42

Horizon	Sol. salts		Organic matter				Particle size analysis %						Flocc. index
			% C	% N	C/N	% OM	Stones	C. sand	F. sand	Silt	Clay	Texture	
Ap			7.64	0.39				13		24	63		
Bg			3.72	0.16				7		28	65		
Cg			8.68	0.17				11		72	17		

[1] Determined after soil thoroughly air-dried.

THIONIC FLUVISOL   **Jt**

Location	Amphoe Nong Sua, Pathum Thani province, Thailand
Altitude	2 to 3 m
Physiography	Flat coastal plain
Drainage	Poor to very poor; flooded by river water for four to five months every year
Parent material	Clayey brackish water deposits
Vegetation	Broadcast rice
Climate	Monsoon tropical; rainfall 1 450 mm (approx.) from May through October

---

Profile description

Apg   **0-15 cm**   Very dark grey to black (10YR 3/1 to 2/1) clay with common fine distinct yellowish brown mottles, mainly in pores; moderate coarse subangular blocky, breaking to medium and fine blocky; firm moist, sticky and plastic wet; few very fine interstitial and tubular pores; many fine roots; gradual slightly wavy boundary; pH 5.0.

Ag   **15-30 cm**   Very dark grey and black (10YR 3/1 and 2/1) clay with many fine and medium yellowish brown and few fine red mottles; weak to moderate medium angular blocky breaking to fine blocky; firm moist, sticky and plastic wet; few slickensides; common very fine interstitial and few very fine tubular pores; few very fine roots; gradual wavy boundary; pH 4.5.

ABg   **30-49 cm**   Greyish brown (10YR 5/2) and very dark greyish brown (10YR 3/2) clay with very many medium and coarse red and dark red, many fine and medium yellowish brown mottles; moderate medium and fine angular blocky; firm moist, sticky and plastic wet; common slickensides and pressure faces; many very fine interstitial and few very fine tubular pores; few very fine roots; gradual smooth boundary; pH 4.5.

Btg1   **49-59 cm**   Brown (7.5YR 4/2) with few small inclusions of very dark grey clay; many medium and coarse red and dark red, many fine pale yellow (jarosite) and few fine yellowish brown mottles; moderate medium and fine angular blocky; firm moist, sticky and plastic wet; common pressure faces and slickensides; many very fine interstitial, few fine tubular pores; few very fine roots; clear wavy boundary; pH 4.5.

Btg2   **59-110 cm**   Brown (7.5YR 5/2) clay; many medium and coarse yellow (jarosite) and few fine yellowish brown mottles, mainly as vertical streaks (fillings of coarse tubular pores and cracks); moderate coarse prismatic, breaking to angular blocky; firm moist, sticky and plastic wet; few slickensides; few very fine tubular and few fine and medium vertical tubular pores; pH 4.5.

Btg3   **110-160 cm**   Brown (7.5YR 5/2) clay; common medium and coarse yellowish brown, few medium yellow (jarosite) mottles; half ripe; pH 6.0.

BCg   **160-190+ cm**   Dark grey to dark greenish grey (5Y 4/1 to 5GY 4/1) clay; half ripe; pH 6.0.

THIONIC FLUVISOL

Thailand

Horizon	Depth cm	pH H₂O 1:1	pH KCl 1:1	CEC	TEB	% BS	Ca	Mg	K	Na	Extr. acidity	P ppm Bray	K ppm ammon. acetate
Apg	0–15	4.4	3.3	20.0	11.0	33	4.4	4.8	0.3	1.5	21.9	5	143
Ag	15–30	4.2	3.4	20.3	9.7	28	4.0	4.4	0.2	1.1	23.9	5	113
ABg	30–49	3.9	3.1	22.8	13.1	39	4.7	6.0	0.3	2.1	20.4	3	149
Btg1	49–59	4.2	3.0	24.6	14.7	43	5.3	6.7	0.3	2.4	19.4	3	160
Btg2	59–110	4.0	3.1	24.9	15.7	49	5.3	7.7	0.4	2.3	16.6	3	172
Btg3	110–160	4.2	3.1	23.2	14.6	46	4.6	7.1	0.5	2.4	17.2	6	190
BCg	160–190+	3.5	2.9	30.7	19.4	41	5.0	10.7	0.7	3.0	27.6	24	280

Horizon	Sol. salts		% C	% N	C/N	% OM	Stones	C. sand	F. sand	Silt	Clay	Conduc-tivity 1:5	Flocc. index
Apg			1.21						11	48	41	250	
Ag			0.91						11	43	46	200	
ABg			0.26						7	34	59	250	
Btg1			0.21						5	33	62	300	
Btg2			0.19						1	36	63	340	
Btg3			0.33						19	26	55	450	
BCg			2.04						8	43	49	1 300	

FERRIC LUVISOL   Lf

Location	Table estate, Tawau, Sabah
Altitude	150 m (approximately)
Physiography	Gently undulating to rolling plateau
Drainage	Well drained
Parent material	Residual clay from Quaternary basalt
Vegetation	Industrial crops; cocoa, oil palm
Climate	Humid tropical; rainfall 1 800 mm with maximum from May to September

Profile description

Ah   **0-2 cm**   Very dark grey (5YR 3/1) silty clay; strong medium crumb structure; loose; few quartz fragments; very few fragments of decomposing rock (basalt); few roots; abrupt smooth boundary.

AB   **2-17 cm**   Dark brown (7.5YR 3/2) clay; strong medium fine subangular blocky, breaking into fine crumb structure; few angular fine quartz fragments; many pores; distinct cutans; little gravel; few roots; gradual smooth boundary.

BA   **17-55 cm**   Brown to dark brown (7.5YR 4/2) clay; strong fine subangular blocky breaking into fine crumb structure; very friable; few quartz fragments; many pores; distinct cutans; few roots; gradual smooth boundary.

Bt1   **55-150 cm** Dark yellowish brown (10YR 3/4) clay; strong fine crumb structure; very friable; few quartz fragments; few pores; distinct cutans.

Bt2   **150-200 cm** Similar to the above horizon.

FERRIC LUVISOL

Sabah

Horizon	Depth cm	pH		Cation exchange me %									CaCO₃ %
		H₂O	KCl	CEC	TEB	% BS	Ca	Mg	K	Na	Al	H	
Ah	0–2	7.3	6.6	39.74		88	27.81	5.15	1.81	0.28		0.72	
AB	2–17	6.3	5.6	14.35		69	7.96	1.20	0.60	0.19		1.20	
BA	17–55	6.2	5.6	10.81		67	6.17	0.69	0.19	0.16		0.88	
Bt1	55–150	6.0	5.5	8.01		61	3.05	1.35	0.40	0.08		3.28	
Bt2	150–200	5.8	5.5	8.58		52	2.93	0.68	0.77	0.06		1.25	

Horizon	Sol. salts		Organic matter				Particle size analysis %						Flocc. index
			% C	% N	C/N	% OM	Stones	C. sand	F. sand	Silt	Clay	Texture	
Ah			7.18	0.79				7.7	18.7	51.3	22.3		
AB			1.16	0.22				6.1	11.5	32.5	49.9		
BA			0.37	0.13				4.7	8.2	24.3	62.8		
Bt1			0.30	0.06				3.1	5.5	20.6	70.8		
Bt2			0.34	0.06				19.0	13.3	14.6	52.4		

GLEYIC LUVISOL   Lg

Location	Amphoe Muang, Nakhon Pathom province, Thailand
Altitude	5 to 7 m
Physiography	Low terrace
Drainage	Poorly drained
Parent material	Semi-recent alluvial deposit
Vegetation	Rice field
Climate	Monsoon tropical; rainfall 1 300 mm (approx.) from May through October

Profile description

Ap   **0-15 cm**   Very dark greyish brown (10YR 3/2) loam with many fine and medium yellowish red mottles; moderate fine subangular blocky; slightly sticky and nonplastic wet, friable moist; many very fine interstitial and common very fine tubular pores; many very fine roots; clear smooth boundary; pH 6.0.

Ag   **15-31 cm**   Very dark greyish brown (10YR 3/2) silty clay loam; few fine brown to dark brown mottles; weak to moderate medium subangular blocky; many very fine interstitial and tubular pores; few pieces of brick; common very fine roots; gradual smooth boundary; pH 7.0.

BAg   **31-50 cm**   Dark greyish brown (10YR 4/2) silty clay; many fine and medium dark yellowish brown mottles; moderate to strong, medium subangular blocky, breaking to small blocky; sticky and slightly plastic wet, friable moist; patchy thin clay coatings; many very fine interstitial and tubular pores; few small soft manganese concretions; common very fine roots; gradual smooth boundary; pH 7.0.

Btg1   **50-85 cm**   Dark greyish brown (10YR 4/2) to brown (10YR 4/3) silty clay; many fine and medium dark yellowish brown and yellowish brown mottles; moderate to strong, medium subangular blocky, breaking to small blocky; sticky and slightly plastic wet, friable moist; thin broken clay coatings on ped faces and in pores; many very fine interstitial and tubular pores; few small soft manganese concretions; common very fine roots; gradual smooth boundary; pH 8.0.

Btg2   **85-105 cm**   Brown (7.5YR 4/2) silty clay loam; very many medium yellowish brown mottles; moderate to strong, medium subangular blocky; sticky and slightly plastic wet; thin broken clay coatings; slightly calcareous; many very fine interstitial and tubular pores; few very small soft manganese nodules; few very fine roots; pH 8.0.

GLEYIC LUVISOL

Thailand

Horizon	Depth cm	pH H₂O 1:1	pH KCl 1:1	Cation exchange me % CEC	TEB	% BS	Ca	Mg	K	Na	Extr. acidity	P ppm Bray	K ppm ammon. acetate
Ap	0–15	5.8	5.2	17.8	22.7	77	13.1	6.5	0.3	2.8	6.9	42	140
Ag	15–31	6.5	5.8	18.6	19.8	79	10.9	6.7	0.3	1.9	5.3	44	117
BAg	31–50	6.7	5.9	19.8	22.4	83	10.1	9.1	0.3	2.9	4.6	31	117
Btg1	50–85	7.3	6.6	20.0	26.3	85	10.3	10.2	0.2	5.6	4.5	31	93
Btg2	85–105	8.0	7.5	19.0	39.3	94	24.1	9.3	0.2	5.7	2.3	32	93

Horizon	Sol. salts		Organic matter % C	% N	C/N	% OM	Particle size analysis % Stones	C. sand	F. sand	Silt	Clay	Conductivity 1:5	CaCO₃ %
Ap			1.62					24	50	26		420	0.6
Ag			1.02					18	48	34		440	0.4
BAg			0.68					10	49	41		410	0.4
Btg1			0.36					4	54	42		490	0.9
Btg2			0.30					6	56	38		650	4.2

CALCIC LUVISOL   Lk

Location	Amphoe Muang, Nakhon Pathom province, Thailand
Altitude	5 to 8 m
Physiography	Nearly level terrace
Drainage	Well drained
Parent material	Old alluvial deposit
Vegetation	Gardens and orchards with some maize and sugar cane
Climate	Monsoon tropical; rainfall 1 300 mm (approx.) from May through October

Profile description

Ap   0-30 cm   Brown to dark brown (10YR 4/3) clay loam; weak coarse subangular blocky; non-sticky and non-plastic wet, friable moist, hard dry; many very fine interstitial and tubular pores; common very fine roots; diffuse smooth boundary; pH 6.5.

Bt   30-65 cm   Dark yellowish brown (10YR 4/4) clay loam to clay; weak to moderate medium subangular blocky; slightly sticky and slightly plastic wet, friable moist, hard dry; thin broken brown to dark brown clay coatings in pores and on ped faces; many fine and very fine tubular and interstitial pores; few mica flakes; many fine and medium and common very fine roots; gradual smooth boundary; pH 7.5.

BC   65-90 cm   Brown to dark brown (7.5YR 4/4) clay loam; moderate medium and fine subangular blocky; slightly sticky and slightly plastic wet, friable moist; thin patchy clay coatings; many fine and very fine interstitial and tubular pores; much white powdery lime, strongly calcareous; common mica flakes; common fine and very fine roots; gradual smooth boundary; pH 8.0.

C   90-130 cm   Strong brown (7.5YR 5/6) loam; moderate medium subangular blocky; non-sticky and non-plastic wet, friable moist; small amount of soft powdery lime; many mica flakes; many very fine interstitial, few fine and very fine tubular pores; few very fine roots; pH 8.0.

CALCIC LUVISOL

Thailand

Horizon	Depth cm	pH H₂O 1:1	pH KCl 1:1	CEC	TEB	% BS	Ca	Mg	K	Na	Extr. acidity	P ppm Bray	K ppm ammon. acetate
						Cation exchange me %							
Ap	0–30	7.1	6.4	15.0	13.4	80	10.6	1.6	0.4	0.8	3.3	48	175
Bt	30–65	6.3	5.7	16.1	20.6	85	16.6	2.1	0.2	1.7	3.8	82	70
BC	65–90	7.5	7.0	15.1	53.5	99	37.2	5.1	0.2	11.0	0.5	45	88
C	90–130	8.3	7.5	11.5	28.9	99	19.5	2.7	0.1	6.6	0.2	20	47

Horizon	Sol. salts		% C	% N	C/N	% OM	Stones	C. sand	F. sand	Silt	Clay	Conductivity 1:5	CaCO₃ %
			Organic matter				Particle size analysis %						
Ap			3.22					40	41	19		10	0.9
Bt			2.02					19	48	33		680	0.3
BC			1.42					14	59	27		1 800	6.9
C			0.82					69	14	17		700	3.0

ORTHIC LUVISOL   **Lo**

Location	Amphoe Pak Tho, Ratchaburi province, Thailand
Altitude	10 to 14 m
Physiography	Mainly flat old river levee
Drainage	Well drained
Parent material	Old alluvial deposit
Vegetation	Vegetable gardens and orchards
Climate	Monsoon tropical; rainfall 1 200 mm (approx.) from May through September

---

Profile description

Ap   **0-10 cm**   Dark yellowish brown (10YR 4/3) sandy loam; weak medium subangular blocky; very friable moist, slightly sticky and slightly plastic wet; many worm casts; many very fine interstitial, common very fine and few fine tubular pores; many very fine and few fine medium roots; pH 8.0.

AB   **10-30 cm**   Dark yellowish brown (10YR 3/4) with many inclusions of brown (7.5YR 4/4) sandy loam; weak to moderate subangular blocky; very friable moist, non-sticky and non-plastic wet; many pieces of charcoal; many very fine interstitial, common very fine and fine tubular pores; few fine, medium and coarse roots; clear wavy boundary; pH 8.0.

BA   **30-73 cm**   Brown (7.5YR 4/4 moist) and yellowish brown (10YR 5/6 dry) sandy clay loam; weak to moderate subangular blocky; slightly hard dry, very friable moist, slightly sticky and slightly plastic wet; thin patchy clay coatings; many very fine interstitial, many very fine and few fine tubular pores; few very fine, fine, medium and coarse roots; gradual smooth boundary; pH 7.5.

Bt   **73-105+ cm**   Reddish brown (5YR 5/4) sandy clay loam with many medium faint yellowish red mottles; moderate medium subangular blocky; slightly hard dry, friable moist, sticky and slightly plastic wet; thick continuous clay coatings in pores and on ped faces; many very fine interstitial and tubular pores.

ORTHIC LUVISOL

Thailand

Horizon	Depth cm	pH H₂O 1:1	pH KCl 1:1	CEC	TEB	% BS	Ca	Mg	K	Na	Extr. acidity	P ppm Bray	K ppm ammon. acetate
Ap	0–10	7.3	6.7	7.1	6.9	82	5.4	0.8	0.5	0.2	1.5	40	204
AB	10–30	7.3	6.6	6.7	5.7	77	4.3	0.8	0.4	0.2	1.7	27	181
BA	30–73	7.1	6.2	5.4	4.1	68	2.5	0.8	0.6	0.2	1.9	3	213
Bt	73–105	6.6	5.4	6.7	5.4	64	2.7	1.8	0.6	0.3	3.0	3	260

Horizon	Sol. salts		% C	% N	C/N	% OM	Stones	C. sand	F. sand	Silt	Clay	Conductivity 1:5	CaCO₃ %
Ap			0.87					73	22	5	10		
AB			0.59					71	21	8	40		
BA			0.78					58	34	8	31		
Bt			0.17					49	32	19	34		

PLINTHIC LUVISOL   **Lp**

Location	Phan Thiet, Viet Nam
Altitude	40 to 50 m
Physiography	Flat to gently undulating old terrace
Drainage	Imperfectly drained; slow internal drainage
Parent material	Heterogeneous old alluvial deposits
Vegetation	Dry short grass savanna with locally rainfed paddy fields
Climate	Dry monsoon; rainfall 800 to 1 000 mm from August through December

Profile description

Ap	**0-24 cm**	Dark greyish brown (10YR 4/2) sandy loam with mottling along previous root channels; very weak medium subangular blocky to massive structure; locally slightly platy; very hard consistence; clear smooth boundary.
E	**24-37 cm**	Yellowish brown (10YR 5/6) sandy loam, fine mottling; very weak subangular blocky structure; hard consistence; clear irregular boundary.
Btg	**37-76 cm**	Brownish yellow (10YR 6/6) sandy loam, strongly mottled; weak coarse subangular blocky structure with weak clay coatings; some fine iron concretions; hard consistence; abrupt irregular boundary.
Csq	**76-120 cm**	Plinthite with lateritic gravel of 2 to 10 mm diameter.

PLINTHIC LUVISOL

Viet Nam

Horizon	Depth cm	pH	Cation exchange me %								
			CEC	TEB	% BS	Ca	Mg	K	Na	Al	H
Ap	0–24	5.9	4.14		104	3.38	0.56	0.31	0.06		
E	23–37	6.0	4.04		106	3.13	0.75	0.35	0.06		
Btg	37–76	5.7	3.76		83	2.68	0.13	0.35	0.03		
Csq	76–120	6.4	4.25		79	2.50	0.13	0.59	0.12		

Horizon	Sol. salts		Organic matter				Particle size analysis %					Flocc. index
			% C	% N	C/N	% OC	Stones	Sand > 0.05	Silt 0.05-0.002	Clay <0.002	Texture	
Ap					12	0.73		71	13.3	15.7		
E					9	0.36		69	13.3	17.7		
Btg					9	0.49		65	15.3	19.7		
Csq					8	0.32		60.5	18.6	20.9		

DYSTRIC NITOSOL   **Nd**

Location	Near Ban Nam Kaen, Thailand
Altitude	260 m (approximately)
Physiography	Undulating old terrace
Drainage	Well drained
Parent material	Old slope colluvial deposits derived from shales and metamorphic rocks
Vegetation	Shifting cultivation of upland rice
Climate	Monsoon tropical; rainfall 1 400 mm (approx.) from May to mid-October

---

Profile description

Ap   **0-5 cm**   Dark yellowish brown (10YR 3/4 moist) and dark brown (10YR 4/3 dry) sandy clay loam; moderate fine and very fine subangular blocky; sticky, slightly plastic; friable; slightly hard; few fine tubular and common very fine interstitial pores; many fine pieces of charcoal; many very fine roots; clear slightly wavy boundary; pH 6.5.

AB   **5-15 cm**   Dark brown to brown (7.5YR 4/4 moist) and brown (7.5YR 5/4 dry) sandy clay loam; moderate fine subangular blocky; sticky and slightly plastic; friable, slightly hard; few fine tubular and common fine interstitial pores; common fine charcoal pieces; very few fine subangular quartz fragments; common very fine and fine roots; gradual smooth boundary; pH 5.5.

Bt1   **15-31 cm**   Yellowish red (5YR 4/6 moist) and strong brown (7.5YR 5/6 dry) sandy clay loam; moderate very fine and fine subangular blocky; sticky and slightly plastic; firm; slightly hard; patchy thin clay cutans on horizontal and vertical ped faces; few coarse and very coarse tubular pores made by termites; common fine tubular pores; few pieces of charcoal; common very fine angular quartz fragments; common coarse and very coarse and also medium and fine roots; diffuse smooth boundary; pH 4.5.

Bt2   **31-63 cm**   Yellowish red (5YR 4/8 moist and 5YR 4/6 dry) clay loam; moderate fine and medium subangular blocky; sticky and plastic; firm; hard; patchy thin clay cutans on horizontal and vertical ped faces; few coarse and medium tubular pores; common fine interstitial pores; common medium pieces of charcoal; common very fine and fine subangular quartz fragments; few coarse and very coarse roots; diffuse smooth boundary; pH 4.5.

Bt3   **63-100+ cm**   Yellowish red (5YR 4/8 moist and 5YR 5/8 dry) clay loam to clay; weak fine and medium subangular blocky; sticky and plastic; firm; hard; broken moderately thick clay cutans on horizontal and vertical ped faces; few very fine tubular pores; common very fine and fine interstitial pores; many very fine and fine angular and subangular quartz fragments; common fine roots; pH 4.5.

DYSTRIC NITOSOL

Thailand

Horizon	Depth cm	pH H₂O 1:1	pH KCl 1:1	Cation exchange me % CEC	TEB	% BS	Ca	Mg	K	Na	Extr. acidity	P ppm Bray	K ppm ammon. acetate
Ap	0–5	5.8	5.1	12.3	7.1	46	4.1	2.2	0.6	0.2	8.3	8.8	280
AB	5–15	4.9	3.9	9.8	1.7	15	0.3	0.5	0.7	0.2	9.5	4.4	42
Bt1	15–31	4.8	3.7	8.1	0.5	5	0.1	0.2	0.1	0.2	5.4	1.9	42
Bt2	31–63	5.0	3.9	9.3	0.8	7	0.4	0.2	0.1	0.2	10.1	1.8	15
Bt3	63–100+	5.0	3.8	9.6	0.5	4	0.2	0.1	0.1	0.2	10.9	1.8	15

Horizon	Sol. salts		Organic matter % C	% N	C/N	% OM	Particle size analysis % Stones	C. sand	F. sand	Silt	Clay	Conductivity 1:5	Flocc. index
Ap			1.29	0.16				46.5		42.0	11.5	0.06	
AB			0.74	0.08				39.5		38.5	22.0	0.01	
Bt1			0.55	0.08				36.0		38.0	26.0	0.01	
Bt2			0.47	0.07				32.5		36.5	31.0	0.01	
Bt3			0.33	0.06				38.5		29.5	42.0	0.01	

EUTRIC NITOSOL   **Ne**

Location	Phan Rang area, Viet Nam
Altitude	20 m (approximately)
Physiography	Flat to gently undulating coastal plain
Drainage	Well drained
Parent material	Residual clay from andesitic and granitic rocks
Vegetation	Overgrazed short grass savanna with thorny bushes
Climate	Dry monsoon; rainfall 700 mm (approx.) with maximum from September to November

---

Profile description

A	**0-10 cm**	Brown (7.5YR 4/4) sandy loam; very weak coarse platy structure; friable; clear wavy boundary.
AB	**10-20 cm**	Reddish brown (5YR 4/5) sandy clay loam; weak fine subangular blocky structure; friable; gradual smooth boundary.
Bt1	**20-33 cm**	Yellowish red (5YR 4/6) clay loam; strong fine subangular blocky structure; discontinuous clay coatings; slightly hard; gradual smooth boundary.
Bt2	**33-49 cm**	Yellowish red (5YR 4/7) clay loam; strong subangular blocky structure; discontinuous clay coatings; hard; gradual regular boundary.
Bt3	**49-73 cm**	Yellowish red (4YR 4/7) clay; strong medium subangular blocky structure; prominent continuous clay coatings; hard to very hard gradual regular boundary.
Bt4	**73-150+ cm**	Red (2.5YR 4/7) clay; strong coarse subangular blocky structure; hard to very hard; continuous coatings.

EUTRIC NITOSOL

Viet Nam

Horizon	Depth cm	pH		Cation exchange me %									CaCO₃ %
		H₂O	KCl	CEC	TEB	% BS	Ca	Mg	K	Na	Al	H	
A	0–10	6.2		6.5		118	5.20	1.70	0.41	0.38			
AB	10–20	5.9		9.8		118	8.90	2.20	0.18	0.36			
Bt1	20–33	5.8		11.3		113	9.80	2.70	0.10	0.26			
Bt2	33–49	5.7		11.7		107	9.90	2.30	0.10	0.26			
Bt3	49–73	5.9		13.5		93	10.10	2.20	0.08	0.26			
Bt4	73–150	6.0		10.5		111	9.4	2.00	0.08	0.26			

Horizon	Sol. salts		Organic matter				Particle size analysis %						Flocc. index
			% C	% N	C/N	% OC	Stones	C. sand	F. sand	Silt	Clay	Texture	
A					17	1.84		62	20	18			
AB					20	0.80		48	18	34			
Bt1					16	0.64		46	18	36			
Bt2					13	0.52		46	18	36			
Bt3					16	0.48		48	12	40			
Bt4					13	0.52		44	14	42			

HUMIC PODZOL **Ph**

Location	Kuching airport, Sarawak
Altitude	30 m
Physiography	Flat coastal terrace
Drainage	Poor
Parent material	Old alluvial deposit
Vegetation	Old secondary low forest
Climate	Humid tropical; rainfall 3 500 mm (approx.) with maximum from October through January

Profile description

H	**4-0 cm**	Dark reddish brown (5YR 3/2) finely decomposed humus in root mat; moist, friable.
Ah	**0-23 cm**	Brown (7.5YR 5/2) loamy fine sand; moist, friable; few fine roots; few fine pores; low faunal activity; clear wavy boundary, tongues into most of the next horizon.
E	**23-55 cm**	White (10YR 8/1) loamy fine sand; massive, very compact; no roots; no pores or cracks; contains common tongues of material of above horizon.
Bh	**55-60 cm**	Very dark (10YR 3/1) fine sandy loam; very compact and firm.

HUMIC PODZOL

Sarawak

Horizon	Depth cm	pH		Cation exchange me %									Free Fe
		H_2O	KCl	CEC	TEB	% BS	Ca	Mg	K	Na	Al	H	Fe_2O_3
H	4–0	3.6	3.2	78.98		19	10.10	3.32	1.18	0.20		89.50	0.02
Ah	0–23	4.4	3.4	4.09		37	0.36	1.01	0.09	0.05	6.92	6.92	0.003
E	23–55	5.2	4.8	0.41		84	0.35	0.01	0.03	0.03	0.00	0.00	0.000
Bh	55–60	4.1	3.3	25.18		2	0.21	0.02	0.16	0.04		0.21	0.004

Horizon	Sol. salts		Organic matter				Particle size analysis %						Flocc. index
			% C	% N	C/N	% OM	Stones	C. sand	F. sand	Silt	Clay	texture	
H			24.23	1.19	20			—		—	—		
Ah			1.38	0.06	23			75.8		16.9	7.3		
E			0.01	0.01	—			78.0		16.8	5.2		
Bh			4.64	0.09	52			72.6		10.7	4.1		

ORTHIC PODZOL   Po

Location	Mardi experimental station, east coast, Malaysia
Altitude	10 m (approximately)
Physiography	Coastal plain, level
Drainage	Excessively drained
Parent material	Sandy marine alluvial deposit
Vegetation	Shrub, coconut and cashew
Climate	Humid tropical; rainfall 2 600 mm (approx.)

Profile description

Ap   **0-10 cm**   Pale brown (10YR 6/3) sand; structureless; few fine roots; no biological activity; clear boundary.

E1   **10-25 cm**   White (10YR 8/1) sand; structureless; very loose; very few grass roots; no biological activity; diffuse boundary.

E2   **25-55 cm**   White (10YR 8/1) sand; structureless; very loose; roots up to a depth of about 35 cm; sand consists almost entirely of quartz; diffuse boundary.

E3   **55-94/100 cm**   White (10YR 8/1) sand; lower part grey (10YR 6/1); structureless, loose; no roots; no biological activity; sharp wavy boundary.

Bh1   **94/100-104 cm**   Black (10YR 2/1) sand; hard cemented humic pan which can be broken with the fingers; quartz grains are coated; no roots; no biological activity; diffuse boundary.

Bh2   **104-122 cm**   Very dark grey (10YR 3/1) sand; weak cemented humic layer, easily broken between fingers; sand grains coated; no roots; no biological activity; diffuse boundary.

Bhs1   **122-150 cm**   Strong brown (7.5YR 5/8) sand; friable coated sand containing a few yellowish red nodules (5YR 5/8) which can be broken by pressure between the fingers; no roots; no biological activity; diffuse boundary.

Bhs2   **150-200 cm**   Yellowish brown (10YR 5/6) sand; friable.

ORTHIC PODZOL
Malaysia

Horizon	Depth cm	pH		Cation exchange me %									Free iron %
		H$_2$O	KCl	CEC	TEB	% BS	Ca	Mg	K	Na	Al	H	
Ap	0–10	5.0	4.3	1.20			0.22	0.06	0.04	0.06		1.66	0.09
E1	10–25	4.9	4.2	0.41			0.55	0.03	0.03	0.06		0.48	0.02
E2	25–55	4.8	4.4	0.24			0.02	0.02	0.02	0.06		0.36	tr.
E3	55–95	4.7	4.4	0.06			0.01	0.01	0.02	0.06		0.12	0.01
Bh2	104–122	4.5	4.2	1.02			0.01	0.01	0.01	0.06		3.98	0.52
Bhs1	122–150	4.6	4.5	0.54			0.01	0.01	0.02	0.01		2.48	0.90
Bhs2	150–200	4.7	4.4	0.18			0.02	0.01	0.06	0.06		1.56	1.10

Horizon	Sol. salts		Organic matter				Particle size analysis %						Flocc. index
			% C	% N	C/N	% OM	Stones	C. sand	F. sand	Silt	Slay	Texture	
Ap			0.68					58.6	38.8	1.8	0.7		
E1			0.23					56.5	41.7	0.7	0.9		
E2			0.09					60.1	38.3	1.1	0.5		
E3			0.03					52.4	46.4	1.2	0.0		
Bh2			0.40					58.5	40.2	0.6	0.7		
Bhs1			0.24					64.7	34.1	1.2	0.1		
Bhs2			0.11					82.0	17.2	0.4	0.4		

CAMBIC ARENOSOL   Qc

Location	Amphoe Pak Tho, Ratchaburi province, Thailand
Altitude	30 m (approximately)
Physiography	Gently undulating (1-3 percent slope) high terrace
Drainage	Somewhat excessively drained
Parent material	Old alluvial sandy deposits
Vegetation	*Dipterocarpus* forest
Climate	Monsoon tropical; rainfall 1 200 mm (approx.); rainy season from May through October

---

Profile description

A   **0-18 cm**   Brown (7YR 4/2 moist) to pinkish grey (7.5YR 6/2 dry) loamy sand; single grain; slightly hard dry, very friable moist, non-sticky, non-plastic wet; many very fine interstitial, few fine tubular pores; many charcoal pieces; common very fine and few fine and medium roots; clear smooth boundary; pH 6.0.

AB   **18-50 cm**   Reddish brown (5YR 5/3 moist) to pinkish grey (5YR 7/2 dry) loamy sand; single grain; slightly hard dry, very friable moist; many very fine interstitial, few very fine tubular pores; few worm casts; common very fine and few fine, medium and coarse roots; gradual smooth boundary; pH 7.0.

Bw   **50-120+ cm**   Light reddish brown (5YR 6/4 moist) to pinkish grey (5YR 7/2 dry) loamy sand; single grain; slightly hard dry, very friable moist; many very fine and fine interstitial pores, few very fine tubular pores; few very fine roots; pH 7.0.

CAMBIC ARENOSOL

Thailand

Horizon	Depth cm	pH H₂O 1:1	pH KCl 1:1	CEC	TEB	% BS	Ca	Mg	K	Na	Extr. acidity	P ppm Bray	K ppm ammon. acetate
A	0–18	7.3	4.9	3.5	1.9	48	1.2	0.3	0.2	0.2	2.1	13	79
AB	18–50	7.1	5.2	1.5	0.9	64	0.6	0.1	0.1	0.1	0.5	17	35
Bw	50–120	7.1	5.6	0.9	0.5	83	0.3	0.1	tr.	0.1	0.1	9	21

Horizon	Sol. salts		Organic matter % C	% N	C/N	% OM	Particle size analysis % Stones	C. sand	F. sand	Silt	Clay	Texture	Conductivity 1:5
A			0.52					86		11	3		20
AB			0.10					83		12	5		10
Bw			0.10					84		11	5		10

HUMIC ANDOSOL   **Th**

Location	Palestina, Pile, Camarines Sur, Philippines
Altitude	
Physiography	Rolling locally steep slopes
Drainage	Well drained
Parent material	Fine volcanic ash
Vegetation	Annual crops
Climate	Monsoon tropical; rainfall 2 000 mm (approx.) from May through December

---

Profile description

Ah   **0-30 cm**   Black (N2/, moist) loam; very fine granular to weak subangular blocky structure; friable, non-sticky and non-plastic; pH 5.3; gradual boundary.

AB   **30-58 cm**   Very dark brown (10YR 2/2 moist) loam; weak fine to coarse subangular blocky structure; friable, non-sticky, non-plastic; pH 5.5; gradual boundary.

Bw1   **58-88 cm**   Natural ped dark brown (10YR 3/3 moist) and crushed ped brown (10YR moist) silt loam; fine to coarse subangular blocky structure; slightly compact; friable; pH 5.65.

Bw2   **88-120 cm**   Natural ped dark yellowish brown (10YR 4/3 moist) and crushed ped dark yellowish brown (10YR 4/4 moist) silt loam; very fine to coarse subangular blocky structure; slightly compact; friable; a few tubular fillings (0.5 cm diameter) with the dark surface soil; 10x grass showed some light-coloured mineral crystal (0.5 mm diameter) in the brown soil at about 100 cm; pH 6.0.

BC   **120-150 cm**   Natural ped dark brown (10YR 3/3 moist) and crushed ped brown (10YR 4/3 moist) silt loam; fine to coarse subangular blocky structure; slightly compact, friable; pH 5.9.

HUMIC ANDOSOL
Philippines

Horizon	Depth cm	pH		Cation exchange me %									CaCO, %
		H₂O 1:1	KCl 1:1	CEC	TEB	% BS	Ca	Mg	K	Na	Al	H	
Ah	0–30	5.3	4.7	61.43	9.54	15.5	7.76	1.44	0.17	0.17		51.89	
AB	30–58	5.5	5.0	42.36	2.41	5.7	1.44	0.59	0.20	0.29		39.94	
Bw1	58–88	5.7	5.3	33.79	2.59	7.7	1.63	0.59	0.25	0.12		31.20	
Bw2	88–120	6.0	5.4	33.06	3.73	11.3	2.50	0.80	0.26	0.17		29.33	
BC	120–150	5.9	5.4	33.92	3.14	9.3	2.18	0.59	0.25	0.12		30.78	

Horizon	Sol. salts		Organic matter				Particle size analysis %						Flocc. index
			% C	% N	C/N	% OM	Stones	C. sand	F. sand	Silt	Clay	Texture	
Ah			12.0					—	40.80	48.7	10.5	l	
AB			5.2					12.72	40.88	40.0	6.4	vfsl	
Bw1			1.6					8.88	51.52	33.2	6.4	vfsl	
Bw2			1.5					9.01	64.39	22.0	4.6	vfsl	
BC			1.2					—	44.90	45.7	9.4	l	

MOLLIC ANDOSOL   **Tm**

Location	Tjikolo forestry station, Java, Indonesia
Altitude	1 200 m (approximately)
Physiography	Undulating to rolling volcanic ridge
Drainage	Well drained
Parent material	Volcanic ash
Vegetation	Experimental forest plot
Climate	Humid tropical; rainfall 2 200 mm

Profile description

Ah1   **0-21 cm**   Dark greyish brown (10YR 3/2) loam; weak very fine crumb; very friable; clear smooth boundary.

Ah2   **21-64 cm**   Brown to dark brown (10YR 4/3) silt loam; weak very fine crumb to subangular blocky; very friable; clear smooth boundary.

C1   **64-83 cm**   Dark brown (10YR 4/3-3/3) clay loam; moderate fine subangular blocky; friable to firm; abrupt smooth boundary.

C2   **83-165 cm**   Black (10YR 2/1) silt loam; weak very fine crumb; friable; clear smooth boundary.

C3   **165+ cm**   Dark brown (10YR 3/3) clay loam; moderate medium subangular blocky; firm; clay illuviation.

MOLLIC ANDOSOL
Indonesia

Horizon	Depth cm	pH		Cation exchange me %									CaCO₃ %
		H₂O	KCl	CEC	TEB	% BS	Ca	Mg	K	Na	Al	H	
Ah1	0–21	5.2	4.7										
Ah2	21–64	5.7	5.3										
C1	64–83	5.6	5.3										
C2	83–165	5.1	4.7										
C3	165+	5.6	5.3										

Horizon	Sol. salts		Organic matter				Particle size analysis %						Flocc. index
			% C	% N	C/N	% OM	Stones	C. sand	F. sand	Silt	Clay	Texture	
Ah1			10.8	0.89	12			16		74	10		
Ah2			6.2	0.52	12			20		68	12		
C1			n.d.[1]	n.d.				33		59	8		
C2			n.d.	n.d.				7		83	10		
C3			n.d.	n.d.				7		79	13		

[1] Not determined.

CHROMIC VERTISOL **Vc**

Location	Nakhon Luang irrigation scheme, Amphoe Tua Rua, Thailand
Altitude	7 m
Physiography	Flat
Drainage	Somewhat poorly drained
Parent material	Old clayey alluvial deposit
Vegetation	Transplanted paddy rice
Climate	Monsoon tropical; rainfall 1 200 mm (approx.); rainy season from May through October

Profile description

Ap1 **0-4 cm** Dark greyish brown (10YR 4/2) clay with few coarse sand grains; many fine distinct yellowish red mottles in pores; massive but coarse granular on surface; hard dry, very firm moist, very sticky and very plastic wet; many medium vesicular, common very fine and fine tubular and few fine interstitial pores; abrupt smooth boundary.

Ap2 **4-19 cm** Dark greyish brown (10YR 4/2) clay with few coarse sand grains; few fine and medium distinct yellowish red mottles in pores and on ped faces; weak coarse angular blocky; very hard dry, very firm moist, very sticky and very plastic wet; few very fine and fine tubular, very few fine vesicular and interstitial pores; clear smooth boundary.

Bw1 **19-60 cm** Dark greyish brown (10YR 4/2) clay; very many dark faint yellowish brown and brown mottles; moderate very fine and fine angular blocky; firm moist, very sticky and very plastic wet; many pressure faces; few medium and coarse hard iron-manganese concretions; many fine and very fine tubular and interstitial pores; gradual smooth boundary.

Bw2 **60-100+ cm** Dark yellowish brown (10YR 4/4) clay with few coarse sand grains; common fine distinct grey mottles; moderate very fine and fine angular blocky; firm moist, very sticky and very plastic wet; many pressure faces and slickensides; few fine and medium iron-manganese concretions; many fine and very fine tubular and interstitial pores.

CROMIC VERTISOL

Thailand

Horizon	Depth cm	pH H₂O 1:1	pH KCl 1:1	CEC	TEB	% BS	Ca	Mg	K	Na	Al	H	CaCO₃ %
Ap1	0–4	5.0	3.7	25.4	21.0	64	11.7	8.2	0.3	0.8		11.8	—
Ap2	4–19	5.1	4.1	26.1	23.7	70	13.8	8.4	0.4	1.1		10.2	—
Bw1	19–60	5.6	4.5	29.2	24.0	75	13.0	10.2	0.3	1.5		8.2	—
Bw2	60–100	5.5	4.5	28.6	26.8	77	15.8	8.5	0.3	2.2		7.9	—

Horizon	Conductivity 1:5 EC × 10⁵	% C	% N	C/N	% OM	Stones	C. sand	F. sand	Silt	Clay	Texture	Flocc. index
Ap1	25	0.7										
Ap2	31	0.6										
Bw1	32	0.2										
Bw2	26	0.2										

PELLIC VERTISOL   **Vp**

Location	San Roque, Gapan, Nueva Ecija, Philippines
Altitude	
Physiography	Slight depression in broad flat alluvial terrace
Drainage	Poorly drained
Parent material	Weakly stratified clayey old alluvial deposit
Vegetation	Rainfed paddy rice
Climate	Monsoon tropical; rainfall 2 000 mm (approx.) from May through December

---

Profile description

Ap   **0-18 cm**   Dark grey (10YR 4/1 moist) and grey (10YR 5/1 dry) heavy clay; many medium coarse prominent clear yellowish brown (10YR 5/8) and few fine greenish grey (5G 5/1) mottles concentrated in the lower 10 to 18 cm of the horizon; strong very coarse prismatic structure breaking under pressure to strong medium and coarse angular blocky; cracks among the prisms average about 6 cm across and increase to a maximum of about 10 cm as the dry season progresses; very sticky, very plastic, extremely hard; common fine continuous random mass tubular simple open pores; few small soft and medium hard spherical black and very dark brown Mn-Fe concretions; many fine and medium dead rice roots; abrupt smooth boundary; pH 6.5.

AB   **18-35 cm**   Dark grey (10YR 4/1 moist) and grey (10YR 5/1 dry) heavy clay; common medium prominent clear strong brown (7.5YR 5/6) inprism mottles; strong very coarse prismatic structure extending from above and breaking under pressure to weak coarse blocky cracks extending from above among prisms which are lined with darker grey mottle-free clay; common coarse oblique slickensides; very sticky; very plastic, hard; few fine discontinuous random inprism tubular simple pores; common small soft spherical black and very dark brown Mn-Fe concretions; few fine dead rice roots concentrated in prism cracks; gradual wavy boundary; pH 6.8.

Bwg1   **35-57 cm**   Light olive grey (5Y 6/2 moist) and light grey (5Y 7/2 dry) heavy clay; moderate very coarse prismatic structure extending from the surface; dark grey clay material from above coats prism faces along cracks up to 1 cm wide; common coarse oblique slickensides; firm, very sticky, very plastic; few fine discontinuous random inprism open pores; common small hard and soft spherical black and very dark brown Mn-Fe concretions and films; few fine dead rice roots; gradual smooth boundary; pH 6.8.

Bwg2   **57-85 cm**   Olive grey (5Y 5/2 moist) and pale olive yellow (5Y 7/3 dry) heavy clay; few medium faint diffuse light olive brown (2.5Y 5/6) mottles; weak coarse and medium prismatic structure breaking to weak medium and coarse blocky; dark grey clay exprism coatings; cracks among prisms are essentially closed; common coarse and medium oblique slickensides form most of the blocky structure aggregate surfaces; sticky, very plastic, firm; very few fine discontinuous random inprism open pores; few fine soft black and dark brown Mn-Fe concretions and common medium white CaCO$_3$ nodules; very few fine dead mostly exprism rice roots; gradual wavy boundary; pH 6.8.

BCg   **85-150 cm**   Light olive grey (5Y 6/2 moist) and light grey (5Y 7/2 dry) heavy clay; weak coarse prismatic structure breaking to weak coarse and medium blocky diminishing to structureless (massive below 150 cm); common coarse and medium oblique slickensides; very sticky, very plastic, firm; very fine discontinuous random inprism tubular simple pores; few small soft and medium hard spherical black and very dark brown Mn-Fe concretions and white CaCO$_3$ nodules; very few fine dead rice roots; pH 7.0.

Cg1   **150-170 cm**   Olive (5Y 5/3) heavy clay; few fine faint light grey mottles; very sticky, very plastic, very firm; few small soft spherical black and dark brown Mn-Fe concretions and white irregular CaCO$_3$ nodules; pH 7.0.

Cg2   **170-220 cm**   Dark greyish brown (2.5Y 4/2) very fine clay; few fine light grey mottles; very sticky, very plastic, very firm; few small soft spherical black and very dark brown Mn-Fe concretions and white irregular CaCO$_3$ nodules; pH 7.0.

Cg3   **220-250 cm**   Grey (N5) heavy clay; common fine brownish yellow mottles; very sticky, very plastic, very firm; common small soft and hard spherical black and dark brown Mn-Fe concretions; pH 7.2.

Cg4   **250-300 cm**   Grey (5Y 5/1) heavy clay; few fine bluish grey and common fine brown mottles; very sticky, very plastic, very firm; common small soft and hard spherical black and very dark brown Mn-Fe concretions; pH 7.5.

PELLIC VERTISOL
Philippines

Horizon	Depth cm	pH H₂O 1:1	pH KCl 1:1	CEC	TEB	% BS	Ca	Mg	K	Na	Al	H	CaCO₃ %
Ap	0–18	6.1	5.3	41.8		73.2	18.7	10.4	0.19	1.3		7.5	1.8
AB	18–35	6.7	5.7	39.9		84.5	20.7	11.0	0.18	1.8		4.9	2.0
Bwg1	35–57	7.0	5.9	43.7		78.1	21.0	10.7	0.22	2.4		4.4	2.0
Bwg2	57–85	6.9	5.7	34.3		93.0	19.0	9.4	0.17	3.3		2.1	1.8
BCg	85–150	7.2	6.0	37.8		90.0	20.4	11.3	0.19	2.2		2.8	2.0
Cg1	150–170	7.2	5.8	48.4		89.3	24.2	13.2	0.24	2.3		4.8	0.9
Cg2	170–220	7.2	6.1	50.2		89.0	22.2	14.9	0.23	2.6		5.0	0.9

Horizon	Sol. salts		% C	% N	C/N	% OM	Stones	C. sand	F. sand	Silt	Clay	Texture	Flocc. index
Ap			1.24	0.035	35.4	2.13		0.6	1.2	27.4	70.6	c	
AB			0.56	0.027	20.0	0.97		1.0	1.4	25.0	72.6	c	
Bwg1			0.22	0.023	9.6	0.38		1.0	1.8	20.6	76.6	c	
Bwg2			0.19	0.025	7.6	0.33		1.0	2.6	23.8	72.6	c	
BCg			0.17	0.021	8.5	0.29		0.2	6.2	26.4	68.6	c	
Cg1			0.24	0.036	6.6	0.41		0.6	5.4	22.4	71.6	c	
Cg2			0.18	0.030	6.0	0.30		0.4	4.0	20.6	75.6	c	

Horizon	Moisture equivalent %		At pF 2 %	At pF 4.2 %			Bulk density g/cc	Total K ppm	Avail. P ppm	Free Fe₂O₃ %
Ap	44.1		51.3	28.4			1.82	179	22	1.40
AB	55.4		51.9	28.8			1.88	245	18	1.00
Bwg1	43.4		55.5	31.6			1.77	158	4	0.54
Bwg2	39.1		57.3	30.3			1.59	165	2	0.45
BCg	41.8		55.3	26.9			1.73	112	2	0.65
Cg1								210	9	1.10
Cg2								292	26	1.30

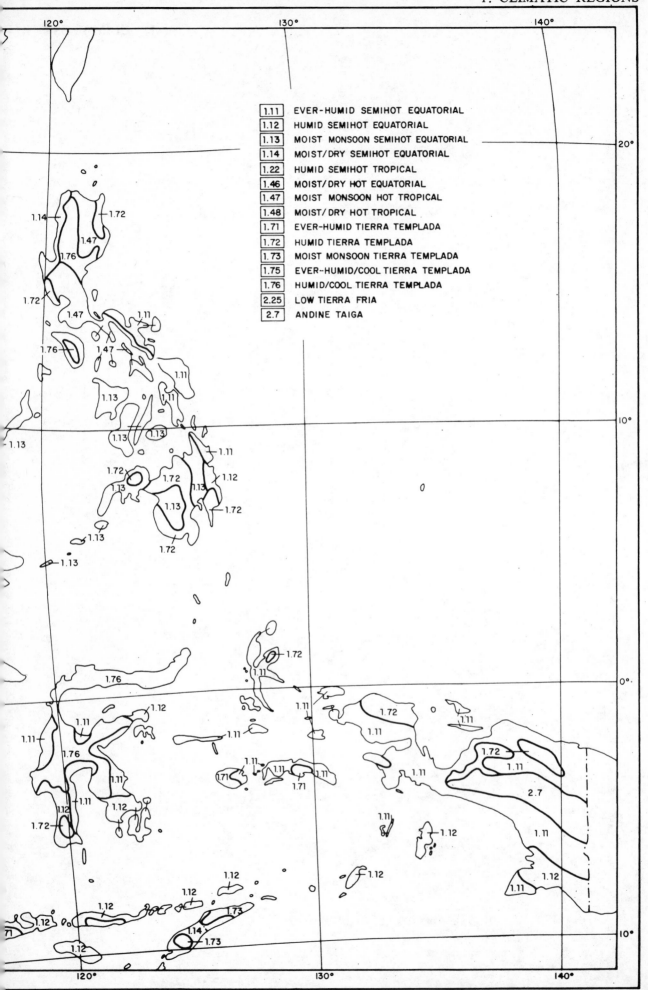

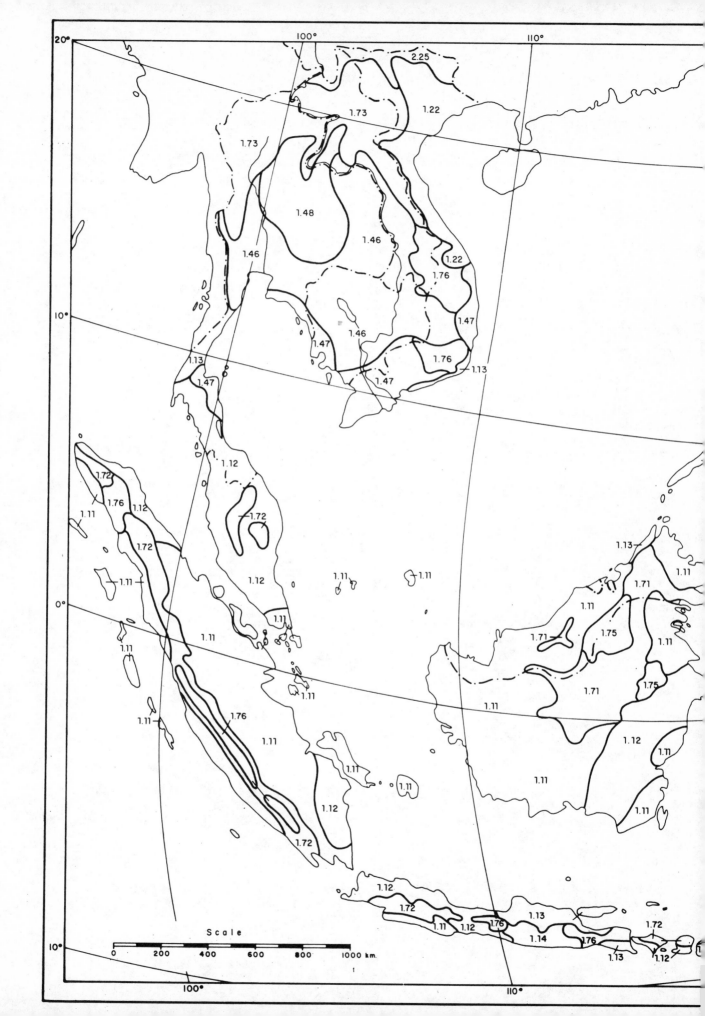

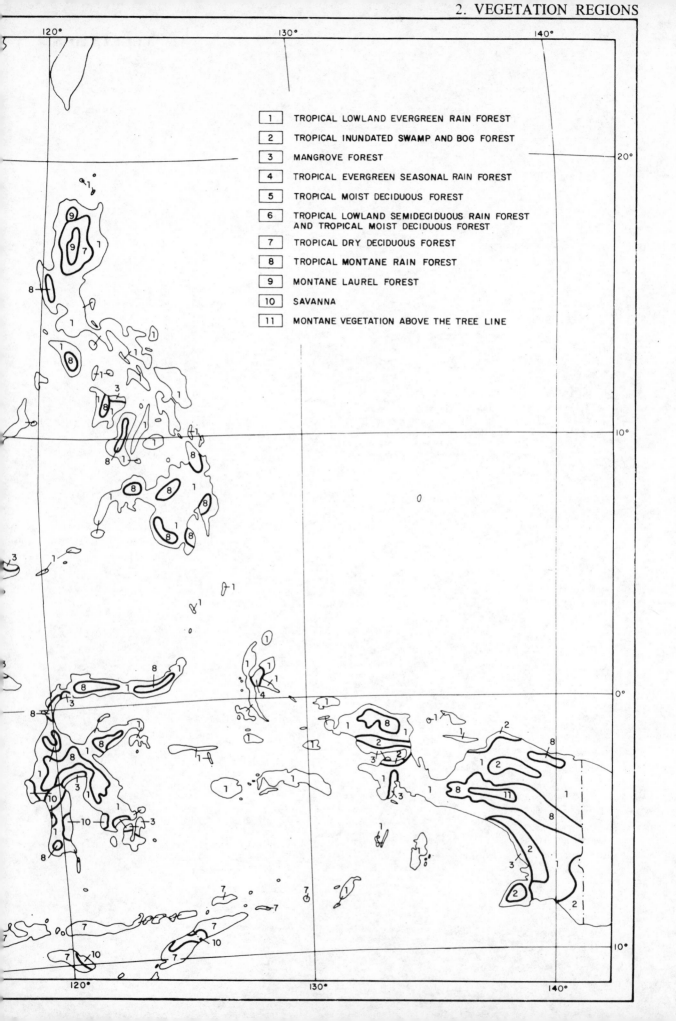

1 | TROPICAL LOWLAND EVERGREEN RAIN FOREST
2 | TROPICAL INUNDATED SWAMP AND BOG FOREST
3 | MANGROVE FOREST
4 | TROPICAL EVERGREEN SEASONAL RAIN FOREST
5 | TROPICAL MOIST DECIDUOUS FOREST
6 | TROPICAL LOWLAND SEMIDECIDUOUS RAIN FOREST AND TROPICAL MOIST DECIDUOUS FOREST
7 | TROPICAL DRY DECIDUOUS FOREST
8 | TROPICAL MONTANE RAIN FOREST
9 | MONTANE LAUREL FOREST
10 | SAVANNA
11 | MONTANE VEGETATION ABOVE THE TREE LINE

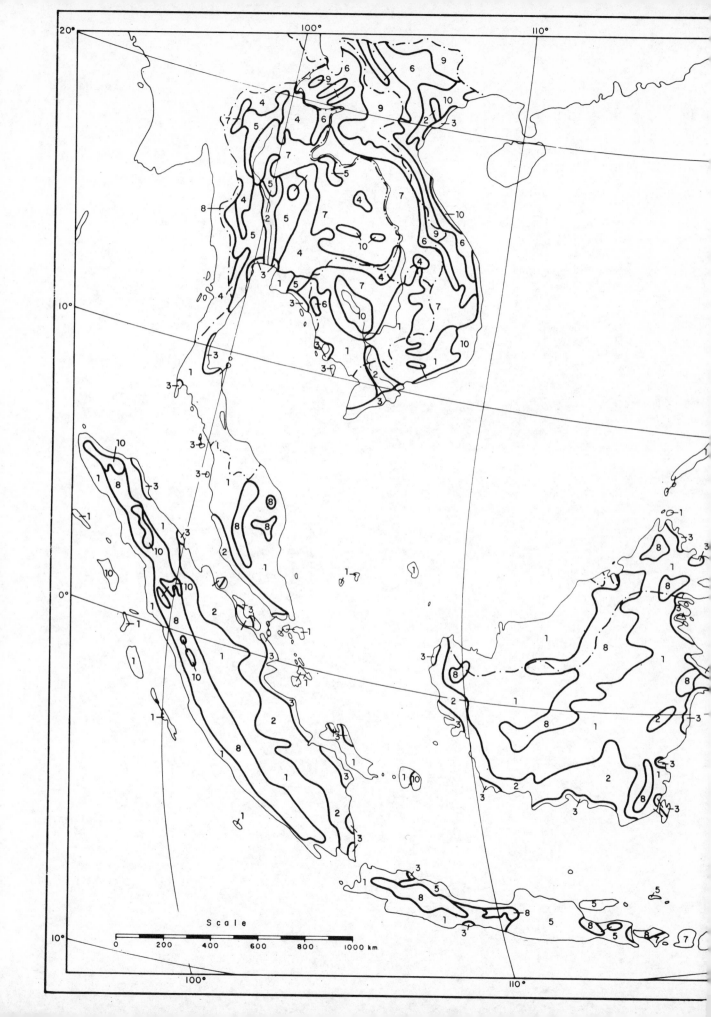

3. OCEANIC BASINS AND MORPHOSTRUCTURAL REGIONS

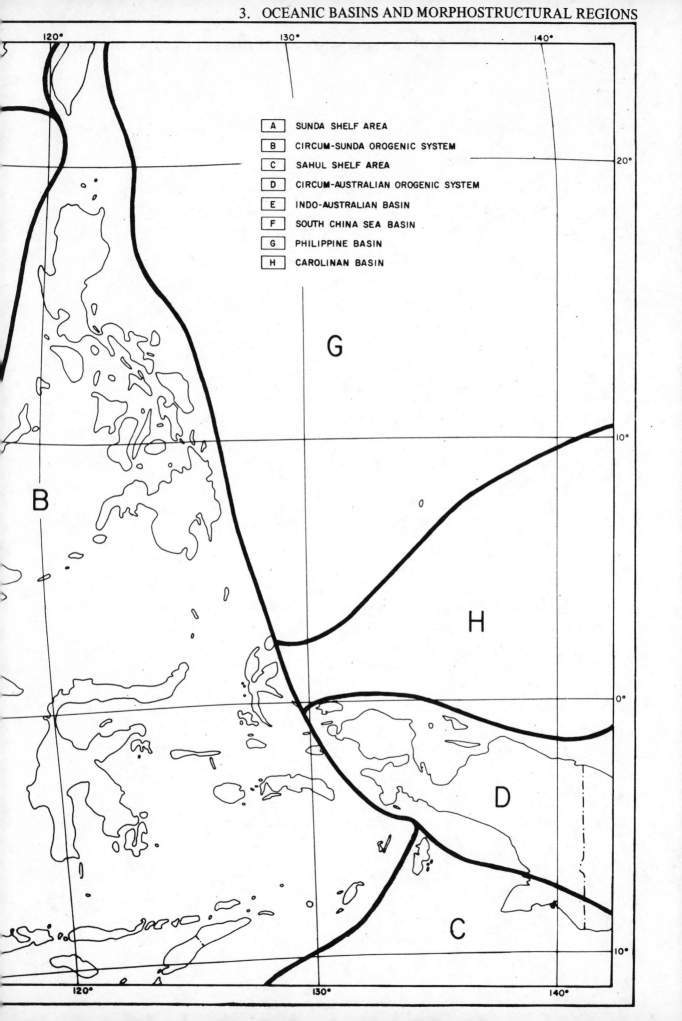

A	SUNDA SHELF AREA
B	CIRCUM-SUNDA OROGENIC SYSTEM
C	SAHUL SHELF AREA
D	CIRCUM-AUSTRALIAN OROGENIC SYSTEM
E	INDO-AUSTRALIAN BASIN
F	SOUTH CHINA SEA BASIN
G	PHILIPPINE BASIN
H	CAROLINAN BASIN

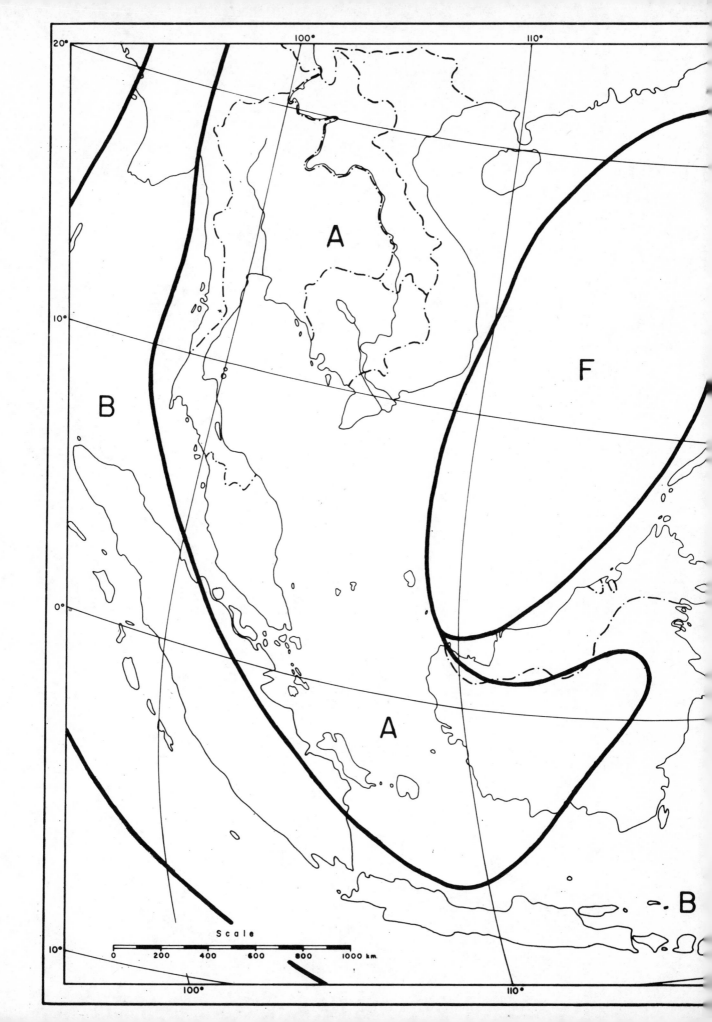

A SUNDA SHELF AREA

A1 MALAY PENINSULA AND WESTERN THAILAND GEOSYNCLINAL SYSTEM
    A1.1 MALAY PENINSULA
    A1.2 WESTERN THAILAND GEOSYNCLINAL SYSTEM

A2 INDOCHINESE COMPLEX

A3 INDOCHINESE MASSIF
    A3.1 KORAT AND VIENTIANE MASSIFS
    A3.2 EASTERN MASSIFS
    A3.3 TONKIN MASSIF

A4 QUATERNARY BASINS
    A4.1 MEKONG RIVER BASIN
    A4.2 CHAO PHRAYA RIVER BASIN

A5 BORNEO
    A5.1 CONTINENTAL SUNDA SHELF SECTOR
    A5.2 EMBALUH ZONE
    A5.3 KUCHING AND MERATUS ZONES

B CIRCUM-SUNDA OROGENIC SYSTEM

B1 PHILIPPINES
    B1.1 LUZON
    B1.2 MINDORO
    B1.3 PANAY
    B1.4 NEGROS, CEBU AND BOHOL
    B1.5 SAMAR AND LEYTE
    B1.6 MINDANAO
    B1.7 PALAWAN

B2 MOLUCCAS
    B2.1 CERAM
    B2.2 BURU
    B2.3 MISOOL
    B2.4 SULA ISLANDS
    B2.5 HALMAHERA GROUP

B3 SULAWESI
    B3.1 NORTHERN ARM
    B3.2 CENTRAL
    B3.3 SOUTHEASTERN ARM
    B3.4 SOUTHERN ARM

B4 LESSER SUNDA ISLANDS
    B4.1 WETAR
    B4.2 ALOR
    B4.3 FLORES
    B4.4 SUMBAWA
    B4.5 LOMBOK
    B4.6 BALI
    B4.7 SUMBA
    B4.8 TIMOR
    B4.9 TANIMBAR

B5 JAVA AND MADURA
    B5.1 SOUTHERN BELT
    B5.2 CENTRAL BELT
    B5.3 NORTHERN BELT

B6 SUMATRA
    B6.1 NORTHERN MOUNTAINS
    B6.2 BARISAN RANGE
    B6.3 NORTHEASTERN LOWLANDS
    B6.4 ISLANDS WEST OF SUMATRA
    B6.5 ISLANDS EAST OF SUMATRA

C SAHUL SHELF AREA

C1 ARU ISLANDS

D CIRCUM-AUSTRALIAN OROGENIC SYSTEM

D1 IRIAN JAYA
    D1.1 DOBERAI PENINSULA
    D1.2 CENTRAL IRIAN JAYA
    D1.3 SOUTHERN ALLUVIAL PLAIN

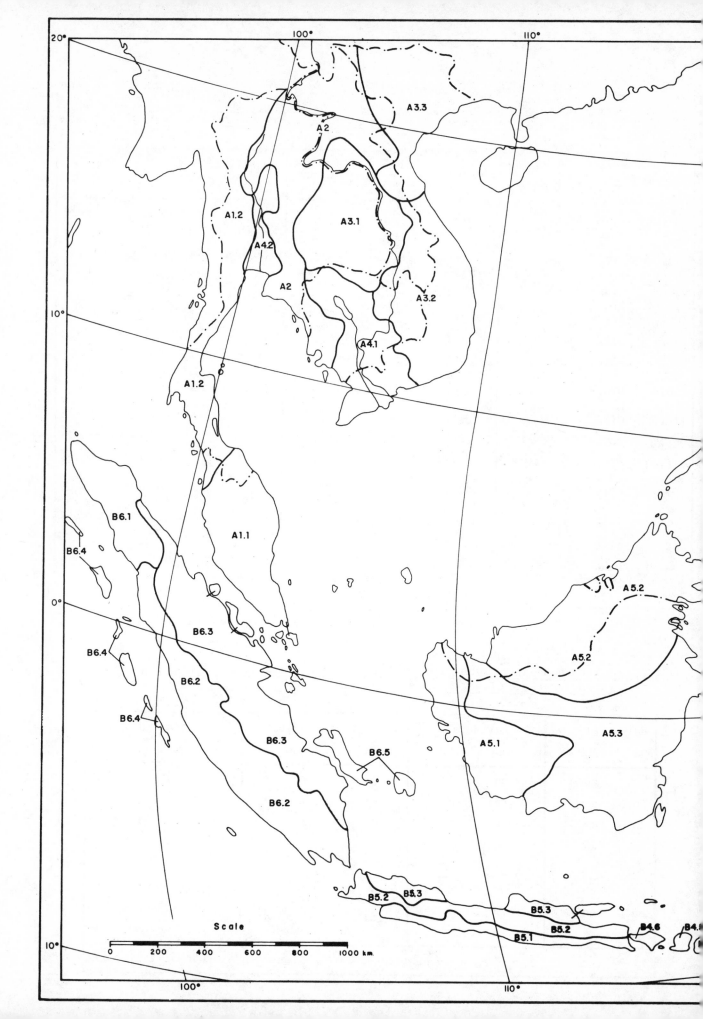

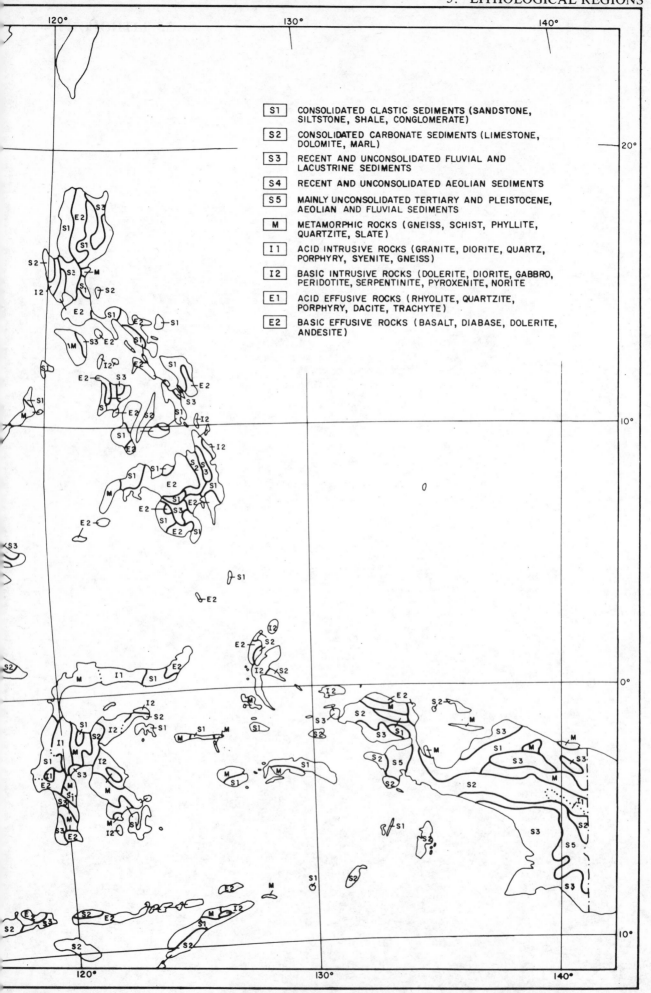

S1	CONSOLIDATED CLASTIC SEDIMENTS (SANDSTONE, SILTSTONE, SHALE, CONGLOMERATE)
S2	CONSOLIDATED CARBONATE SEDIMENTS (LIMESTONE, DOLOMITE, MARL)
S3	RECENT AND UNCONSOLIDATED FLUVIAL AND LACUSTRINE SEDIMENTS
S4	RECENT AND UNCONSOLIDATED AEOLIAN SEDIMENTS
S5	MAINLY UNCONSOLIDATED TERTIARY AND PLEISTOCENE, AEOLIAN AND FLUVIAL SEDIMENTS
M	METAMORPHIC ROCKS (GNEISS, SCHIST, PHYLLITE, QUARTZITE, SLATE)
I1	ACID INTRUSIVE ROCKS (GRANITE, DIORITE, QUARTZ, PORPHYRY, SYENITE, GNEISS)
I2	BASIC INTRUSIVE ROCKS (DOLERITE, DIORITE, GABBRO, PERIDOTITE, SERPENTINITE, PYROXENITE, NORITE
E1	ACID EFFUSIVE ROCKS (RHYOLITE, QUARTZITE, PORPHYRY, DACITE, TRACHYTE)
E2	BASIC EFFUSIVE ROCKS (BASALT, DIABASE, DOLERITE, ANDESITE)

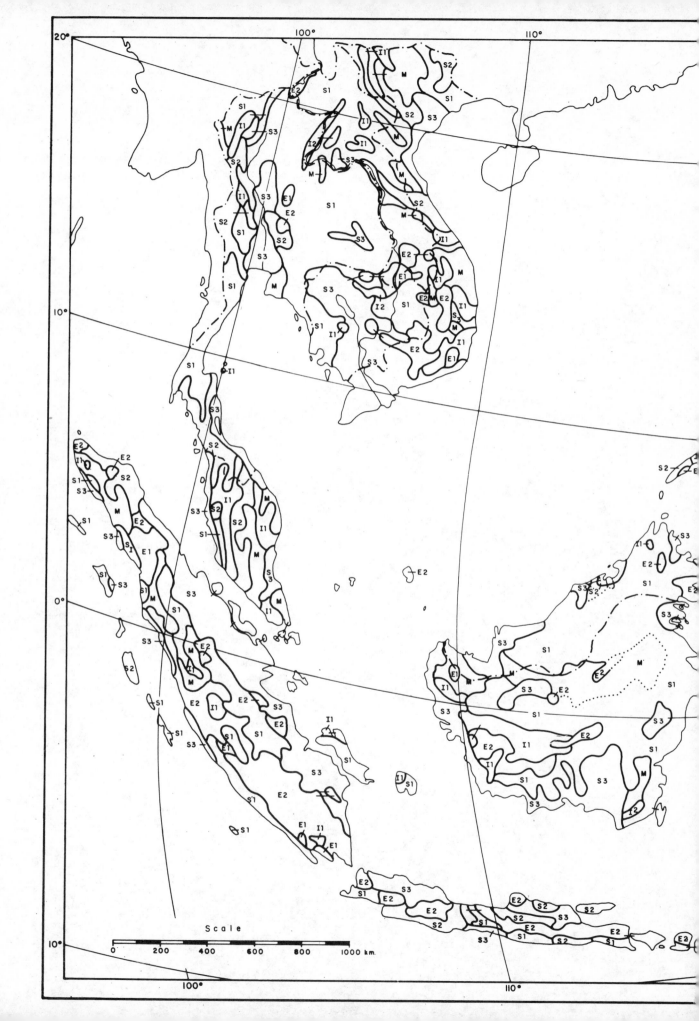

6. **PHYSIOGRAPHY**

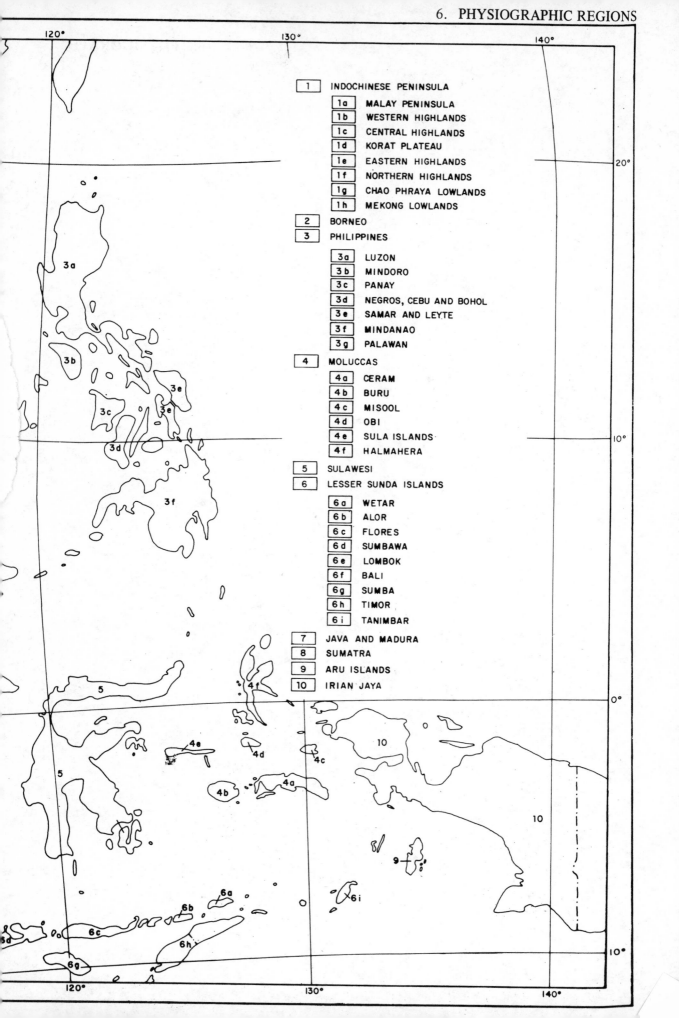

1	INDOCHINESE PENINSULA
1a	MALAY PENINSULA
1b	WESTERN HIGHLANDS
1c	CENTRAL HIGHLANDS
1d	KORAT PLATEAU
1e	EASTERN HIGHLANDS
1f	NORTHERN HIGHLANDS
1g	CHAO PHRAYA LOWLANDS
1h	MEKONG LOWLANDS

2	BORNEO
3	PHILIPPINES

3a	LUZON
3b	MINDORO
3c	PANAY
3d	NEGROS, CEBU AND BOHOL
3e	SAMAR AND LEYTE
3f	MINDANAO
3g	PALAWAN

4	MOLUCCAS

4a	CERAM
4b	BURU
4c	MISOOL
4d	OBI
4e	SULA ISLANDS
4f	HALMAHERA

5	SULAWESI
6	LESSER SUNDA ISLANDS

6a	WETAR
6b	ALOR
6c	FLORES
6d	SUMBAWA
6e	LOMBOK
6f	BALI
6g	SUMBA
6h	TIMOR
6i	TANIMBAR

7	JAVA AND MADURA
8	SUMATRA
9	ARU ISLANDS
10	IRIAN JAYA

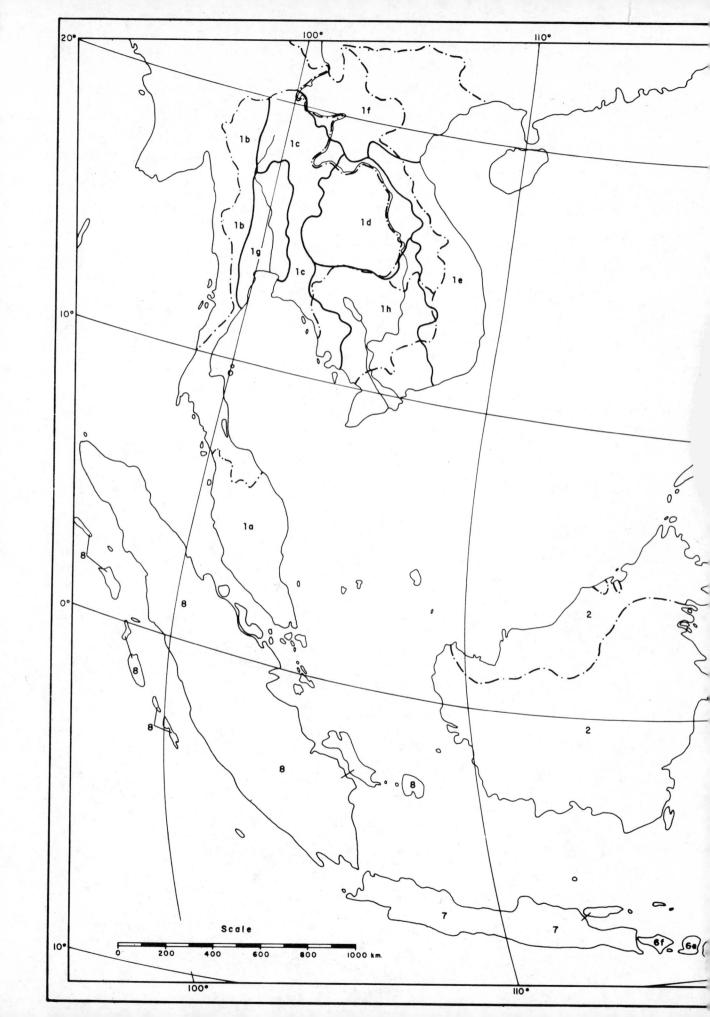

Scale

0   200   400   600   800   1000 km.

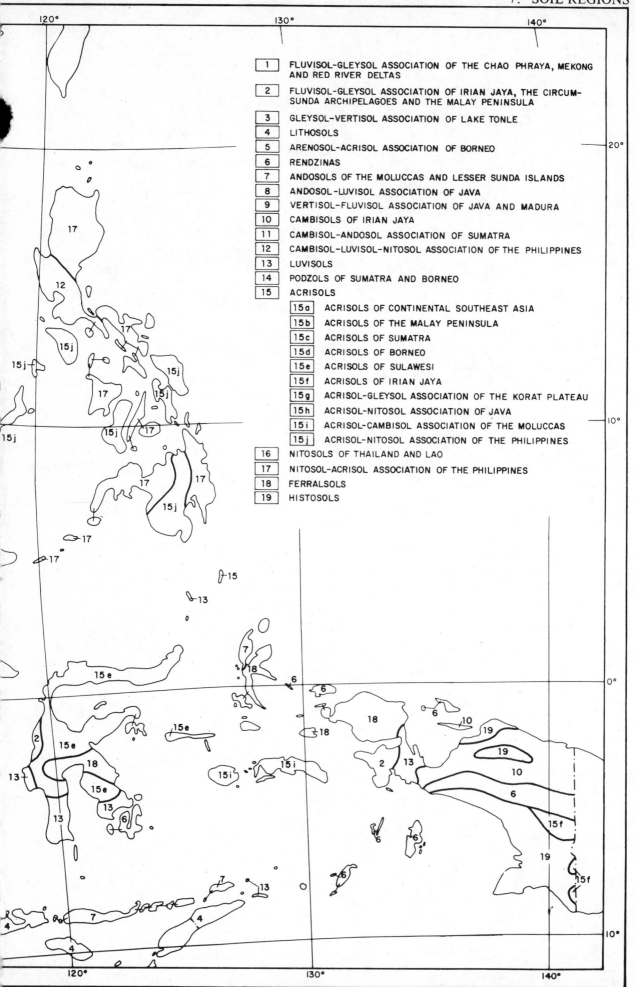

1	FLUVISOL-GLEYSOL ASSOCIATION OF THE CHAO PHRAYA, MEKONG AND RED RIVER DELTAS
2	FLUVISOL-GLEYSOL ASSOCIATION OF IRIAN JAYA, THE CIRCUM-SUNDA ARCHIPELAGOES AND THE MALAY PENINSULA
3	GLEYSOL-VERTISOL ASSOCIATION OF LAKE TONLE
4	LITHOSOLS
5	ARENOSOL-ACRISOL ASSOCIATION OF BORNEO
6	RENDZINAS
7	ANDOSOLS OF THE MOLUCCAS AND LESSER SUNDA ISLANDS
8	ANDOSOL-LUVISOL ASSOCIATION OF JAVA
9	VERTISOL-FLUVISOL ASSOCIATION OF JAVA AND MADURA
10	CAMBISOLS OF IRIAN JAYA
11	CAMBISOL-ANDOSOL ASSOCIATION OF SUMATRA
12	CAMBISOL-LUVISOL-NITOSOL ASSOCIATION OF THE PHILIPPINES
13	LUVISOLS
14	PODZOLS OF SUMATRA AND BORNEO
15	ACRISOLS
15a	ACRISOLS OF CONTINENTAL SOUTHEAST ASIA
15b	ACRISOLS OF THE MALAY PENINSULA
15c	ACRISOLS OF SUMATRA
15d	ACRISOLS OF BORNEO
15e	ACRISOLS OF SULAWESI
15f	ACRISOLS OF IRIAN JAYA
15g	ACRISOL-GLEYSOL ASSOCIATION OF THE KORAT PLATEAU
15h	ACRISOL-NITOSOL ASSOCIATION OF JAVA
15i	ACRISOL-CAMBISOL ASSOCIATION OF THE MOLUCCAS
15j	ACRISOL-NITOSOL ASSOCIATION OF THE PHILIPPINES
16	NITOSOLS OF THAILAND AND LAO
17	NITOSOL-ACRISOL ASSOCIATION OF THE PHILIPPINES
18	FERRALSOLS
19	HISTOSOLS

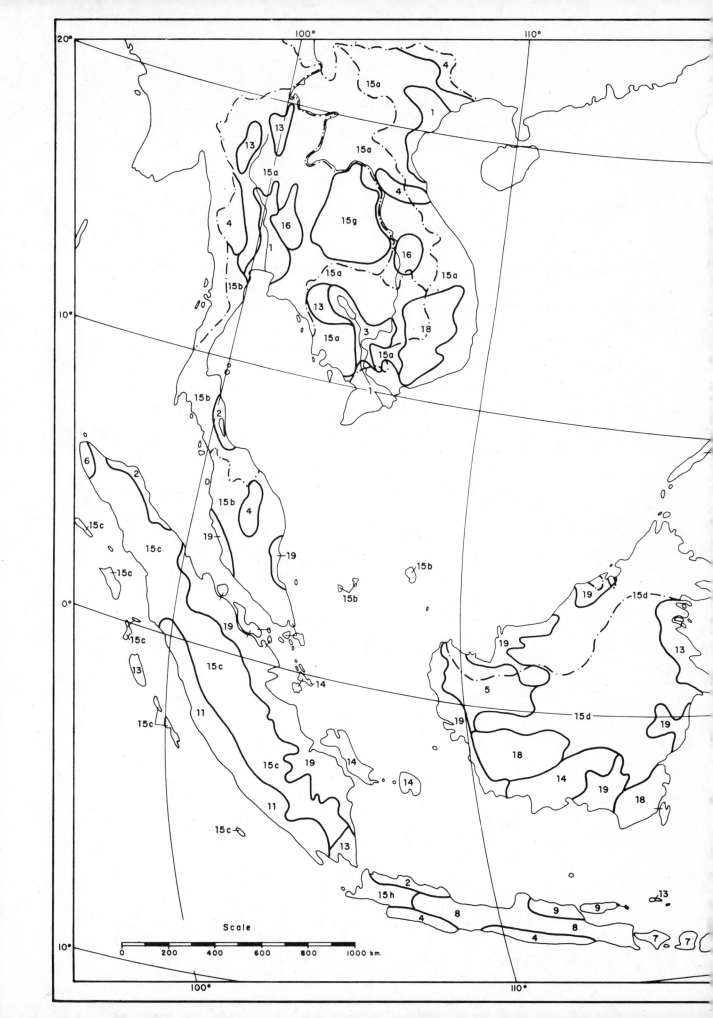